THE GLASS INDUSTRY
OF THE WEALD

FOR
FRANCIS STEER

THE GLASS INDUSTRY
OF THE WEALD

by

G. H. KENYON, F.S.A.

With a Foreword by

D. B. HARDEN, O.B.E., Ph.D., F.S.A.

LEICESTER UNIVERSITY PRESS
1967

© G. H. KENYON, 1967

PRINTED AND BOUND IN ENGLAND BY
HAZELL WATSON AND VINEY LTD
AYLESBURY, BUCKS
FOR LEICESTER UNIVERSITY PRESS

FOREWORD

THE Wealden glass industry which endured and prospered in the Surrey and Sussex Wealden area from the thirteenth to the seventeenth century, has in the past received perhaps less than its due consideration from archaeologists and historians of technology. For long those who have had an interest in one or more aspects of the subject, and have wished to broaden and deepen their knowledge of it, have sought in vain for an up-to-date and authoritative account of its many facets, which would provide a fuller and more all-embracing story than S. E. Winbolt was able to give, in 1933, in his *Wealden Glass*.

It is to fill this gap that Mr Kenyon has prepared this book, which is based on his long experience with the glasshouse sites and finds and his personal experience of excavating them in the company of Winbolt and others, and I deem it a great honour to have been invited to write this foreword.

Mr Kenyon has spared no pains in seeking out all the available evidence, not only about the sites, but also about those families and individuals who worked them from century to century. Having amassed his material, he has set it out chapter by chapter in a consistent pattern which makes his book a pleasure to use, and puts all those who wish to study this fascinating subject permanently in his debt. I commend it to them with conviction, sure in the knowledge that they will not be disappointed and that this important account of Wealden glassmaking will for many years to come remain a source book for the social and economic history of glassmaking in medieval England, as well as for the history of glass in general.

D. B. HARDEN

CONTENTS

LIST OF PLATES
(between pages 218 and 219)

LIST OF TEXT FIGURES

The author wishes to thank the following for the use of illustrations reproduced in this book: Mr T. Pape, F.S.A. (Plate VI, 1 and 2; Fig. 8); Mr E. S. Wood, F.S.A., and the editor of *Surrey Archaeological Collections* (Plate VII, 1; Figs. 4, 5, 6, 7); Mr J. C. Harrington and The National Park Service, U.S.A. (Plate VII, 2; Plate VIII; Fig. 9); Science Museum, London (Plate IX, Crown copyright); Trustees of the British Museum (Plate X); Hampshire County Council (Plate XV); Mr J. W. Daniels, nephew of the late Mr J. S. Daniels (Plate XIX); Mr A. D. R. Caroe, F.R.I.B.A., F.S.A. (Plate XXI).

EXPLANATORY NOTE

ALTHOUGH the scope of this book is stated on pp. 1 and 2, it has to be emphasized that considerable repetition is inevitable in a book designed for specialist
readers and in which a number of basically similar sites are discussed.

The Introduction attempts to give an overall picture of the Wealden glass industry,
and the subsequent chapters expand those various aspects as will be seen from the list
of contents on pp. vii–xii. Also, to avoid a cumbersome index of subjects, numerous
cross-references have been included in the text and it is hoped this system, coupled
with the list of contents, will be found convenient.

Any unevenness of style, and any variation in the spelling of surnames is partly due
to a wish to quote accurately and acknowledge, rather than paraphrase, the work of
other people. Those who have assisted were experts in various skills, which they
shared with great generosity and patience, whereas I can offer little more than a deep
interest in an industry closely associated with the district where I have lived and
worked for many years.

After this book was in page proof, Dr D. B. Harden, Director of the London
Museum, kindly agreed to write a Foreword: I want to take this opportunity of
expressing my deep sense of obligation for the honour he has done me.

G. H. KENYON

Kirdford
December 1966

BIBLIOGRAPHY AND ABBREVIATIONS

This bibliography only includes works quoted and used by the author.

Abbreviation

C. H. Ashdown, *History of the Worshipful Company of Glaziers of the City of London* (1919).

J. Aubrey, *The Natural History and Antiquities of the County of Surrey* (1718-19).

J. Barralet, *La Verriere en France* (1953).

T. Barrett-Lennard, 'Glass-making at Knole,' in *The Antiquary*, vol. 41 (1905).

N. P. Bridgewater, 'Glasshouse Farm, St. Weonards: a Small Glass-working Site,' in *The Woolhope Naturalists Club Trans.*, vol. 37 (1963).

R. J. Charlston, 'Ancient Glass-Making Methods,' in Circle of Glass Collectors, Duplicated paper No. 124, March 1961.

R. J. Charlston, *The Connoisseur Period Guides. Tudor Period: Pottery, Porcelain and Glass.*

E. G. Clark, 'Glassmaking in Lorraine,' in *Society of Glass Tech. Journal*, vol. 15, No. 58, June 1931.

J. W. Cobb, *Alfold* (1935).

C. T. S. Cooper, *History of Chiddingfold* (unpublished).

J. S. Daniels, *The Woodchester Glass House* (1960).

E. Gerspach, *L'Art de la verrerie* (1885).

D.E.G. E. S. Godfrey, *The Development of English Glassmaking, 1560–1640* (unpublished doctorial thesis, University of Chicago, 1957).

GMR Guildford Muniment Room.

Grazebrook H. S. Grazebrook, *Collections for a genealogy of the Noble families of Henzey, Tyttery and Tyzack (De Hennezel, De Thiétry and Du Thisac), 'Gentilshommes Verriers' from Lorraine* (1877).

Guttery   D. R. Guttery, *From Broad-glass to Cut Crystal* (1956).

               D. B. Harden, 'Domestic Window Glass, Roman, Saxon and Medieval,' in E. M. Jope (ed.), *Studies in Building History* (1961).

               J. C. Harrington, *Glassmaking in Jamestown* (1952).

Hartshorne   A. Hartshorne, *Old English Glasses* (1897).

               E. B. Haynes, *Glass through the Ages* (1948).

               W. B. Honey, *Glass* (Victoria and Albert Museum, 1946).

               W. Horridge, 'Documents Relating to the Lorraine Glassmakers in N. Staffs. &c.,' in *Glass Notes*, No.15, Dec. 1955.

               E. Wyndham Hulme, 'English Glassmaking in the Sixteenth and Seventeenth Centuries,' in *The Antiquary*, vols. 30, 31.

               Journal of British Archaeology, vol. 17 (1861).

J.M.G.   *Journal of the British Society of Master Glass Painters.*

               Journal of the Society of Glass Technology.
               This ceased publication in 1959; the Society then commenced to issue two new journals, namely *Glass Technology* and *Physics & Chemistry of Glasses.*

               J. A. Knowles, 'The Source of the Coloured Glass used in Medieval Stained Glass Windows,' in *Glass*, March-June 1926.

               J. A. Knowles, 'Medieval Processes of Glass Manufacture,' in *Glass*, July-Sept. 1927.

               J. A. Knowles, *The York School of Glass Painting* (1936).

               Lord Leconfield, *Petworth Manor in the Seventeenth Century* (1954).

               J. D. Le Couteur, *English Medieval Stained Glass* (1926).

               London Museum Medieval Catalogue (1st ed., 1940).

O.S.   Ordnance Survey.

Pape   T. Pape, 'Medieval Glassworkers in North Staffordshire,' in *North Staffs. Field Club Trans.*, vol. 68 (1934).

               H. J. Powell, *Glassmaking in England* (1923).

P.R. Parish Register.

M. H. Ridgway and G. B. Leach, 'Further Notes on the Glasshouse Site at Kingswood, Delamere, Cheshire,' in *Journal of the Chester Arch. Soc.*, vol. 27.

L. F. Salzman, *English Industries of the Middle Ages* (1923).

B.E.S. L. F. Salzman, *Building in England down to 1540* (1952).

The Scottish Antiquary, vol. 7 (1893).

C. Singer and others, *A History of Technology*.

E. Straker, *Wealden Iron* (1931).

Sy.A.C. *Surrey Archaeological Collections* (in progress).

Surrey Record Society publications (in progress).

S.A.C. *Sussex Archaeological Collections* (in progress).

S.C.M. *Sussex County Magazine*.

S.N.Q. *Sussex Notes and Queries* (in progress).

S.R.S. Sussex Record Society publications (in progress).

Theophilus (trans. and ed. C. R. Dodwell). *De Diversis Artibus* (1961).

W. A. Thorpe, *English Glass* (2nd ed., London, 1949).

T. Tithe Award Map and/or Schedule (in description and schedule of glasshouse sites).

S.A.G.T. W. E. S. Turner, 'Studies in Ancient Glasses and Glassmaking Processes,' in *Journal of the Society of Glass Technology* (vol. 40, 1956).

W. E. S. Turner, 'A Notable British Seventeenth-century Contribution to the Literature of Glassmaking,' in *Glass Technology*, vol. 3, (1962).

V.C.H. Hants *The Victoria History of the County of Hampshire* (vol. 5, 1912).

V.C.H. Surrey *The Victoria History of the County of Surrey* (vol. 2, 1905).

V.C.H.
  Sussex   *The Victoria History of the County of Sussex* (vol. 2, 1907).

              P. A. L. Vine, *London's Lost Route to the Sea* (1965).

W.G.   S. E. Winbolt, *Wealden Glass* (1933).

              C. Winston, *Hints on Glass Painting* (1846).

For a full Bibliography of Glass, see the book of that title by G. S. Duncan. It was published in 1960, has over 15,000 entries, a foreword by Professor W. E. S. Turner and a subject index by Frank Newby. The *Bibliography* was edited by Violet Dimbleby.

INTRODUCTION

General

THE object of this book is three-fold: to collect and select from the work of the late Rev. T. S. Cooper, the late S. E. Winbolt and myself; to bring the available information up to 1965; and to provide a provisional framework to which any fresh documentary evidence or glasshouse excavation can be added. Extracts are given from valuable material of the late Professor W. E. S. Turner, Dr L. F. Salzman, Mr R. J. Charleston, Mrs E. S. Godfrey,[1] and Mr E. S. Wood, plus some technical information on Wealden glass. The great bulk of the evidence for the English forest glass industry comes from the Weald and as all the forest glasshouses outside the Weald about which anything is known up to 1965 are discussed in Chapters IV and X, this book treats of much of the forest glass industry in England.

It was my good fortune to be associated with Winbolt as a friend and a raw recruit at all the glasshouse sites on which he worked, except No. 36[2] which I visited later. I owe much to the ideas of the two pioneers, Cooper and Winbolt, although not always agreeing with, but always stimulated by, them. They would certainly have modified their ideas if they had been alive today; both have long been dead. Cooper's notes were probably completed nearly fifty years ago and Winbolt's book was published more than thirty years ago. It is very easy to be wise a generation or more later; but there is tidying-up to be done and fresh conclusions to be drawn now as there will be fifty years hence. Possibly local patriotism tended to exaggerate the importance of this small industry. The tendency is more objective today and one of the aims of this book is to distinguish between fact and fancy and to get the industry into focus in England and possibly in Europe.

Where the bulk of material is considerable, *e.g.*, that relating to families, I have selected drastically, but where the evidence is scanty and little is known, *e.g.*, that relating to vessel form, I have included everything. The balance of the book has been less a matter of choice than of necessity.

I soon discovered it was almost impossible to revise Winbolt's *Wealden Glass*,[3]

---

[1] Doctoral thesis, University of Chicago, 1957. *See* p. 12, note 38.

[2] A numbered schedule of glasshouse sites is included in Chapter IX.

[3] S. E. Winbolt, *Wealden Glass* (Combridges, Hove, 1933), hereafter abbreviated *W.G.* Winbolt wrote two later articles in the *Sussex County Magazine*, December 1935 and May 1940, bringing the furnace site information up-to-date. Since then I have put brief notes on the industry in various journals: *News and Reviews of the Society of Glass Technology*, Vol 35, pp. 6–11 (1951), Vol. 43, pp. 17–20 (1959); *Journal of the British Society of Master Glass Painters*, Vol. 12, pp. 103–07 (1956–7); *Sussex Archaeological Collections*, Vol. 96, p. 73, Vol. 99, pp. 106–08; *Sussex Notes and Queries*, Vol. 14, p. 26, Vol. 16, p. 168.

and so I started afresh using selections[4] from his chapters on glasshouse sites covering, with the *Sussex County Magazine* articles, about two-thirds of the thirty-six proved or probable sites.[5] The remainder have been found since he died in 1944 or evidence for them has come to light in the Cooper material. I have not reprinted Winbolt's valuable Appendices (pp. 74–83) containing summaries from Theophilus, Månnson and Agricola.

Scope of the Book

Cooper used the term 'Wealden Glass'; this and Straker's *Wealden Iron* (1931) no doubt suggested the title for Winbolt's book. I have not used that title because the industry in the Weald was small compared with the far more important and wide-spread iron industry, and because this is a new assessment, though owing much to Cooper and Winbolt. It would have been a more congenial and simple task if I had been using only my own material; this was particularly true of the ground plans of Fernfold and Vann. The book is intended for people interested in the industry as a whole and is not a specialist, technical or archaeological treatise though it does include some recent work on these aspects. Roughly one-third of the text is devoted to descriptions of the thirty-six proved and probable and the six possible glasshouse sites in the Weald. Another nine sites suggested by Cooper, but for which I can find no satisfactory evidence, are discussed in Chapter IX but not included either in the schedule or on the map. Six of these were queries in *W.G.* Seven English forest glasshouses, all after *c.*1550, outside the Weald,[6] are also discussed and plans given for Buckholt (Fig. 20), and Bishop's Wood (Fig. 8).

Lack of Remains on Sites

As the industry ceased only 350 years ago some written evidence is available; this is fortunate because the majority of the sites are archaeologically disappointing. This is not unusual and other workers such as Professor R. Newstead and the Rev. M. H. Ridgway in Cheshire (1935 and 1945) and Mr N. P. Bridgwater in Herefordshire (1961) found very little or no surviving structure; the last says the furnace and buildings were completely demolished. Mr T. Pape at Bishop's Wood in Staffordshire (1931) was exceptionally fortunate in finding one untouched ruined kiln, but his other five sites were structurally barren.

The historian and economist may find something of interest, but the study is less rewarding for the archaeologist and museum curator because the majority of glass-

---

[4] Where I have used *W.G.*, I have made this quoting clear.

[5] The titles, proved, probable and possible, their definitions and the sites to which they refer are discussed in Chapter IX, pp. 149, 150.

[6] The glasshouses were at Graffham and Northiam in Sussex, in Hampshire, Kent, Staffordshire, Gloucestershire and Herefordshire. The glasshouse at Jamestown, Virginia, is also discussed as is its conjectural reconstruction by Mr J. C. Harrington. There was also a probable glasshouse at Kingswood, Cheshire; a summary of the work done there is given in Chapter X. A number of fresh glasshouse sites in Staffordshire were found in 1966 during land clearance operations (*see* p. 214, note 15).

house sites produce little except a few crucible and glass fragments and a surviving burnt patch. The end-product is usually very scarce,[7] because all waste was carefully husbanded and went back into the next batch (*see* p. 18). In general the only exceptions to this in my experience are on three Late sites (Nos. 14, 23 and 38) – probably the last to be worked. What might have been a fascinating and useful study of vessel forms is impossible, because even where fragments survive, they are tiny and usually dispersed by stone plunderers, cullet seekers, roots and earlier workers.

The Problems of the Forest Glasshouse Sites

One has a fair idea of what a forest glasshouse looked like from the early description by Theophilus (Plate IX) perhaps written in the early twelfth century and from the fine fifteenth-century drawing (Plate X), but almost nothing is known about vessel forms in the Weald, except to some extent by analogy with the late sixteenth-century Woodchester (Glos.) fragments (*see* p. 218). There are very few vessels depicted in English illuminated MSS. which can be recognized as glass.[8]

When I started this book I was conscious of the lack of photographs and plans of glasshouse sites. Only two, both Late,[9] of the twenty-four certain sites[10] examined by Winbolt and/or myself had provided evidence of the furnace structure, and the plans were unsatisfactory. I then knew of only one photograph showing any structural remains, but thanks to the expert excavation in 1960 of the Blunden's Wood, Hambledon site (No. 35) by Mr E. S. Wood, a large gap is filled and there is a clear and convincing illustrated description of a complete Early glasshouse.[11]

Thanks also to the invaluable help of Mr A. D. R. Caroe, Winbolt's ground plan of the working furnace at Vann (provisionally Late; *W.G.* 31) becomes comprehensible and as satisfactory as can be made (*see* Fig. 17). I have long puzzled over Winbolt's plan of Fernfold (No. 25)[12] and with one suggestion the plan becomes more intelligible, but it is not entirely satisfactory nor do I know of any photographs. The Vann and Fernfold sites are fully discussed in Chapter IX and both were probably

[7] Only some of the more promising Wealden sites have been closely examined, but even at the untouched glasshouse in Blunden's Wood which was minutely examined, it (in common with other Early sites) provided only a small quantity of glass and few glass vessel fragments of any interest. Harrington at Jamestown (Va.) where a large area was minutely examined, found very little of the end-product.

[8] I am indebted to Dr L. F. Salzman for this information.

[9] I have divided Wealden glass into two basic types, Early (*c.*1330–*c.*1550) and Late (*c.*1567–1618) with a little possibly Transitional. The reasons for this are mentioned on p. 17 and fully discussed in Chapter VI.

[10] See Chapter IX, Description of sites and schedule, pp. 149 and 150. I tabulated the 42 sites on the schedule as: 26 certain (No. 33 was excavated and No. 42 will be, by Mr E. S. Wood), 10 probable and 6 possible. I do not know if site No. 4 was seen by Winbolt before it was destroyed, but all the known glass from it was found by the Cooper family.

[11] *Surrey Archaeological Collections* (abbreviated hereafter to *Sy.A.C.*), vol. 62. I have made full use of his paper in Chapter IV.

[12] *S.C.M.*, vol. 9, p. 789.

worked in the latter half of the sixteenth century. Unhappily, I spent only the odd half-day at them and I accepted the authorized version as final. I had no idea that one day I should attempt a revised version or that we should find nothing better.

Winbolt and I had nothing to compare with Mr Wood's excavation of Blunden's Wood glasshouse; his methods were better than ours thirty years earlier and, with one possible exception, we found no site so completely untouched. With tiny resources, we concentrated on the working furnace rather than the whole glass-house which, as Harrington in 1948 and Wood in 1960 have shown, is a formidable but worthwhile task.

Although most of the first sites we examined or re-examined proved to be dis-appointing,[13] we made our main contribution to the work on the industry by the tracking down, identification and mapping of its extent; this was no quick or simple exercise. A statement on the condition of the sites and a summary of the results of work on this small industry may temper the disappointment felt by everyone approaching a site, seeing the great poverty of museum material, or reading this book.

Of the known Wealden sites we examined and proved,[14] two-thirds appeared to have been destroyed in whole or in part by cultivation or robbing, or were known to have been turned over by earlier workers.[15] Of the remainder, two glasshouses, Blunden's Wood, has been, and No. 42 will be, excavated by Mr Wood; two working furnaces were excavated and planned by Winbolt and six were examined (two closely) and proved by us. Some of the later Wealden glass furnaces were built of brick, but the design of the working furnace, as distinct from its appendages, was probably basically the same (*see* Chapter IV, p. 76). All the known furnaces in the Weald, in 1965, appear to have been rectangular; they differed in size and capacity, but with the limitations of wood-billet firing and flame-heated crucibles on siege platforms, the general design is unlikely to have varied greatly. No doubt the personal whims of a Schurterre in the fourteenth century or a Hensey in the sixteenth century decided how to achieve the greatest sustained heat, whether to have solid or cavity walls, how wide the fire box and siege platform should be and where to carry out the annealing.

Mr Wood points out in his authoritative paper the close similarity of the Blunden's Wood structure of c.1330 to that of the Jamestown (Va.) furnace in 1608. This suggests that, unless another wholly untouched glasshouse site or a Late site is found producing vessel glass as at Woodchester, any extensive work (except proving new sites), may provide little fresh basic information, though there is still much to dis-

---

[13] I am not suggesting that these sites will produce nothing of interest. A robbed glasshouse site can be very unrewarding, as workers in other districts have found.

[14] Proving is defined and suggestions are made on how to find a glasshouse site. For a detailed summary of the twenty-six sites and the work done on them, *see* Chapter IX, p. 150.

[15] We found only the leavings of earlier workers on seven sites. Unhappily these included the Sidney Wood glasshouse which produced the finest vessel glass known in the English forest glass industry; tiny scraps we found were fragmented into insignificance.

cover about the details, in particular where and how annealing was carried out. The labour involved is considerable, but such is the enthusiasm today that Mr Wood had twenty helpers for three weekends – resources undreamt of thirty years ago.

For a few years after 1931 I spent a fair amount of my leisure on various sites and after much labour realized how structurally unrewarding they could be, particularly in arable fields. I tended therefore to concentrate firstly on the search for new sites since there was always the chance of repeating Pape's good fortune, secondly on determining the extent of the industry, and thirdly on investigating the problems of colour and vessel form. A detailed examination of site No. 29 produced evidence that ruby glass was made there, but the pursuit of vessel forms has so far proved fruitless. I also spent time, which I do not regret, on the antiquarian project of collecting enough window glass to glaze a small lancet window in Kirdford church[16] as Cooper had done at Chiddingfold (see p. 8).

Of the twenty-eight proved and probable glasshouse sites before 1939, two-thirds were established by Winbolt and myself and the remaining known sites re-examined.[17] The scale and distribution of the industry was broadly decided and the great change in the mid-sixteenth century in the Weald observed; both were reinforced later. We spent more time searching for and proving than on the detailed examination of sites; however, I now wish that I had examined the site at Wephurst (No. 21) more thoroughly for any traces of structure.

My experience of material from Wealden glasshouse sites suggests that the rare and interesting glass fragments are probably imported cullet or waste glass (see p. 18) and therefore useless as evidence of production. It is also most unwise to assume from a few handfuls of glass fragments that the glasshouse produced only, or even mainly, window or vessel glass. Waste glass was so valuable that what is found, even if it was the local product, may only be scraps from the last batch produced at the site and it provides no reliable guide as to the glasshouse production. Such glass as survives can be highly misleading and needs very cautious interpretation (see p. 18). The evidence is often further confused, when the site has been dug over for its stone and bricks or so disturbed by tree roots that fragments from different batches are all muddled up.

Searchers are not always welcome in carefully preserved woodland and on some sites I had only an odd half-day or two – conditions not unknown today on rescue digs. On the whole owners were interested.

It is difficult, without endless qualifications, to preserve the delicate balance of correct emphasis and yet provide a clear picture, and firmly to separate fact from fancy because much slight evidence belongs to a shadowy world of part truth and part opinion.

Cooper and Winbolt

Winbolt drew some of his material, in particular Chapter II of *Wealden Glass*, from the Rev. T. S. Cooper's 'History of Chiddingfold' and he gratefully acknow-

---

[16] Dedicated June 1933 as a memorial to the industry.
[17] A summary of work on the sites is given on p. 150.

ledges in his introduction that the book 'would never have been attempted had not the Rev. T. S. Cooper and Mrs Halahan of Chiddingfold shown the way.'

Mrs Halahan, Cooper's daughter, found and examined a furnace site in Fromes Copse (No. 5) three years after her father died. She lectured to the Newcomen Society in 1925 on the industry.[18] Though she lacked her father's meticulous accuracy, she tells us the dates when some glasshouses were found and the useful fact that the interesting crucible fragment containing ruby glass, now in Guildford Museum, was found at the Chaleshurst Lower kiln (No. 4).

In general I have used her father's evidence, except in a few instances in Chapter IX where her evidence is marked (H). I think there is a possibility that her and her father's theory that the flints found on glasshouse sites were used for cutting glass may be correct; it is a possible reason for their presence. Flints will mark the soft Early glass and before the diamond cutters of the sixteenth and seventeenth centuries they may have been useful but whether glass was 'cut' on the forest sites, except for convenience of transport,[19] is by no means certain.

Three sites are marked on the O.S. maps, No. 37 on the 2½-in., Nos. 23 and 31 on the 25-in. sheets.[20] Apart from these and some stray finds in Hovel Copse, Chiddingfold (see p. 157), Cooper was the pioneer investigator of glassmaking in the Weald. He lived in Chiddingfold from 1875 to 1918 when he died,[21] and assisted the vicar from 1880. He was the secretary of the Surrey Archaeological Society,[22] a Fellow of the Society of Antiquaries, and did an extensive uncovering of the Roman Villa site in the parish from 1888 onwards although he published no findings. He knew Chiddingfold intimately and devoted much time to studying its history, in particular the remarkable collection of ancient documents then belonging to the Sadler family of Pockford, Chiddingfold, and mostly relating to that parish. The deeds are now in the Guildford Muniment Room (GMR) and are extensively referred to in Chapter I.

Cooper's 'History of Chiddingfold,'[23] with its twenty-seven page appendix on 'Glass,' was possibly started soon after he came to live in the parish. Unhappily the first proved glasshouse site was not found by the family until 1911, two years after he had become a semi-invalid, so the actual handling of local glass was possible only at the end of his life when his health was failing.

[18] *Trans. Newcomen Soc.*, Vol. 5, pp. 75–85 (1924–5).   [19] *See* site No. 14.
[20] The O.S. records were unhappily destroyed during the Second World War; it is unlikely that any information relating to these sites has survived.
[21] His obituary is in *Sy.A.C.*, vol. 31, p. viii.
[22] Seventy years later, Mr E. S. Wood was Secretary of the Society; Cooper would have rejoiced at his work.
[23] This detailed and scholarly work remained in MS., inaccessible to students, until 1957, when a copy (730 pages including the appendices, in two bound volumes) was typed by his daughter Mrs E. Brodhurst Hill and most kindly deposited, together with his loose notes, in Haslemere Museum, by her and two other daughters, the late Mrs P. Baker and Miss A. Cooper. I am very grateful to them for their help.

The 'Glass' appendix, from internal evidence, seems to have been completed by him before 1911 and therefore based only on documents. The last few pages must have been added later by his family to try and bring it up to date.[24]

It is clear from his loose notes that four sites, Nos. 2, 3, 4 and 7, had all been examined by the family before he died in 1918 and provided much of the Cooper material now in Haslemere and Guildford Museums. There were six daughters and a son and some competition among them to find glass. Due to ill-health Cooper did little excavation on the glasshouse sites and though he saw the four sites above, he had to rely largely on what the family unearthed.[25] The only kiln he excavated was at Messels, c.1904; he was then in his prime and left a good plan and photographs among his notes. Unhappily this is almost certainly a tile kiln, no trace of any glass or crucible having been found there (see p. 156). Such careful work would have been most welcome at other sites, e.g., No. 7 found in 1912, though he laments that it was almost completely destroyed.

The whole of his 'History,' including the appendix on 'Glass' but excluding additions, by his family, was probably written before he had seen or handled any quantity of the local glass. Therefore for the archaeological side of his work we must go to his loose notes, apparently made between 1911 and 1918, and to his glass material. This has been a difficult task, but it would have been impossible to sort out and discuss the Chiddingfold sites in Chapter IX otherwise. In his last seven years he had handled much Early glass, which fascinated him, since he had seen only the documentary side for thirty years or more.

As Chiddingfold had long been known to have been a centre for glassmaking,[26] and Cooper had found glassmakers in the parish registers and in the Sadler deeds, it was natural that he and his family should start hunting for furnace sites. Cooper's 'History' shows that the Schurterres were making glass in the fourteenth century and were associated with Chiddingfold from the fourteenth to the seventeenth centuries, as were the Peytowes from the fifteenth to the seventeenth centuries (see Chapter VIII). Although no member of either family can be traced as glazier or

---

[24] On p. 72 it says 'When a selection of the Chiddingfold glass was taken to the Castle Arch Museum, Guildford, in 1919, it was noticed that the glass from the Chaleshurst kiln was remarkably similar to that brought from Chertsey Abbey.' Cooper died in 1918 so this comparison was not his. From the context the comparison appears to have been made with some painted window glass found at Chaleshurst furnace site. Glass painting was done by town glaziers not forest glass-makers, so the painted fragments were probably cullet (see p. 18) and could have originated anywhere in northern Europe. I suggest that all uncoloured north European forest glass looks much the same and that it is probably impossible to decide its origin by appearance.

[25] I am indebted to Miss A. Cooper for this information and also for providing the photograph of her father (Plate I).

[26] Aubrey (1626–97), Surrey, Vol. 4, p 36, Chidingefold: 'In Queen Elizabeth's time here eleven Glass-houses, which as nuisances, and in regard there were others at Hindhead, were put down by a petition of Part of this County.' There may have been eleven glasshouses working in Surrey at various times during Elizabeth's reign, but it is very unlikely they were all in Chiddingfold. I know of no clues at Hindhead.

glassmaker in the fifteenth century, some of them may have practised the art and kept the tradition alive until the first recorded Peytowe glassmaker in 1536. Thereafter, until the industry shut down, another seven Peytowe glassmakers are known.

Cooper confined his activities to Chiddingfold glass and knew or suspected all the sites in the parish except No. 5, but only Nos. 2, 3, 4 and 7 seem to have produced any significant amount of material before 1918. In 1916 he glazed a small window in Chiddingfold Church, made up of 427 fragments (224 being coloured)[27] from three glasshouse sites, probably sites Nos. 2, 3 and 7. The inscription under the window should be read in conjunction with the family associations discussed in Chapters I and VIII. Cooper realized that cullet was used but it is not clear from his notes if he understood that painted window glass fragments must have been cullet brought in from outside.

Both Cooper and Winbolt were well aware of the value of field-name clues, and Cooper followed up all those in Chiddingfold.[28] Both appreciated the possible value of pottery fragments for dating purposes. Cooper's best collection of pottery came from a site, Schurterreshurst, for which the evidence of glassmaking is poor. Winbolt and I found pottery on six of the easily dated Late sites, but nothing significant on the Early ones.[29]

To Cooper the parish was his world. The reverse was true of Winbolt. Cooper was a meticulous worker who, if he had had the luck to find a glasshouse site in his hey-day, would have made a fine job of it. There were two within about 500 yards of his house, a major consideration forty years ago. Winbolt, the pioneer who revelled in the challenge of distant horizons, was always eager to be off over the next range of hills. A great optimist, he may have hoped to return and complete his provisional work on some sites. As a scholar he was far from irresponsible and was careful to publish such work as he had been able to do. Such an outlook had its drawbacks as well as its virtues in an archaeologist.

Compared with the present burst of archaeological activity the digging resources of Cooper and Winbolt were very small and usually consisted of members of their families. The aim of Winbolt and myself was to track down a site and, with the usual absence of any surviving structure, to prove its existence by exposing traces of the furnace floor or burnt area, and to discover such glass as remained, with any associated

[27] The coloured fragments are almost certainly all cullet, imported for English windows from northern Europe (*see* also Chapter V).

[28] I have examined thirty-five Tithe Apportionment schedules in an attempt, I think successful, to find the limits of glassmaking in the Weald. The task was laborious but relatively simple today, with the schedules and maps grouped in County Record Offices, a situation unknown thirty years ago. Field-names are fully discussed in Chapter IX, p. 147.

[29] The explanation is that we followed the Coopers on four Early sites and found no pottery. Twelve of our fresh sites were Late, only six being Early, of these three had been wholly or largely destroyed (Nos. 12, 15 and 18), one (No. 20) showed no promise and we only proved its existence; one (No. 21) produced only an intrusion of pottery and the remaining glasshouse (No. 29) nothing.

pottery. Apart from Fernfold and Vann (Nos. 25 and 35), five other promising sites were examined, two being re-examined in detail. The glass fragments were interesting and though some traces of floors survived, no traces of any structure were found.[30]

When Cooper began on the Chiddingfold glass industry, probably before A. Hartshorne's monumental book *Old English Glasses* was published in 1897,[31] he naturally accepted the one authority then available, Charles Winston's *Hints on Glass Painting*.[32] Winston considered that ancient window glass could be closely dated by its thickness. This set Cooper off measuring with great accuracy and dating to very close limits; to a lesser extent Winbolt followed this dating by appearance.

It would be tedious to contradict such of Cooper or Winbolt's writings with which I disagree[33] on the grounds of insufficient evidence or because new material has changed their interpretations. Both men were scholars and would welcome additions and amendments to their work. In general I simply omit the differences but three examples of such omissions may be mentioned:

1. Close dating by appearance and thickness. For example, Winbolt mentions, *W.G.*, p. 37, at Broomfield Hanger (site No. 2) that the glass was 'light milky green of the thirteenth and fourteenth century and a piece of crucible with an inturned rim seems to corroborate this dating.' I suggest that today we can do no more than divide the Weald glass by its appearance and quality into pre- and post-mid-sixteenth century, with some Transitional, but I have added a rider that in general the bulk of very thick, poor glass is probably the earliest and the bulk of very fine quality thin glass the latest (*see* p. 104).[33a]

2. The idea put forward in *W.G.* that crucibles having inturned rims, as described by Theophilus, are early, is not confirmed by the site evidence. Both in- and out-turned rims are found on a number of sites and the most heavily inturned rims are found at site No. 32, one of the last furnaces to work, possibly in the early seventeenth century.

3. I have omitted most of the *W.G.* (p. 72) family associations and mentioned only those for which there is some evidence, albeit slight. Most of it is confined

[30] Such were Nos. 7 (re-examined), 14, 23, 29 and 38 (re-examined) and to a less extent Nos. 12, 17 and 21. These are discussed in Chapter IX.

[31] Hartshorne quotes (p. 132), from the Glasewryth deed (*see* p. 31) in the Sadler collection, so Cooper must have told him of it. Cooper, later in life, and Winbolt probably made use of Hartshorne.

[32] Among Cooper's loose notes at Haslemere is a letter to W. E. Hulme saying that 'Winston's excellent book *Hints on Glass Painting* (1846) had enabled me to date this glass approximately.'

[33] For this reason, and because some of the sites given cannot be substantiated, I suggest that the tentative synopsis of sites in *W.G.*, p. 51, might be disregarded. I have substituted my own tentative list in the schedule to the distribution map in Chapter IX. Winbolt would certainly have abandoned his close dating into centuries, which he attempts in this synopsis and probably also his 'rough chronological classification' of Weald vessel forms into three periods (*W.G.*, p. 69), because too little is known about the forms. But he is broadly correct in placing our blue-green glass into his third period, 1550–1620 (*see* p. 100).

[33a] Dr D. B. Harden kindly tells me that some of the Saxon window glass from Glastonbury and Monkswearmouth was very thin.

to Chiddingfold and Kirdford[34] in the Late period. Where I differ from Winbolt on any important point, such as the re-use of furnace sites, both views are discussed.

To Winbolt goes the credit for getting some information into print and for extending the limits of this glass industry into other parishes, mainly south and east of Chiddingfold. The first fifty-two pages of *Wealden Glass* were articles which had appeared in the now defunct *Sussex County Magazine*. Winbolt, writing for that popular but excellent magazine, realized the shortcomings of these articles but because of lack of funds they could not be altered and he was determined to get some of his own and Cooper's work into more permanent form.

Winbolt was a gay, delightful and generous companion, a great enthusiast, and something of a journalist eager to share his knowledge and get the public interested. He was much in demand to excavate ancient sites in Sussex and Surrey. Thirty years ago when only a very few archaeologists were paid, the odd press contribution provided modest and necessary car expenses, a fact sometimes forgotten then, and now. He used to put short notes in *The Times* as soon as a new glass site was found; he had little patience with a paper buried in a learned journal ten years late, a trait which carried obvious dangers. I think he realized this but had decided that if the closed shop of forty years ago was to be opened and public interest aroused, he must be prepared to risk an occasional tumble. He took these tumbles with great good humour. One I remember came in a letter from an eminent west country archaeologist, who strode solemnly down from Sinai and broke the tables of the law on Winbolt's head for daring to say that archaeology was fun. Both men served their generation well. Possibly the ideal lies between the two extreme schools of thought, the quick and the dead, and Winbolt's *Wealden Glass* would, I think, have been better for a longer gestation, but life is short and a great mass of knowledge has died with over-leisurely perfectionists.

Winbolt excelled as a field archaeologist; the photograph shows him as such (Plate II). Roman roads fascinated him and I think his best and most matured work was *With a Spade on Stane Street* (1936). He lived near it for many years. His eager pioneering spirit could not be confined to a single patch of ground and he delighted in being involved at one time with an Iron Age camp, a stretch of Stane Street and a new glasshouse site.

Our site work was done mainly with the spade rather than the trowel. The admirable technique of the leaders of archaeology in the '20s and '30s had not penetrated down to become common practice. Such a lag occurs and no doubt will occur, in all skills. It is too often forgotten that the ordinary archaeologists of forty years ago did some good work and that only their relatively hasty methods, due in part to trifling resources, and their destruction of evidence, in key sites are remembered and scorned. Much work would never have been done but for them; they stimulated

[34] The history of both parishes has been closely studied, Chiddingfold by Cooper and Kirdford by myself. The glassmaking families are fully discussed in Chapter VIII.

public interest which has made possible the cash and labour available today. I doubt
if the present generation appreciates the great leap forward in the standards, technique and knowledge in the general run of archaeological work which has taken
place in the last thirty or forty years.

Winbolt was educated at Corpus Christi College, Oxford, and retired, c.1930,
after thirty-five years as classics master at his old school, Christ's Hospital; he died in
1944, aged 76.

Mr I. D. Margary, in the last paragraph of his obituary of Winbolt in *S.N.Q.*,
vol. 10, p. 47, admirably sums up the latter's work: 'To his friends he showed great
charm of manner, and as a correspondent nothing was too much trouble. Perhaps as
a result of his school life, he had the gift of encouraging beginners and young helpers
in archaeology which the writer, for one, most gratefully acknowledges, and this
human touch undoubtedly helped the popular side of his work. Science owes much
to such leaders at the present time.'

After 1939 very little was done for twenty years, though I kept in touch and
checked any reported sites. One, No. 9, turned up in 1951 having been destroyed
by a bulldozer. In 1959 Dr D. B. Harden suggested that I attempted a re-assessment
of Winbolt's *Wealden Glass* and since then seven[35] fresh sites have come to light;
two, Nos. 33 and 42, which showed some promise have been or will be completely
excavated by Mr E. S. Wood.

I have examined all the known evidence for the Coopers sites. They are the
ten, and one possible, Chiddingfold sites, two of which were suspected by Cooper
and confirmed on the ground by myself. Winbolt and I found another eighteen (two
being refound) and seven were found by A. D. R. Caroe, F. W. Cobb, N. Farmer,
F. Holling, A. B. Nicholls, W. Taylor and N. P. Thompson.

Some Authorities

For the technical details of medieval glassmaking we must rely on Theophilus, a
monk, writing in Germany, probably in the first half of the twelfth century. He
describes our 'northern' processes and rectangular furnace, whereas the two later
more specialized writers, Månsson and Agricola, writing in the sixteenth century
from long Italian experience, describe the processes and round furnace of the 'south'.[36]
Theophilus is valuable because there is no other medieval description. His account

[35] Nos. 8, 16, 27, 33, 39, 41 and 42. They are discussed in Chapter IX. Three are certain and four
are probable.

[36] Extracts from these three writers are given in a valuable appendix of *W.G.*, pp. 74-81. W. B.
Honey in *Glass* (1946), p. ix, says 'The most important modern book on the glassmaker's practice
was Antonio Neri's *L'arte vetraria* (Florence, 1612) which was translated into English, with a commentary by Christopher Merret in 1662...' In 1962 Professor W. E. S. Turner read a paper on
Merret to the Society of Glass Technology; see *Glass Technology*, Vol. 3, no. 6 (1962), pp. 201-13. Of
Neri he says 'references to furnaces and processes are few and casual, a knowledge of these aspects of the
subject being taken for granted.'

is readily accessible and I have made some use of it to amplify our slender evidence.[37]

The second volumes of the Victoria County Histories of Sussex (1907) and Surrey (1905) include sections on the industry. The former by Dr L. F. Salzman, has some interesting documentary material relating to the Beckley glasshouse in 1579 which is included in Chapter IX. Cooper's work on the Sadler deeds is used and acknowledged in the Surrey volume but with no reference to the source of the material. There are two errors: that charcoal was used in the forest furnaces and that the industry moved to Lambeth. The fuel was wood billets and the Wealden glassmakers moved principally to the West Midlands and later to Newcastle upon Tyne; only two individuals can be traced to London.

I hope that any material used for direct quotation has been acknowledged. Such quotations are not unusually large except for those in Chapters VII and VIII which owe much to Mrs E. S. Godfrey's thesis on 'The Development of English Glassmaking 1560–1640.'[38] It is to be hoped this will be published as it is of great value for the Weald industry in general and for Isaac Bungar, glassmaker, of Wisborough Green and Billingshurst, a leader in this industry during its last twenty years or so, in particular (see Chapter VIII).

Possible Origins

Knowledge of glassmaking in England until the latter half of the sixteenth century is very meagre. There are Roman glasshouse sites at Wilderspool, Cheshire, and Caistor-by-Norwich, and a late Saxon one at Glastonbury,[39] but there are only about a dozen medieval furnace sites in England, compared with 168 in France.[40] The numbers reflect the relative importance of the industry in France and England.

There is no evidence of its place of origin, but the most likely is the forêt de Lyons region in Normandy, fifteen miles east of Rouen, which had a flourishing glass industry at least from the early years of the fourteenth century.[41] The industry is known to have been established in Chiddingfold by 1351 (see Chapter I) but may have started about a hundred years earlier. The shipping link between Fécamp or Rouen and Littlehampton was easy and some enterprising Norman may have penetrated up the Arun to Wisborough Green, Kirdford and Chiddingfold.

In 1560 the glassworks of Burgundy, Lorraine and Normandy were famed for

[37] Theophilus. *De Diversis Artibus*. Translated and edited by C. R. Dodwell (1961).

[38] Abbreviated hereafter to *D.E.G.* I am very much indebted to Mrs Godfrey for kindly allowing me to use her work and to Mr R. J. Charleston, Keeper of Ceramics at the Victoria and Albert Museum, for lending me his photostat copy of this thesis.

[39] D. B. Harden, 'Domestic Window Glass: Roman, Saxon and Medieval,' in E. M. Jope (ed.) *Studies in Building History* (London, 1961), p. 53, and the extensive bibliography given there. *See also* D. B. Harden, *Glastechnische Berichte* 32K (1959), Heft VIII, Sunderband V, pp. viii, 15 (for Caistor).

[40] J. Barrelet, *La Verrerie en France* (Paris, 1953), p. 153. G. H. Kenyon, 'Some Comments on the Medieval Glass Industry in France and England', *News and Reviews of the Society of Glass Technology*, 43, 18 (1959). The dating evidence is discussed in Chapter VI.

[41] E. Gerspach, *L'art de la verrerie* (1885), p. 229 et seq.

the quality of their window glass, the best, coming from Normandy, was readily accessible for England. Even as late as 1690 'French glass' was used in the windows of the main rooms at Petworth House.[42]

The Beginnings in the Weald

There were glasshouses in Kirdford and Hambledon, adjoining Chiddingfold, in the fourteenth century, but the main expansion of the industry did not come until after the mid-sixteenth century when, following its fuel supply southeastwards into the Weald, it had spread to the neighbouring parishes of Wisborough Green, Lurgashall, Alford, Ewhurst and probably Billingshurst. But even at its peak, c.1600, it was almost entirely confined to a district about ten miles square in the extreme northwest of the Weald Clay on both sides of and close to the Surrey–Sussex border. More than three-quarters of the known glass furnaces were in the old parishes of Chiddingfold, Kirdford and Wisborough Green, the latter being the centre of Elizabethan Wealden glass production.

The industry could have settled wherever fuel was plentiful[43] but, apart from the vague shipping link mentioned, there is no apparent reason why the Chiddingfold area was selected. Perhaps it was one of those accidents of history – or industry. It is true that fuel was plentiful and local sand from Hambledon may have been used but it is unlikely that any local clay was used for crucibles. The district is remote from port, river or trading centre. The scanty records suggest that the industry survived in Chiddingfold for at least 260 years until it moved to coal-producing areas in c.1618, but until the mid-sixteenth century very little is known about it.

Fine vessel glass was imported and the crude forest wares are unlikely to have found a wide market, except for bottles, phials, and apothecaries' wares. But with the increasing use of both window and vessel glass in houses, due to the sharp rise in the standards of dwelling and of living in the sixteenth century, demand grew rapidly and a small industry expanded to meet it with a great improvement in quality. There is no evidence to suggest that until the mid-sixteenth century this industry was more than small.

The Great Change

The fact that for at least 200 years the woodlands of three parishes could support this industry is probably some indication of its small size. The most interesting and significant stage was reached in the second half of the sixteenth century when owing to the enterprise of Jean Carré, this undistinguished forest industry grew into something four or five times its former size:[44] from possibly one or two glasshouses

[42] S.A.C., vol. 96, pp. 99.

[43] It takes between seven and ten tons of coal (D.E.G., p. 362), and a greater weight of wood billets to produce a ton of glass so that forest siting was economically desirable for any sustained glass production.

[44] There are thirteen Early sites known in about 250 years, three being provisional. There are sixteen Late sites known in the last fifty or so years, three being provisional.

working at one time to probably about six[45] and some of these probably producing a much greater weight of glass. The larger production was brought about by much increased demand and vastly improved technique. The primitive and uneven beginning is interesting but the technical renaissance largely brought about by Carré and his Frenchmen and their descendants is the really fascinating development, and is also more adequately documentated.

The window glass industry in the Weald may have fallen on evil times when Carré erected two glasshouses at Fernfold, Sussex, in 1567, and the art may have been temporarily lost[46] Carré was also the founder of the English crystal glass industry[47] in London, later taken over by Verzelini.

Two quite separate markets were catered for—the Weald window and vessel glass for widespread domestic use, and the London crystal for the luxury trade; in the 1570s under Verzelini the latter equalled the finest Venetian product. The last twenty years of the sixteenth century saw the development of English glassmaking after a shadowy and undistinguished prelude stretching from the fourteenth century and possibly earlier.

During the sixteenth century the evidence increases; we have a few surviving wills, deeds and the start of parish registers. After 1567 and until the industry moved out of the forests fifty years later, there are petitions, quarrels, inquiries by the authorities and, in the last three years (1615–18), the conflict between the wood-fired Wealden forest glasshouses represented by Isaac Bungar and the Henseys (see Chapter VIII) and the coal-fired town glasshouses represented to an increasing extent by Mansell.[48] There is more known because there was more happening. Quarrels and fuel troubles, which may have become acute with the increased number of glasshouses, no doubt led to difficulties in the industry, but it was the development of the more efficient, coal-fired furnace and Mansell's determination to enforce the Proclamation of 1615 prohibiting the use of wood fuel in glass furnaces that finally drove it away.

Some Glassmaking Families

It has usually been assumed that the industry was worked entirely by foreigners. This was not so in the Weald, where two prominent, long-established yeoman

[45] In 1589 George Longe said 'there are now fifteen glasshouses in England' (see Chapter VIII, p. 143). This is the only evidence and the figures seem likely. The number of known glasshouse sites in the Late period was sixteen for the Weald and possibly twenty-seven in the rest of England and so we might expect about six glasshouses working in the Weald in 1589.

[46] See Chapter V, p. 84.   [47] D.E.G., p. 306.

[48] Admiral Sir Robert Mansell came into the industry as a company promoter in 1615 shortly before the Proclamation prohibiting the use of wood fuel in glasshouses. W. B. Honey, Glass, p. 97, says of him: 'By 1618 Mansell had bought out his partners, and in 1623 a comprehensive patent gave him the sole right to make "all manner of drinking glasses, broad glass, window glasses, looking glasses . . .".'

families, the Peytowes of Chiddingfold and the Strudwicks of Kirdford[49] were also making glass. There were at least seven Peytowes in the trade between 1536 and 1616 and at least six Strudwicks between 1557 and 1614; the Peytowes were established as landowners in Chiddingfold for at least a century before they are described as glass-makers, though some may have practised the art, and the Strudwicks are an ancient Sussex family. It is such well-rooted families who provide a vital link transforming history into something more than a meaningless fantasy. They bring a hint of life to dead and despoiled furnace sites. At least one Strudwick furnace site is known and, thanks to Cooper's work on the Sadler deeds, two or three possibilities for those of the Peytowes can be suggested.

Glassmaking could probably be fitted into the cycle of the farming year, because the furnaces shut down for two or three months in summer; it provided an alternative source of income and absorbed some floating winter labour in the provision of fuel. Both families farmed on a considerable scale for this district, and the Strudwicks of Idehurst in Kirdford were also ironmasters in a small way from at least 1584 to at least 1634.[50] Presumably both families benefited from the mid-sixteenth-century improvements; the Late site evidence supports this without exception. Both families continued in the district until recently, whereas by 1620 the immigrant French glassmakers had moved away with their trade to other districts.[51] An example of the French glassmakers' clear-cut movements can be found in the parish registers of Wisborough Green in which they appear in 1567 and disappear fifty years later. Wisborough Green was the centre of Elizabethan forest glassmaking in the Weald.

These whole-time professionals had been the leaders in a boom period, whereas our yeoman glassmakers were probably followers only and resumed their husbandry when the industry moved away.

The social and economic effects on the district until after the mid-sixteenth century were probably negligible and even at the peak time of our glass production farming was the basis of local economy.

Glasshouse Sites

Nothing is visible at any of the Wealden glasshouse sites. The industry here was based on its fuel supply, and with few tools[52] and small rough furnaces it was readily

---

[49] There is a single reference to a third yeoman family in 1547 when Richard Mose of Plaistow in Kirdford, is described as 'glassmaker.' Ten years later he appears again, as a plain yeoman. (Sussex Archaeological Society deeds, B. 541 and B.542).

[50] S.N.Q., vol. 13, p. 238. The forge hammers also would probably be out of water power in the summer and their working would also fit in with the farming year.

[51] An exception was Isaac Bungar who died at Pulborough in 1643 (see p. 135), but there is no evidence that he made any glass in the Weald after 1618.

[52] Glassmaker's tools are illustrated by Dr D. B. Harden and Mr R. J. Charleston in C. Singer and others, A History of Technology, vol. 2, p. 331, and vol. 3, p. 219. Dr Harden says that they 'have always been of primitive kind, and it is likely their shapes and varieties have changed very little from very early times.'

mobile and could follow its fuel; in a stoneless country it is not surprising that the sites were thoroughly robbed.

An Early glassmaker might rent some woodland for a few years and build a rough temporary furnace on it before moving to another source of fuel. Late glassmakers, possibly using larger furnaces such as Fernfold (No. 25), may have had more permanent, better built furnaces and carted their fuel some distance as Isaac Bungar appears to have done.[53]

In the Weald there is no such thing as a 'typical' site, though about one-third tend to conform to some pattern. Beech and oak billet-fired furnaces probably had of necessity some rough general pattern.[54] From the collective evidence of the glasshouse sites, there was no fairly uniform glass until the mid-sixteenth century and there were no 'typical' crucibles, though two shapes appear to have been common.

Types of Wealden Glass

Perhaps the most significant event in the English forest glass industry was the progressive improvement in quality probably brought about by Carré's imported French glassmakers and their descendants from c.1567 onwards. The change was probably due to a greatly improved technique and the result in the Weald is two usually unmistakable types of glass; pre- and post-mid-sixteenth century – the primitive and the modern – which may be called Early and Late.[55] The crucial evidence for suggesting that Carré was primarily responsible for the great and permanent improvement in Wealden glass is:

(a) Having obtained his licence and acted on it, Carré stated in 1567, 'I have erected two glasshouses at Fernefol, Sussex for Normandy and Lorraine glass by H.M. Licence, and one in London for crystal glass; and also brought over workmen at my own great cost and to the benefit of the kingdom.'[56] The names of the French glassmakers imported by Carré are known, and there is ample evidence that these families stayed in England. They and their descendants can be traced as leaders of the industry during the last fifty years of forest glassmaking, principally in the Weald, until its end in 1618, when some of the Lorraine glassmakers became leaders in the new coal-fired glasshouses in Stourbridge and Newcastle upon Tyne. So much is recorded history.[57]

(b) The great and sustained change in glass type can be shown to have largely come about during the fifty years following Carré's licence in 1567, because most of the sites where the Late type glass is found in the Weald and other counties can be dated by surviving pottery or documents.

---

[53] *See* p. 133.   [54] *See* p. 76.
[55] This distinction is essential and is emphasized by capital letters throughout.
[56] *The Antiquary*, vol. 30, p. 211. The letter may be dated to July 1567.
[57] This is all set out in Chapter VIII.

There may have been other attempts to revive the industry and some Late type glass of moderate quality may ante-date Carré by a few years, but there is, in 1965, no evidence that they were sustained. I am much indebted to Mr E. S. Wood for discussing his glasshouse site at Knightons (No. 42) and for persuading me that this proviso about earlier attempts is necessary; it is probably unwise to be too precise as to the date of the great change.

From the early fourteenth to the mid-sixteenth century 'Early' Wealden glass was usually soft with no sharp fracture, semi-opaque, and pale milky-green with a, now, rough and often corroded surface. Apart from the individual batch variations which are considerable, and some has completely decayed, there appears to be little general difference for two or three centuries, so that any exact dating of the product before the mid-sixteenth century, by its appearance or by qualitative analysis, is probably impossible.

After the mid-sixteenth century to c.1618 the 'Late' glass, at its best indistinguishable from modern glass, was mostly hard with a sharp fracture, fairly clear, dark blue-green with a burnished surface which is seldom corroded,[58] and much more uniform in appearance than the earlier, poorer glass.

There are three glasshouse sites (Nos. 13, 16 and 17), whose indeterminate glass does not fit into the two main (Early and Late) types, but might belong to either. Two of these glasshouses were probably working in 1557 and so I have provisionally suggested the name 'Transitional' for this glass.[59]

I have abandoned the terms fougère (potash) and barilla (soda) glass because analysis has shown that all Weald glass was potash glass.

I am much indebted to Mr N. P. Bridgewater, who excavated the St Weonards glasshouse in 1961, for most kindly and firmly refusing to accept Carré's possible use of barilla soda as the reason for the great progressive change brought about in the Weald.[60] Mr Bridgewater has been amply supported by subsequent evidence: it was improved technique and not any change of chemical composition that brought about the improvement, although Late glass shows a markedly lower alkali content.

There is no evidence that 'crystal' glass was made in the Weald, or at any of the forest glasshouses. The few scraps found on the Late sites are cullet.

The late Mr E. Barrington Haynes, who was head of Messrs. Churchills, and a great authority on vessel glass of all periods, wrote in *Glass Through the Ages* (Pelican books, 1948), p. 114, of the Late Weald glass:

'But there is also a later type of metal of the Carré period, to which too much praise can hardly be given. The fragments betray excellent workmanship, the metal is homogeneous and free from bubbles, while its texture and finish is surprisingly good ... Latterly it was a rather deep blue-green, not unlike that found in Spanish coastal glass of relative and later date. In fact, the whole range

[58] There are two exceptions to this, Nos. 37 and 42.
[59] *See* p. 103.   [60] *See* Chapter II, pp. 41, 42.

of tints rather recalls the varying colours of seventeenth-eighteenth century Spanish peasant glass.'

He was much interested in the industry and shared my disappointment at the poverty of our vessel material with its vague hints only of beautiful forms.

Cullet

The glass industry feeds on its own waste which is collected and goes into the next batch, so there is often little surviving on a site.[61] Another source of confusion is that, owing to constant demand, a high proportion of the surviving fragments may represent the last phase in the life of the glasshouse. A glasshouse site is therefore seldom a promising source of glass evidence,[62] and that evidence needs careful assessing: it cannot be taken at its face value. A small glass vessel can easily break into 100 fragments, so the best measure is bulk. On the most prolific site one might get two gallons or more of fragments and this is a tiny and probably unrepresentative part of the glasshouse production. Cullet hinders the corrosive action on the bottom of crucibles, assists the melting and thriftily swells the volume of the next batch. The wastage at the glasshouse from faults and breakages was probably high[63] The proportion of cullet used depended on the available supply and a batch could be made up wholly of cullet.[64] Waste also came from glaziers' workshops[65] and any place through which our glass carriers passed and might include broken church windows; such glass could have originated in France[66] so any fragments of glass not

[61] Mr J. C. Harrington's extensive, over 4,000 sq. ft., excavation of the glasshouse at Jamestown (Va.) produced very little glass. I suggest the reason, as in some of our sites, may simply be that every scrap of cullet was used and that any from the last batch was taken to some fresh, unknown kiln nearby.

[62] 'The evidence of excavation on glasshouse sites is diminished by the fact that glass-cullet may be used again, unlike the shards and wasters of a pottery kiln, which are usually found in much greater abundance.' W. B. Honey, *Glass*, p. 4, note 6.

[63] Winbolt (*W.G.*, p. 57), quoting from *The Journal of Glass Technology*, Sept. 1932, p. 385, gives the amount of wastage in a model glassworks in Sweden during nine months as: 'glass faults 6·7%, bad work 6·3%, lehr breakage 0·8%, losses incurred by breaking during cracking off, grinding, cutting, etching and painting 10·6%,' a total of 24·4%.

[64] I am indebted to Dr D. B. Harden for this information. He also tells me that the workers at the reconstructed Jamestown furnace today, for instance, use only cullet.

[65] On 29 November 1579 the *Mayflower* of 8 tons brought to Rye from London 'broken glass and glass-making tools.' (*See* The Port Books of Rye, S.R.S., vol. 64. I am much obliged to Mr R. F. Dell for allowing me to use his material before publication and to Dr L. F. Salzman for kindly sending me the proofs.) The cullet and tools were probably for the Beckley or Northiam glasshouses (*see* Chapter X, p. 212). Normal furnace wastage was probably insufficient for their requirements. For Mansell's difficulty in getting cullet, *see* Chapter II, p. 38.

Cullet was so valued that it was shipped to France and in 1612 there were four separate shipments of broken glass from Meeching [Newhaven] to Deepe [Dieppe] and one to St Palleres in Somme. The amounts varied from six to twelve barrels and the dues collected were 3*d.* a barrel; *see* Port Books of Meeching and Lewes, P.R.O., 756/21.

[66] It is probably impossible to distinguish any medieval north European forest glass, window or vessel, away from its site of manufacture.

found in a crucible are theoretically suspect. In practice the mass of ordinary fragments is likely to be home-made, but the rare, unusual and interesting fragments are, unhappily, of doubtful origin. However, the site evidence has some value because if, say, a pint of blown-glass fragments remain scattered around a site and if more than ninety per cent. are fairly uniform and fall within the type limits defined on p. 17 and in Chapter VI, I suggest that the scraps were probably made on the site and may be used as evidence for showing that vessel and window (muff and/or crown) were produced there. They can rarely provide a guide to the relative proportions of the production (see also p. 5).

It is evident that cullet was brought in to supplement the normal furnace waste because broken window with painted decoration and lead marks has been found on furnace sites, and windows were not painted or leaded up in a forest. I suspect that fragments of window glass showing grozed edges[67] are also cullet, because such shaping by crushing, mainly before the advent of diamond cutters, is generally the work of glaziers not glassmakers.[68] Some sites appear to have been almost stripped of their waste so that the amount of glass surviving on any site has little significance. The three sites, Nos. 14, 23 and 38, where a considerable quantity, perhaps a gallon or more, of glass fragments survived, were Late and in all probability were simply abandoned when the makers moved to the coal producing areas in about 1618.[69] The same explanation can perhaps be given for the collections of fragments from Woodchester (Glos.) and Bishop's Wood (Staffs.).[70] An attempt was made by Messrs Powell in about 1920 at reconstructing twenty forms based on the Woodchester fragments. The late J. Stuart Daniels's book, *The Woodchester Glass House* (Bellows, Glos., 1960), has valuable illustrations of the suggested types, some of which can be matched in the Weald (see Plate XIX). Fragments of Early glass are found on very few Late sites; the break, excluding possible Transitional sites, was clean.

Furnace Structure and Destruction

The discovery of a site is usually a matter of following up a field-name clue, identifying the site and its type of glass and seeing if anything remains to provide

[67] Grozed edges look as if a mouse had nibbled them; it can be compared in method and appearance to secondary flaking on flint implements.

[68] There is at least one probable exception to this, because at a Late site, No. 14, possibly working up to *c*.1618, quarries, small diamond-shaped window panes, were almost certainly produced (see p. 174, note 61). This would provide the waste normally found in a glazier's workshop and be one reason why so many fragments of window glass survived on the site.

[69] Four Early glasshouse sites (Nos. 3, 4, 5 and 7) may have had a considerable quantity of glass fragments but they were dug over by the Cooper family and the best appear to have been removed.

[70] The Bishop's Wood glass furnace, with crucible bases still in situ, is the most interesting and complete survival known. Conjectural reconstruction was unnecessary as only the roof had collapsed. This Elizabethan furnace was fully described by T. Pape, 'Medieval Glassworkers of North Staffordshire,' published in the *North Staffs. Field Club Trans.*, vol. 68 (1934). The paper includes useful material on the glassmaking families. The furnace is discussed in Chapter IV, p. 68.

some structural detail of interest, which it rarely does.[71] In rather more than half the known glasshouse sites a field-name was the reason for discovery.

The sites are described and eight-figure map references are given in Chapter IX, but some general comments may be useful here. Twenty-six glasshouse sites have been examined, twenty-one before 1939, by spade and spear, but only four so far, provided any useful structural result, Fernfold (No. 25), Blunden's Wood (No. 33) Vann (No. 35) and Knightons (No. 42).

Of the forty-two Wealden sites discussed and shown on the distribution map, sixteen including the four mentioned above, had varying amounts of furnace floor or baked clay base[72] surviving, depending on how thorough the stone robbers had been, and ten provided adequate evidence of glassmaking[73] but, for various reasons, in most cases the furnace was destroyed. In two cases, Nos. 13 and 32, sites were proved but not excavated; they might be worth further examination. There are ten probable sites, all having field-name clues plus a small amount of material evidence, and six possible sites which are shown in italics in the schedule (p. 152). Seven of the known sites had been turned over by earlier diggers, five by the Cooper family, one, No. 38, by the Rev. F. W. Cobb and at least one, No. 37, by someone unknown in the nineteenth century.[74]

How many glasshouses there were is unknown but it is likely that more will turn up.[75] The furnaces were little larger than bread ovens, with a working space roughly roofed in with timber supports; such poorly built affairs could be swallowed up long ago in the thousands of acres of copse and woodland surviving in the eight parishes which supported this small industry.

It is impossible to say how many Wealden glasshouses were originally in copses or woodland, because a very large area was planted in this district in the eighteenth and nineteenth centuries. Now that old pasture is ploughed up a few more sites have come to light as burnt areas with fragments of crucible and glass around them. What is quite certain is that all glasshouses were very close to, or actually in, copse or woodland, and if sites are found well out in a field, it is due to woodland clearance.[76] Because of copse planting, as well as the growth of tree roots, ploughing, and the demand for stone already mentioned, the chance of finding more than a burnt patch

---

[71] The search for and identification of glasshouse sites is given in the opening sections of Chapter IX.

[72] See p. 147.

[73] Details are given on p. 149, but in general, crucible fragments, plus a field-name, plus glass fragments, in that order of priority, are evidence of a glass furnace close by. Thinly glazed brick or stone alone are not. The waste dross produced at various stages of glassmaking at all forest glass furnaces is not always easy to distinguish from other vitreous slags (see also p. 76, note 25).

[74] See Chapter IX. The site was known in 1874. (Sy.A.C., vol. 6, p. 2.)

[75] I should not be surprised if there were at least a hundred of these primitive furnaces at various times during about three centuries in this small but heavily timbered district.

[76] A glance at the 1-inch O.S. map and the distribution map, shows that glasshouses were usually in or close to large areas of woodland.

is not good; these small, low furnaces in a clay country had to be built on top of the ground, with thick walls to conserve heat, and needed no foundations.

Two of the three best surviving glass furnace sites are in the extreme north of the Weald Clay district where it joins the Greensand ridge. This may be significant because here stone was easy to get and no one troubled to dig out the furnaces. Possibly the nearer to the Greensand ridges to the north and south of our district, the better the chance of finding an untouched glasshouse.

Wealden Iron and Glass: a Comparison

The Wealden industries of iron and glass had much in common except size, labour employed, geographical distribution and economic importance. Both:

1. Were attracted by ample fuel supplies and other raw materials.
2. Were practised in other suitable districts.
3. Were arts rather than sciences. Thus in 1611 glassmaking was referred to as 'the art, feat and mystery,'[77] and John Fuller, the great gun-founder, in a letter of 1754 wrote 'a furnace is a fickle mistress and must be humoured and her favours not to be depended upon.'[78]
4. Were sometimes sidelines for enterprising farmers. Glassmaking needed little capital equipment whereas the costly water-powered works of the Tudor iron industry were usually, in this district, provided by landowners and rented to the ironmaster.
5. Vastly improved their techniques in the sixteenth century.
6. Reached their peak in this district between c.1570 and c.1620.
7. Departed in general for the same reason, that coal firing was more efficient and less costly.[79]

But whereas techniques of ironfounding are well recorded, and the structural remains massive, little is known about the traditional process of glassmaking here, and structural remains are small.

Museums

I have seen glass from all except three (Nos. 1, 31 and 41) of the forty-two sites and it is a disappointing collection. The material is described in Chapter IX. Winbolt and I gave our best fragments to museums, but the bits were not exciting and were not always exhibited; in two instances they are lost and in others the labels have been

[77] V.C.H., *Surrey*, vol. 2, p. 300. This description in a Patent Roll is legal verbiage, but glassmaking remained an art and, to some extent, a mystery for many years to come. Prof. Turner (*S.A.G.T.*, vol. 5, p. 298, T.) says that glass making until well past the mid-nineteenth century has been 'generally rated as a precarious and secretive business. . . The day of a chemical industry making standardized products had yet to come.'

[78] Fuller Letter Book, 24 Oct. 1754, in Barbican House, Lewes.

[79] Fuel shortage is discussed in Chapter III, p. 45. In this district, in particular, the ore supply may have become worked out. *See* 'Iron ore working in the Weald Clay of the Western Weald' by B. C. Worssam, in *Proc. of The Geologists' Assn.*, vol. 75 (1964), pp. 529-546.

moved and the material is therefore of little value. This may not be important, apart from the loss of the material from Lorraine,[80] as long as Haslemere and Guildford Museums continue to stage a good exhibit of local glass. Luckily, I kept samples for comparative purposes from about two-thirds of the sites and I have revisited others, so there are only three (Nos. 15, 30 and 40) of the thirty-six certain and probable glasshouse sites for which there is no surviving evidence. These three certainly existed and are fully considered. In spreading our humble scraps around various museums, Winbolt's purpose was educational: he was showing people what to look for. In general the fragments were simply specimens of either crucible or glass, just as, on a much larger scale, specimens of bloomery cinder, blast furnace slag or forge clinker might be distributed from the thousands of tons still available.

My museum information in the schedule of sites is correct up to 1964. The great bulk of Cooper's and my material is or will be, eventually deposited at Haslemere Museum; the industry is not confined to one county and it would be unwise to split the evidence. Moreover Haslemere was originally a chapelry of Chiddingfold and is only a mile and a half from the nearest glasshouse (No. 8). The best of the Cooper collection is in Guildford Museum as is the small complete crucible together with some fragments of glass from Sidney Wood given by Winbolt and the finds from Blunden's Wood. There remains a little material in the Victoria and Albert Museum, with a small amount of comparative evidence from other counties. There is a very small amount in museums at Lewes and Littlehampton.

In Guildford Museum there is an excellent exhibit, recently (1965) carried out by Mr F. Holling, relating to the Wealden Glass industry, it includes:

1. A small model of a typical forest glass furnace based on the excavation of the Blunden's Wood site.

2. Two fine specimens of small crucibles, one complete from Sidney Wood and another less complete, from Lower Chaleshurst. The latter is particularly interesting because it contains some ruby glass, conclusive proof that ruby glass was made there.

3. Fragments of the more usual heavy and larger crucibles, which provide the most important evidence of a glasshouse site.

4. Fragments of vessel, showing the difference between the appearance of Early and Late glass.

5. Three large fragments of spun (crown) window glass.

6. Other interesting glasshouse finds mainly from Blunden's Wood.

On the wall behind is a brief description of the Wealden Glass industry together with:

1. Two distribution maps of the glasshouse sites in Surrey.

2. A photograph of a suggested reconstruction of a medieval glasshouse made

---

[80] This loss may be due to the labelling difficulty (*see* p. 151). The Lorraine glass is discussed under site No. 38.

by Mr J. Gardner for the Pilkington Museum. It is largely based on the Blunden's Wood glasshouse.

3. Photostat copies of two fourteenth-century documents relating to the industry, the originals of which are now in the adjoining muniment room.

The material from Knighton's glasshouse (No. 42) will no doubt be added to this collection when the excavation is complete.

Such modest individual exercises as ours may seem strange today when excavations are done by and for County Archaeological Societies. Straker's life work on Wealden Iron was an example of one-man research; our work was similar but far less important.

Acknowledgments

I owe a great debt of gratitude to Francis Steer for tackling the formidable task of editing and improving my text and seeing it through all its stages to book form. To him and two other friends, Dr L. F. Salzman, C.B.E., and Miss A. Reeve, B.A., I am deeply grateful for their interest and most helpful advice at all stages of the compilation of this book extending over several years. Its shortcomings are my own.

The late Professor W. E. S. Turner, F.R.S., and the late Mr J. A. Knowles, F.S.A., were always happy to share their immense knowledge and were most generous with their help. I am very grateful to both of them.

I am much indebted to Miss G. M. A. Beck, M.A., for much assistance with Chapter I; Mr N. P. Bridgewater, B.Sc., for his advice on the problem of the Carré renaissance; Mr A. D. R. Caroe, F.R.I.B.A., for his most valuable help with the structural details of Vann furnace; Mr R. J. Charleston, Keeper of Ceramics at the Victoria and Albert Museum, for constant help and advice, and for giving me copies of his papers (*see* Bibliography) from which I have quoted; Mrs E. S. Godfrey of North Carolina for kindly allowing me to use material from her thesis 'The Development of English Glassmaking, 1560–1640'. To Dr D. B. Harden O.B.E., F.S.A., Director of the London Museum, I am most grateful for his suggestion that I should attempt a reassessment of *Wealden Glass*, and for his invaluable comments at proof stage. To Mr J. C. Harrington of Virginia, Regional Chief of Interpretation of the National Park Service, for his enthusiasm and permission to use material from his interim report, *Glassmaking in Jamestown* (1952) (*see* also Chapter IV, p. 72); Mrs A. Kentish, Winbolt's daughter, who worked on a number of the glass sites, kindly lent me her fathers' copy of *Wealden Glass*, provided a photograph of him and has given her encouragement and blessing to my attempt to offer a fresh point of view on the industry; Mr T. Pape, F.S.A., for his help and for permission to use his material on Bishop's Wood furnace (*see* p. 68); Mr W. Taylor of Horsham, a keen field archaeologist, for telling me of four fresh sites, two (Nos. 16 and 27) are probables and two are possibles (Nos. 22 and 24); Mr E. S. Wood, F.S.A., who generously sent me a copy of his paper on the Blunden's Wood glasshouse and allowed me to make full use of it, before it was published in *Sy. A.C.* vol. 62. The editor gave me permission to use it, and it has been invaluable, particularly in Chapter IV; Miss V. Smith for her careful vessel drawings, plans and the drawing of a Chartres panel, and for her helpful ideas.

The impressive list of acknowledgments and the bibliography promise, I fear, far more than is forthcoming.

I

THE MEDIEVAL PERIOD

WE have much information about glazing and glass-painting in medieval England in the writings of Dr L. F. Salzman[1] and the late Mr J. A. Knowles.[2] Both have also written on medieval glassmaking,[3] and I am very greatly indebted to them for their interest and advice over many years. However, we know very little indeed of actual glassmaking in England before the mid-sixteenth century from documentary sources, and such is confined to the Chiddingfold district.

It is, however, clear from surviving accounts that Chiddingfold had no monopoly in glassmaking. Dr Salzman sums up what is known of the other medieval English sources:[4]

'From 1284 to 1309, and probably later, the abbey of Vale Royal were carrying on its manufacture in Cheshire.[5] That it was made in other places is more than likely, and it would seem that the "glashous" belonging to Salisbury Cathedral and frequently mentioned in the fifteenth century accounts of that church, was the seat not only of glazing but of glassmaking, judging from the quantities of sand that were carried thereto. For the glazing of St Stephen's Chapel, John de Brampton was ordered in 1349, to buy glass in Shropshire and Staffordshire and this must obviously have been of local manufacture;[6] but when John Geddyng was sent in July 1352, on the same errand into Kent and Essex we cannot be certain that he did not obtain foreign glass from the ports.'

---

[1] L. F. Salzman, *Building in England down to 1540* (O.U.P., 1952), pp. 173–186; hereafter abbreviated *B.E.S.*

[2] J. A. Knowles, *The York School of Glass Painting* (S.P.C.K., 1936), and many other papers.

[3] L. F. Salzman, *English Industries of the Middle Ages* (O.U.P., 1923), pp. 183–193. J. A. Knowles, 'Medieval processes of glass manufacture,' in *Glass*, July–Sept. 1927.

[4] *B.E.S.*, p. 182.

[5] The glasshouse site at Kingswood, Delamere, Cheshire, was examined in 1935 and 1945 'but the date of the glass-house and destruction must remain obscure.' *See* 'Further notes on the glasshouse site at Kingswood, Delamere, Cheshire' by M. H. Ridgway and G. B. Leach in *Journal of the Chester Arch. Soc.*, vol. 37, pp 133–140. This site might have been connected with the Vale Royal Abbey. [G.H.K.]

[6] Confirmation about the Staffs. glass industry can be found in a 1380 lease of half a (glass)house in Kirdford to John Glasewryth of Staffordshire. GMR. 105/1/117. (*See* p. 31.) I have acknowledged my great debt to Cooper's pioneer work. He was a very careful worker but unhappily rarely gave his references, except in his loose notes and transcriptions. Most of these have been very kindly traced and checked by Miss G. M. A. Beck in the Guildford Muniment Room and are marked

It is far from easy to put any convincing flesh on the bare bones of medieval glass-house sites and to say who worked there. Even the approximate dating of a furnace is rarely possible. It happens that the history of two principal glass-producing parishes, Chiddingfold and Kirdford, has been closely examined, so that something is known of land ownership and occupation, but there remains the difficulty – usually insuper-able in this district – of determining the precise limits of a farm at a given date.

The name Laurence Vitrearius in the much-quoted grant of 20 acres in 'Chidinge-falde'[7] probably indicates some glassmaking activity here in the first half of the thirteenth century, but the earliest conclusive documentary evidence of a glass industry in the Weald comes from the Exchequer K.R. rolls in 1351[8] and from the Sadler collection of Chiddingfold deeds in 1380[9].

GMR. They all occur in this chapter (pp. 29 and 31) and in the Family chapter pp. 115–117. The few not traced (9) in this chapter are marked (C) and may probably be safely accepted. I am also much indebted to Miss Beck for adding some references from the Loseley MSS. now deposited in the GMR. and two from the Surrey Record Society volume, and for editing the draft of this chapter. The Loseley references are quoted by kind permission of Major J. More-Moleneux.

[7] GMR. 105/1/30. The deed is undated, but from the names of the witnesses it can be safely put not later than 1240. It is a grant of 20 acres of land in Chidingefalde by Simon de Stokas to Lawrence Vitrearius (the glazier at this date could also mean glassmaker). Cooper says the land granted was 'beyond question' a small holding known later as Dyers Cross, which is found afterwards in the hands of a member of the glassmaking family of Schurterre. We shall see later (p. 115) that the Schurterres were small property owners in the parish and I think the fact that three members of the family were glassmakers can be over-emphasized. Other vague thirteenth-century references in the parish occur in Cooper's appendix on 'Glass'. A deed of 1300 relating to a rent charge on lands now known as Duns farm, on the Chiddingfold–Dunsfold boundary deals with the release of a yearly rent of 6d. charged on 'le Dunhursteslond' by William de Bochstockare of Compton, near Farnham, to the proprietors of the land, William son of William le Verir (glassmaker) and his wife Johanna. Cooper says 'It will be noticed that it was the elder William who was the glassmaker, and not necessarily the younger, though he almost certainly followed his father's trade.' This is surmise as is Cooper's 'there are grounds for thinking' &c. that this William le Verir was the son of Lawrence Vitrearius of the earlier grant. Cooper says he may have been and we must leave it at that. This thirteenth-century material is not conclusive; it is all set out in Cooper's appendix.

[8] Everything of value to the history of glazing in England between 1221 and 1539 in this important series of records (P.R.O. Exchequer, K.R. rolls, bdle. 471, No. 6) was translated by L. F. Salzman and published in the *Journal of the Society of Master Glass Painters* (here *J.M.G.*) in the six numbers April 1926 to April 1929 inclusive. This includes the most complete run of medieval glazing accounts so far known, viz. those of St Stephen's Chapel, Westminster Palace, from 20 June 1351 to March 1352. Dr. Salzman shows that during this period of 37 weeks £240 was spent on the windows, of which 80 per cent was wages and 15 per cent the cost of glass. The remainder was for painting materials, tools, ironwork and small miscellaneous purchases. The accounts give details of materials, fittings, the names of the designer, master glaziers, painters and ordinary glaziers and their wages. Cooper also used this archive.

[9] GMR. 105/1/117 (*see* p. 31 for full text). This collection, deposited in Guildford Muniment Room in 1954 and 1955 by the late Wing Commander Candy, includes some thirty thirteenth-century deeds, about 100 of the fourteenth century, and about 500 deeds from the fifteenth to the nineteenth centuries, mostly relating to Chiddingfold. I am greatly indebted to Miss E. M. Dance, Guildford Borough Archivist, for pointing out to me that this collection was the source of most of the docu-

In the Exchequer K.R. rolls, covering the building and maintenance of the royal palaces for the whole medieval period, there are only six entries which specifically name the source of the purchase of English-made glass (always white glass). All six refer to Chiddingfold or to 'the Weald' which can certainly be taken as meaning Chiddingfold or an adjoining parish. How much can be based on this is pure surmise, but it is probable that the Chiddingfold district was the principal source of glass in southern England in medieval times.

By 1351 we are dealing with historical facts and not pottery-dating in the rare cases where associated pottery is available within useful date limits, as at Blunden's Wood.

The surviving documentary evidence for this small industry is so scanty until the middle of the sixteenth century that I give these few entries in full. We are on solid ground by 1351 and I propose to start the examination of this industry from this date.[10] but with a respectful salute to two Chiddingfold men of the preceding century, Laurence Vitrearius and his dubious son William le Verir, of whom we know nothing but their names.

During the period from 30 April to 12 December 1351, there are four entries showing that 1290 lbs. of 'white' glass from Chiddingfold was sent to the two chapels St George's[11] and St Stephen's of the Royal Palaces of Windsor and Westminster.[12] This might glaze about 500 sq. ft. (see p. 30).

The four entries are:

Windsor[13]

1351, 30 April: To John Alemayne for 324 [87][14] weys of white glass – the hundred at 12s. and the weys at 6d., 43s. 6d.
To William Holmere for carriage of the said glass from Chiddingfold to London, 8s. And for the carriage from London to Westminster, 8d.[15]

mentary evidence for the local glass industry used by the late Rev. T. S. Cooper in his massive and scholarly *History of Chiddingfold*. He passed the information on to the late Mr M. S. Giuseppi, who used it in his article on glass in V.C.H., *Surrey*, vol. 2, p. 295. It has been often copied since then, but without any source being given.

[10] Very little is known about glassmaking anywhere in Europe before the fourteenth century.

[11] This was the older chapel of St George which, becoming ruinous, was replaced by the present building late in the fifteenth century. J. D. Le Couteur, *English Medieval Stained Glass* (1926), p. 96.

[12] 'Of all the fourteenth century glass at St Stephen's and St George's windows, almost nothing has survived.' J. A. Knowles, *J.M.G.* vol. 2, p. 140.

[13] 'Medieval Glazing account,' in *J.M.G.*, vol. 2, p. 188. The earliest conclusive evidence.

[14] The Clerk of Works' entry is clearly incorrect; the figure should read 87 weys. His total cost is no doubt correct, as is the continually repeated formula that a hundred was made up of 24 weys (*pondera*) and that each wey was 5 lbs. The current price of 'white' glass from Chiddingfold in 1351 for these 'long' hundreds of 120 lbs. was 12s. or 1·2d. per lb. This agrees with the clerk's figure of 6d. a wey. Moreover the cost of carriage agrees with other amounts for this weight of glass, if the 324 weys is corrected to 87.

[15] Dr L. F. Salzman suggests that Westminster was a convenient collecting centre.

St. Stephen's, Westminster[16]

30 (sic) October: To John Alemayne for 303 weys [3 hundreds and 3 weys][17] of white glass, each hundred of 24 weys and each wey of 5 lbs., for glazing the said windows, at 12s. the hundred. 37s. 6d.

To William Holmer for carriage of the same glass from Chiddingfold to Westminster, 6s.

To John Geddyng[18] employed in obtaining the said glass for 7 days, going, staying and returning, receiving for himself and his horse 12d. a day, 7s.

7 November: To John de Alemayne for 36 weys of white glass for the windows of the upper chapel, 6d. the wey, 18s.

To William Holmer for carriage of the same glass from the Weald to Westminster, 3s.

12 December: To William Holmere for 60 weys of white glass bought at Chiddingfold for the chapel windows, at 6d. the wey, 30s. For carriage of the said glass from Chiddingfold to Westminster, 6s.

The remaining two of the six entries are:

1355 Windsor: for 400 [i.e., 480 lbs.] of glass bought of John Alemayne at Chiddingfold, 13s. 4d. the hundred, 53s.[19]

1378 Woodstock (Oxon): To John Brampton, glazier, for a seam [120 lbs.] of white glass of the Weald, bought for making the said windows in the King's chamber, with carriage, 30s.[19]

John Alemayne, who is mentioned as supplying glass from Chiddingfold, was a local man. His name occurs in the Godalming assessment for the Fifteenth and Tenth of 1332;[20] and in the second Chiddingfold tithing at the Godalming Hundred View of Frankpledge, Hocktide, 1343.[21] Richard le Holmere, who is named in the same 1332 assessment, may have been related to the William Holmere who carried glass from Chiddingfold.

[16] 'The Glazing of St. Stephen's chapel, Westminster, 1351–2' in J.M.G., vol. 2, No. 1.

[17] i.e., 375 lbs. or 75 weys.

[18] Glass was difficult to get, possibly owing to the Black Death, and Geddyng probably searched the district unsuccessfully. His charges added 20 per cent to the cost of the relatively small amount of glass. John Geddyng was the third Upper Warden of the Glaziers Guild from 1373–81. C. H. Ashdown, History of the Glaziers and the Painters of Glass, 1328–1918. The late Mr J. A. Knowles, who had a profound knowledge of ancient glass and its manufacture, thought it most unlikely that the early glassmakers produced glass to order, but that they built up stocks of their own lines most in demand.

[19] J.M.G., vol. 2, pp. 189, 192. From its price the 1355 entry was white glass. The carriage to Woodstock must have been costly. John de Brampton was the third Master of the Glaziers Guild from 1373–81. See Ashdown, op. cit.

[20] Surrey Record Society, Surrey Taxation Returns, Pt I, p. 18.

[21] Loseley MSS. 197.

There is no direct evidence that either Alemayne or William Holmere was a glassmaker. Holmere appears to have been a dealer and importer of glass with a depot in the City of London, but Alemayne may have actually made the glass which he supplied from Chiddingfold, since it is unlikely that the size of the industry would warrant a local wholesaler. He was a man of some local importance, with a small property at Hazelbridge Hill (afterwards known as Almeyns) and elsewhere in the parish. The first mention of his name in the Sadler deeds is in 1330:[22] the last is in 1370 when he was among the witnesses to a local conveyance to which his armorial seal is attached.[23]

In 1367 he granted to John Schurterre, 'glasier,'[24] a lease for 20 years of his tenement at Heysulbrigg with two gardens and a meadow adjoining; not long afterwards the property passed into Schurterre's absolute possession and remained in his family for 200 years (C). Alemayne must have died between 1370 and Easter 1378, when his widow Joan was a party to a lease.[25] She and his son John were assessed in the Poll Tax of 1381.

Hazelbridge Hill, 1000 yards southwest of Chiddingfold church, and its surrounding woodlands appear to have been a centre of the local glass industry in the fourteenth century. The furnace sites of Fromes (No. 5), 400 yards away, Hazelbridge Hanger (No. 7) and Prestwick (No. 10) about 700 yards away, all provide glass that could belong to this period.

There is another entry in the E.K.R. rolls which almost certainly refers to the Weald:

1400 Westminster: To Peter Shortere for 5 'lodes' of glass at 24s. the lode, £6.[26]

Thereafter for nearly a century only a single reference occurs to the glass industry in the Weald, viz. in 1495 when Thomas Shorter (?Schurterre) conveyed Estlond with a croft called Le Tryvet to Henry Ropley, 'glassecaryour'.[27] The Ropleys were a local family and presumably there was enough glass to be carried to employ a man. Then come the earlier references to the Peytowes as glassmakers in 1536, and the last eighty years of the industry is fairly well recorded.

In the thirty-seven weeks (1351–2) covered by the St Stephen's series of glazing

---

[22] GMR. 105/1/72.   [23] GMR. 105/2/4.

[24] Glasier at this period seems to have covered both glassmaking and glazing. By the early seventeenth century and possibly earlier it had become restricted to its present meaning in this district. GMR. 105/1/110.

[25] GMR. 105/2/5.

[26] J.M.G., vol. 3, p. 25. If the price in 1400 was the same as in 1351, a 'lode' was 2 hundreds, cases, cradles or seams, and the total would be 1200 lbs. of glass, or nearly as much as the four lots from Chiddingfold totalled in 1351. Dr L. F. Salzman says 'It would appear that the case, chest or cradle of glass was equivalent to the seam of 120 lbs. and the wisp to the earlier wey of 5 lbs.' (B.E.S., p. 184.) Peter Shortere may be Peter Schurtere (see section on the Schurterre Family, Chapter VIII).

[27] GMR. 105/1/140. Cooper says he was the son of Wm. Ropley of West End, and grandson of Richard Ropley of Rodgate.

accounts there are thirteen entries of purchases of glass. We have seen that three lots came from Chiddingfold; in two instances carriage was charged from the City to Westminster; in the remaining eight no carriage is mentioned and the glass was presumably imported direct from abroad to Westminster. Rather more than one-third by weight and about one-eighth by value, of the plain white glass[28] for St Stephen's chapel mentioned in these accounts came from Chiddingfold.

About twenty-eight per cent of the glass was coloured, a high proportion for the mid-fourteenth century, and being intended for a Royal chapel, no doubt most of the 'white' glass was 'florisched' (decorated) with flowers, birds, heraldic designs and elaborate canopies in yellow and orange.[29] We may probably assume that all the colour was imported. 'It is a curious fact that there is absolutely no documentary evidence for coloured glass having been made in England'[30] in the medieval period.

In 1351 production went on from April to December. It may have been a year of great demand (the period following the Black Death was exceptional) so we do not know if, in the fourteenth century, production usually continued throughout the year, nor indeed if glassmaking at this time was a whole-time occupation.

Until the middle of the sixteenth century much of the window glass used in England was probably imported and the home production was small.

There is no indication from the furnace sites that vessel glass, until the middle of the sixteenth century, was more than a rather crude but in my opinion, a nevertheless continuous sideline.[31]

We get some idea of the thickness of fourteenth-century window glass from the fact 'that $2\frac{1}{2}$ lbs. was reckoned sufficient to make one foot of glazing.'[32] This is 40 oz. glass which is very thick and heavy by our standards, being over $\frac{3}{16}$ in. thick. It needed heavy iron armatures to carry it. It would have been quite impossible to paint and lead-up panels of so great a weight except on or close to the site for which they were destined. If further evidence were needed it emphasizes the fact that no glass window was finished in the Weald, and that any glass found among the furnace waste showing painting or leading marks must be imported cullet. Such work was done at the few 'Schools' of glass painting such as York and London, far from forest glass-houses.

By the end of the sixteenth century window glass made in the Weald was seldom over $\frac{1}{16}$ in. thick and frequently less. It was light in weight, let in the maximum of light and was suitable for the small leaded diamond-shaped quarries. Much of the

---

[28] The average price of coloured glass was about 6d. a lb. or five times that of white. It is possible with the prices given, to say within very narrow limits how much was coloured and how much was white.

[29] This is confirmed by the silver filings for painting the glass which occur in ten entries, mostly for a few pence worth.

[30] B.E.S., p. 183.

[31] See also Schurterre lease, 1380 (p. 31).

[32] Literae Cant. (Rolls Series), vol. 3, p. 385, ex B.E.S., p. 175.

heraldic glass in England of the sixteenth and seventeenth centuries is of this remarkable thinness.

The Fourteenth-Century Deeds

I know of only two medieval deeds relating to glasshouses in England, their fuel and their products; both concern the Schurterre family in the late fourteenth century. Because of their rarity, their interest and the fact that the glasshouse referred to in them can possibly be identified as the Hog Wood site (No. 15) they are given below.[33]

The earliest record of this family's connection with the glass industry was shown to be 1367 (*see* p. 29) when John Schurterre, 'glasier,' is mentioned. He died *c.*1379 and his widow Joan brought John Glasewryth from Staffordshire, where there must have been a glass industry, to help run the family glasshouse, possibly until her son John, mentioned in the second deed, was old enough to take over five years later. Possibly the husband had been the only glassmaker in the Weald.

(a) 23 April 1380 (GMR 105/1/117)

This indenture witnesseth that Joan who was the wife of John Schurtere of Chudyngfolde has granted and to farm demised to John Glasewryth, of Staffordshire half a [glass] house in Shuerewode, with all my chattels there being, in the parish of Keuredeforde,[34] and with the underwood growing or being in the aforesaid place called Shuerewode and Strowykeswode: To have and to hold to the same John his heirs or executors from the day of St Michael last past to the end of six years next ensuing fully complete. And the aforesaid John shall work all his work and part; at his own cost it shall be. And the aforesaid Joan for her part shall find at her own cost for her portion to be paid to the same John, his heirs or executors, for a 'sheu' of 'brodeglas' 20*d.* and for a hundred of 'vessel' 6*d.* for his labour. And the aforesaid Joan, her heirs or executors shall warrant and defend all the aforesaid house, and with all other its chattels and the appurtenances to the aforesaid John, his heirs or executors during the term aforesaid against all men. In witness whereof to these indentures the parties aforesaid have affixed their seals these being witnesses: John Croft, John Okhurst, John Baudekefolde, John Atte Purie, and John Ybournehond and many others. Given at Plestowe[35] on Wednesday in the feast of St George in the third year of the reign of King Richard the Second after the Conquest of England.

(b) 11 August 1385 (GMR. 105/1/119)

Indenture between Richard Suzonne, bailiff of Atheryngton, procurator of the abbot and convent of Séez, of the one part, and Robert Pikeboussh and John Shertere, of the other part: witnessing that previously the said bailiff had granted

---

[33] The first is in translation and the second summarized. A copy of these deeds in the Sadler collection was sent by the late Lady M. Maxse to Winbolt and he printed them in *Wealden Glass,* p. 45. Like all the Sadler deeds they were known and used by Cooper.

[34] Kirdford.

[35] Plaistow was the northern portion of Kirdford.

to the said Robert all the underwood of Souzwoude and Stroudwikeswoude, with free ingress and egress to make of the said underwood in the said wood a 'Glashous' and to use it as the office of 'Glasiere' requires, for a certain term, now expired: and that the said Bailiff hereby grants to the said Robert and John 'all the tenement of the said underwood in the wood aforesaid not cut down or expended', to have, cut down, cleave[36] and expend it from the feast of St Michael next for one year, paying 40s. If the underwood be not expended in that term, it shall be extended to the 'Nowel' next ensuing, they paying 6s. 8d. If not expended by that time, they shall have a further term to the Annunciation then ensuing, for a like payment. They may not cut any underwood in the months of June and July. Given at Atherington on the morrow of St Lawrence, 9 Ric II.

The fuel was underwood, which is surprising, though it is a very wide term, and could include substantial billets; the mention of cleaving suggests this. Hog and Strudgwick woods taken together would, today, total not far short of 150 acres.

The bailiff of Atherington[37] was the English agent for the abbey of Séez but there is no close link here between the medieval glassmaking district in Normandy of Lyons le forêt, ten miles east of Rouen, and Séez which is in the far south of Normandy, over ninety miles away. The Benedictine abbey of Séez was founded by Roger Montgomery, first Earl of Arundel, early in the reign of Henry I. Of Robert Pikeboussh we know nothing.

The terms forbade the cutting of underwood in June and July, the months of maximum sap flow. The acreage and amount of underwood and its type are not known, but the agreement is flexible and sensible in the provisions for extending the cutting time.

There is a bewildering variety of medieval terms for quantities of window glass and we do not know what a 'sheu' was. The word 'sheffe' occurs in the fifteenth century and '40 sheffes of Flemysh glass' cost 32s.[38] The price was about 9½d. a sheffe; in 1351 Chiddingfold white glass was 6d. a wey at source, which suggests a sheffe and a wey may be variants for the same quantity, but this makes nonsense of John Glazewryth's remuneration of 20d. per 'sheu'. His rate of 6d. for making 100 vessels looks very low.

'Brodeglas' or broad glass[39] suggests that the cylinder or 'muff' process was the usual method of producing window glass.

It is interesting that vessel is recorded as being made. This confirms the site evidence where enough fragments survived, that window and simple vessel were made on all the Early furnace sites, though it was usually much cruder than the Late.

[36] 'Fendre,' to split or cleave.

[37] An office perpetuated by Bailiff's Court, 1½ miles west of Littlehampton; Atherington itself is now under the sea.

[38] B.E.S., p. 184.

[39] Broad glass (discussed on p. 86, Chapter V) was a term probably normally used for window glass produced by the 'muff' process.

The deed of 1380 states that the glasshouse was in Shuerewode and the under-wood was in Shuerewode and Strowykeswode. Hog Wood today is a large area of woodland (100 acres or so) on the shire boundary and the name may have been changed. It is possible that both deeds refer to the same areas of woodland and that an alternative name for Shuerewode was in 1385, Souzwoude, a likely forerunner of Hog Wood.

All this is not completely convincing, but it is as good a combination of clues as we are likely to get and the glass found could belong to that period. These large areas of woodland were probably more extensive in the fourteenth century, and the two areas of Shire or Sows Wood and Strudgwick Wood may have been closer than the 1200 yards which separate them today.

It is the only medieval family and known furnace site link which has much to recommend it.

II

THE RAW MATERIALS OF GLASS:
ANALYSIS AND DECOMPOSITION

General

THE basic facts are well known. Suffice it to say that glass vessels have probably been made for about 3500 years, being blown for about 2000 years and that glass is made up roughly of:

75% silica (usually sand).

10% lime.

15% sodium or potassium oxide (flux).

The basic composition of a batch, sand and vegetable ash (containing lime) has changed little from the earliest times.

'In the later Middle Ages glass-making was roughly divided into two spheres – that of the north (including Germany, France, Belgium, England and Bohemia) and that of the south (mainly Italy). These divisions were based not on geography but on divergent technical traditions. In the north, in the glass-houses surviving in the forested regions after the break-up of the Roman Empire, glass was made with local sands (providing silica) and with the ashes of burnt inland vegetation (impure potassium carbonate) for flux. In the south, silica was frequently obtained by crushing white pebbles from the beds of rivers, while the flux was a soda (impure sodium carbonate) derived from the burning of marine vegetation.'[1]

The northern potash glass such as that from the English forests was of poorer quality than the soda glass from the southern or Mediterranean lands. This deterioration in northern glass seems to have occurred about the tenth century.[2]

[1] R. J. Charleston, in C. Singer and others, *A History of Technology*, vol. 3 (O.U.P. 1957): Glass, sections I–V, p. 206; *see* also R. J. Charleston, 'Ancient Glass-making Methods,' Circle of Glass Collectors, Duplicated paper No. 124, March 1961 (issued for private circulation to members only).

[2] D. B. Harden in C. Singer and others, *A History of Technology*, vol. 2, pp. 325 ff and table on p. 313. Dr Harden discusses the probable date and adds 'the matter is worthy of much further study.' Theophilus, a German Benedictine monk, possibly writing in the early twelfth century, confirms the use of potash in the north by saying: 'If you should decide to make glass, first cut plenty of beech-wood logs and dry them. Then burn them together in a clean spot and carefully collect the ashes, taking care not to mix in any earth or stone.' See *De Diversis Artibus*. Theophilus. Edited by C. R. Dodwell (Nelson, 1961), Book II, section I, p. 57.

'Medieval glass is far more prone to disintegrate by weathering than is the glass of earlier periods in this country. It was forest-glass, with a potash as alkali, by contrast with the soda-glass prevalent up to the tenth century or thereabouts, and it is particularly liable to become flaky or pitted and to disintegrate.'[3]

Sand

Turning to the three main ingredients of glass, there is very little doubt that our glassmakers used sand. White sand outcrops at Hambledon Common close to the Chiddingfold furnaces and we know that white sand from Lodsworth Common[4] was used, at least by the later glassmakers. The Lodsworth sand is only about ten miles, possibly a day's journey there and back, from any of our sites. One site, Broomfield Hanger (No. 2), has sand all around it which the late Mrs B. Halahan described as fine and somewhat greyer than most in this neighbourhood.

The evidence for the Lodsworth source comes from a finely drawn and coloured map of Fitzlea, by James FitzOsberne, 1629, showing the southern part of Lodsworth parish.[5] This map refers to the digging of sand and the selling thereof from the Common to the glassmakers; it is the only documentary evidence of the origin of sand known to me. The sand-pits are shown on the map about half a mile SSW of Fitzlea Farm, on the north slope of Gallows Hill, a Lower Greensand ridge, along which the Graffham-Lodsworth boundary runs.

Sand from this source, dirty white in colour, could have supplied all the requirements of the glass industry in the Weald, but the Chiddingfold and more northerly furnaces may have used the Hambledon sand. The Lodsworth sand was probably used in the Graffham glasshouse (see p. 209).

The late Professor W. E. S. Turner, F.R.S., kindly sent me a report on a sample of the Fitzlea sand: 'I have examined it and although it cannot be said to be a first quality sand or even a second quality judged by our present standards, it could, I think, have furnished material for making glass of a pale colour.'

Our glassmakers probably knew, at least by the late sixteenth century, that only certain sand was suitable for crystal glass, whereas local sands would suffice for green forest glass, whose price would not allow for high transport costs of imported sand. The Late glass[6] from the Weald is very similar to contemporary glass from Hampshire, Gloucestershire, Staffordshire and Herefordshire. It is most unlikely that they used sand from a common source, and they must have depended on local supplies.

[3] D. B. Harden, 'Domestic Window Glass: Roman, Saxon and Medieval,' in E. M. Jope (ed.), *Studies in Building History* (London, 1961), p. 55.

[4] The sand at Hambledon is on the Folkestone Beds at the top of the Lower Greensand whereas Lodsworth sand comes from Hythe Beds in the lower part of the Lower Greensand. I am indebted to Mr B. C. Worssam of the Geological Survey for this information.

[5] This map is in the West Sussex Record Office on loan from Capt. W. Slade Mitford, D.L.; see also *S.R.S.*, vol. 61, p. 8. I am much indebted to Miss A. Reeve for showing it to me. *See* also *S.N.Q.*, vol. 14, p. 26. The date 1629 is no evidence that glass was still being made.

[6] *See* Introduction, p. 16, and Chapter VI for a discussion of Early and Late types of Wealden glass.

We must look elsewhere for a reason for this unmistakable, uniformly good quality hard and usually blue-green glass. There is no evidence as to who worked the St Weonards furnace in Herefordshire, but the same Lorraine families were involved in the other counties, and they may have used some careful and uniform technique. This is in line with the latest work on the problem, discussed on pp. 37–42. The earlier over-simple reason for the great improvement from Early to Late in forest glass being due to a change from potash to soda is no longer tenable.

Lime

Lime is an essential constituent of durable glass and is always present in surviving samples of ancient glass, except the late 'lead' glass. The late Professor Turner said[7] that lime was not intentionally added as a major constituent before the end of the seventeenth century. He goes on to say that

'E. M. Péligot (1862) gives credit for the first true appreciation of the value of lime as a glass component to P. Delauney Deslandes, Director of the St Gobain glass factory from 1758 to 1785, during which period he introduced the use of purified soda instead of soda ash and came to realise that some stabilising constituent was needed to take the place of the earthy constituents of the soda ash. This constituent he found in lime, which he proceeded cautiously and progressively to add but not to a greater extent than six per cent.'

This would account for the fact that the early writers make no mention of lime; presumably there happened to be sufficient, if not a surplus, in the unpurified vegetable ash and it was not until well after the Weald period that its role was appreciated.

Samples of Weald glass Early and Late, when analysed, show a low silica and high lime content, as do the Bishop's Wood, Bagot's Park and Jamestown (Va.) samples.[8]

Flux

Glass cannot be made with sand alone. A flux is needed to facilitate melting, to make it workable and to produce a stable product.

It is reasonably certain that the Early Weald glassmakers used the ash from beech[9] and oak billets with which the furnaces were fired, supplemented by the ash of other inland plants including bracken (fougère).

It was probably Jean Carré, a promoter from Antwerp, and the French glassmakers he brought over, who were responsible for a radical and progressive improve-

[7] W. E. S. Turner, 'Studies in Ancient Glasses and Glassmaking Processes' (hereafter abbreviated to S.A.G.T.). These invaluable papers appeared in the *Journal of the Society of Glass Technology*. This discussion of lime is in vol. 40 (1956, Part III, p. 39). I am much indebted to Mr R. J. Charleston, for suggesting I searched in Prof. Turner's works and to the Librarian of the Society for finding the reference and loaning me the volume.

[8] J. C. Harrington, *Glassmaking in Jamestown* (1952). The analysis of glass from one of our Late sites (No. 38) showed 24·9 per cent lime.

[9] *See* also Theophilus, p. 2, note 1 of this chapter.

ment in Wealden glassmaking. Here the evidence both documentary and archaeological appear to confirm each other. Descendants of Carré's Lorraine glassmakers spread from the Weald to other counties by the end of the sixteenth century (*see* Chapter X).

There is some valuable information in Mrs E. S. Godfrey's thesis (*see* Introduction p. 12) on basic oxides, potash and soda.[10] The possibility that Carré's importation of soda from Spain was responsible for the dramatic and sustained improvement in the quality of Weald glass finds no support in her thesis. Discussing glass of this period she says

'there were two chief types of glass – forest glass made from wood ashes and soda glass or crystal. The distinction between potash K_2O and soda Na_2O would therefore seem to have been recognized in practice, although in fact it was not clearly understood. . . . Since both potash and soda were derived from the ashes of plant materials, it is easy to see why a distinction was not always made. Thus both Neri's work and Merret's commentary on it classify all the products made from the leaching of ashes as "salts." When all sorts of ashes were mixed, some might be from marine plants, and hence much forest glass contains traces of soda. . . . The wood-burning glasshouses which produce window glass and other types of green glass used the ashes from their furnaces as ingredients in their batch. Mansell [early seventeenth century], when noting his higher costs, recounted that Bungar [of the Weald] "burning wood, had the ashes which is part of the material to make a glass and cost him nothing." That such ashes were not usually sufficient in quantity, however, is suggested, by the fact that Lennard had to supply the glassmakers at Knole with bushels of ashes as well as wood for fuel.[11]

The records of Ballynegery glasshouse in Ireland (early seventeenth century) also indicate that while ashes from the castle and tanhouse grates of the town were used for the batch, ashes were also purchased at the high price of 12*d.* a bushel.[12] It is clear that all sorts of ashes were commonly used, mixed together'.

All this appears to be a complete contradiction of the barilla-soda hypothesis. Of soda Mrs E. S. Godfrey says:

'The chief source of a soda supply for Italian and for some English glassmakers was Spain, particularly the region round Alicante. This form is generally called barillia, although the word "saffora" is sometimes found as a synonyme . . . Jean Carré, the founder of the English crystal industry, ordered his soda (le soudre) from Spain[13] and Verzelini did likewise. . . . By the early seventeenth century however, the newly built English crystal factories were using a native soda.'

But 'about 1619 he (Mansell) sent Howell . . . to buy barillia in Spain.'

[10] *D.E.G.*, p. 301.
[11] Lennard, p. 128 [*see* p. 47, note 7].
[12] S.P.14/113 No. 49. S.P.16/378 No. 58. *D.E.G.*, p. 302.
[13] S.P.12/43 No. 42. *D.E.G.*, p. 306.

Soon after the Weald furnaces had shut down Mansell made some interesting comments on his difficulties.[14] He blamed the poor quality of his glass on two factors, the difficulty of securing wood ashes and cullet.

'Wood ashes, one of the chief ingredients of window-glass, his predecessors had secured as a by-product from their wood-burning furnaces. Knowing their value they kept the ashes in a pure state. But Mansell was forced to buy wood ashes, and in spite of raising the price from 7d. to 11d. a bushel, he could not find a supply that was not corrupted with turf and peat. Cullet, or the cuttings and broken pieces of glass, was also an indispensable ingredient of good glass, but the glaziers refused to sell him their cuttings except at very exorbitant rates, and sometimes not at all, preferring to export them to France.'[15]

Mrs Godfrey comments: 'there is no indication that the Lorrainers ever used ashes in anything but their natural state at this time or knew of other methods.[16]'

Professor Turner says that 'the differences between soda and potash were not realized or established until the eighteenth century.'[17]

'During the medieval period, the potash, particularly in window glass, plain or coloured, dominates the soda in the glasses of England, France and Germany. That this should be so is associated with the change of source of alkali from ash derived from maritime plants of the Eastern Mediterranean to that produced in areas remote from the coast from well grown trees, particularly from beech-wood, especially mentioned by Theophilus in the tenth century A.D.'[18]

He shows that ash from coastal or desert plants contains a much greater proportion of sodium salts than potassium, whereas the ash from inland plants shows just the reverse. He amplifies this by saying 'so much so that from the analysis of ancient glasses of European origin, in medieval and Renaissance times, it is easy to determine which were made from the ashes of beechwood, oak, fern, &c., and those derived from polverine or barilla.'[19] Professor Turner also commented on the difficulties of the ancient glassmakers:

'The problem of making and reproducing workable glass from two supposedly simple materials, sand and nitrum or sand and ash, materials which in fact were usually complex and variable in composition, must always have been difficult and inescapable.

The removal of impurities or undesirable constituents could be accomplished by a succession of operations, purification of the raw materials by selection and in the case of ash, by solution, filtration, and evaporation; by fritting the glass-making mixture; and by the subsequent conversion of frit into glass, the prolonged heating of the latter to remove volatile materials and its treatment by quenching in water or by mechanical means, to remove the unincorporated residue.'[20]

[14] S.P.14/113 No. 49. D.E.G., p. 180.   [15] D.E.G., p. 180. [See Introduction, p. 18.]
[16] D.E.G., p. 183.   [17] S.A.G.T., vol. 40, p. 39.   [18] S.A.G.T., vol. 40, p. 177.
[19] S.A.G.T., vol. 40, p. 288.   [20] S.A.G.T., vol. 40, p. 292.

Comparative Analyses **Main Constituents**

	Sample A: Early Weald Site No. 29	Sample A: Late Weald Site No. 14	Sample B: Early Weald Site No. 21	Sample B: Late Weald Site No. 38	Bishop's Park, Staffs.*	Bagot's Park, Staffs.*	St. Weonards average of 5 samples†	Jamestown average of 6 samples‡	Blunden's Wood c.1330§
SiO_2	56	64·7	56·7	59·5	57·7	54·8	58	59·5	57
Fe_2O_2	·5	·7	·39	·96	—	—	1·4	1·6	1·32
CaO	15	20·8	23	24·9	17·2	20·6	19·6	21·5	17·5
MgO	6·7	2·6	3·6	2·7	4	3·9	3·9	3·8	6·95
Na_2O	2·3	·4	2·2	1·2	5·4	·7	2	1·4	3·4
K_2O	11·1	4·7	6·3	4·4	3·3	8·9	9	3·9	9

* *See Glass Notes*, No. 15, Dec. 1955. A. Churchill Ltd. a paper 'Documents relating to the Lorraine Glass-makers in N. Staffs. &c.' by the late Capt. W. Horridge. The analysis was done by I.C.I.

† N. P. Bridgewater, 'Glasshouse Farm, St. Weonards. A small glassworking site,' in *The Woolhope Naturalists Club Trans.*, vol. 37 (1963), appendix II. Analysis by Mr R. F. Sykes, Dept. of Glass Technology, University of Sheffield.

‡ J. C. Harrington, *Glassmaking at Jamestown* (1952).

§ This is similar to another Early site No. 29 and again emphasizes the high total alkali content relative to our Late glass. It is unlikely to have any dating value because of the wide range of quality in the batches of Early glass. *See* also *Sy.A.C.*, vol. 62. I am much obliged to Mr E. S. Wood, for sending me a copy of his paper before publication.

Some Comparative Analyses in Percentages

	Sample A				*Sample B*				*Sample C*			
	SiO_2	Na_2O	K_2O	Total Alkali	SiO_2	Na_2O	K_2O	Total Alkali	SiO_2	Na_2O	K_2O	Total Alkali
Early	56	2·3	11·1	13·4	56·7	2·2	6·3	8·5	—	2	12·6	14·6
Late	64	·4	4·7	5·1	59·5	1·2	4·4	5·6	—	2·4	3·6	6

Sample A. Analysis kindly arranged in 1950–1 by Mr J. Strauss in America.

Sample B. Analysis kindly arranged by Mr J. Gardner in 1963 and carried out at the laboratories of Messrs Pilkingtons.

Sample C. Analysis kindly arranged by Mr R. J. Charleston, Keeper of Ceramics at the Victoria and Albert Museum and carried out by Dr R. G. Newton of the British Glass Industry Research Association in 1963.

Sample A came from the Early site of Malham Ashfold, Wisborough Green, and the Late site of Glasshouse Lane, Kirdford.

Samples B and C came from the Early site of Wephurst, Kirdford, and the Late site of Sidney Wood, Alfold.

Our analyses, A, B and C do not show this 'much greater proportion of sodium salts than potassium,' rather the reverse so this seems to rule out the introduction of barilla soda as the reason for the great improvement in glass quality which occurred after the middle of the sixteenth century.

The total alkali content and the potash content of our three samples A, B and C of Late glass is remarkably uniform and lower than that of the Early glass. This low total alkali content was noted by Prof. Turner in sample A in 1951 (*see* p. 39). There is no doubt about the marked increase in quality of our Late glass measured only by the relative absence of corrosion, hardness and sharper fracture. This purposely leaves out the controversial difference in visual appearance between our Early and Late glass.

Our Late forest glass remains a potash glass though the total alkali content is less than in the Early glass.

The old idea that good quality was related to soda content and that poor quality was related to potash may be partly correct, but only for the finest crystal glass, which was not produced in the forest furnaces. There were three distinct types in England, the poor Early forest glass, the good Late forest glass and the fine quality crystal produced in London from 1571 onwards.[21]

The late Professor Turner kindly commented on the results (30 March 1951) of the analysis of the Early and Late (Sample A) Weald glass:

'Actually the ash from vegetable matter contains a whole series of constituents, including lime, magnesia, iron oxide, soda, potash, alumina, etc. The relative proportions vary greatly in the fibres of different forms of vegetation. In consequence glass derived by the use of wood ashes, including ash from straw, fern and bracken is likely to vary greatly in composition, and in fact it is difficult to make any hard and fast generalisations about the origin of some of these old glasses on the basis of their chemical analysis.'

He noted that the Late Weald glass (Sample A from No. 14) was similar to the Jamestown glass, 'the special features being a low total alkali content, with potash predominating and a high calcium oxide and magnesium oxide content ranging from about 18 to as high as 30% (CaO plus MgO).'

[21] W. A. Thorpe, *English Glass* (2nd edn., London 1949), p. 97.

There is no confirmation in this that soda played a part. The site (No. 14) had so much glass surviving that it almost certainly was one of the last to work *c.*1618.

Commenting on Sample B, the head of the laboratory said the compositions of the two samples (Early and Late) were basically the same.

Commenting on the alkali content in analysis C, which he kindly made, Dr R. G. Newton says:

'These confirm that the post-1567 glass has quite a different composition from the earlier glass. The total alkali content of 6% agrees well for the "late glasses" quoted (*i.e.* samples B and C) and these compositions would be expected to give a more durable glass. I say "expected" because you will have realized that all of these compositions are quite different from those used in modern glasses which would have much higher silica contents and lower lime. Our analyses therefore support the contention that a marked change in composition took place and I wonder whether you have any historical information which would explain this very marked change.'

Unhappily there is nothing, so far, except Carré's statement that he proposed to import barilla soda and, as we have seen, that is not supported by our analyses. Also commenting on the figures in sample C, Dr Thorpe[21a] in a letter to Mr R. J. Charleston says:

(1) If we can assume that all the samples have been exposed to similar conditions[22] then it is reasonable to conclude that the post 1567[23] glasses are of markedly better corrosion resistance than the pre 1567 samples. (2) If point (1) is accepted the difference in corrosion resistance implies a real, and perhaps deliberate, difference in composition between the two types of glass most probably associated with a reduction in the alkali content of the later glass and in my view the differences would be greater than those likely to be occasioned by changing the source of one of the raw materials. For example, the post 1567 material could well have a higher viscosity/temperature characteristic than the pre 1567 material which would therefore require a hotter melting furnace which in turn might set up different requirements in terms of refractories. In other words I am suggesting that a whole range of technological aspects might be involved in moving from the one type of glass to the other. (3) I would also suggest that the line of argument used above could follow from the analyses quoted by Professor Turner.'[24]

Dr Thorpe's 'whole range of technological aspects' enters a country far outside the scope of this exercise and the mystery of the dramatic change from Early to Late is evidently not subject to any single simple explanation such as the introduction of

[21a] of the British Glass Industry Research Association.   [22] As they were.

[23] This report was made in 1963; later I decided to suggest a less precise dating of mid-sixteenth century.

[24] *See* p. 39.

barilla soda. But there does appear to be a marked and constant difference in composition in the total alkali content between the Early and the Late Wealden glass. The uniformity of our Late glass in four other counties may partly be explained by the fact that the same glassmaking families were probably involved and that they carried their new techniques with them.

Seventeenth-Century Glass Founding

Mr Guttery[25] has some illuminating comment on the empiric methods of glass founders:

> 'The mixing of the materials, that is, the preparation of the batch, was always a specialist job. There is (and seems always to have been) a widespread notion that this proceeding is almost a carefree operation; the idea probably arose from the fact that no two manufacturers use mixtures wholly alike in materials and the proportions in which they are used. A glasshouse was never a chemical laboratory; the chemist can command his conditions; he can get his desired heat to the exact degree and in an indestructible vessel from an exactly predetermined mixture produce the purest glass, and he can repeat this exactly on any occasion. Now the same heat and mixture in a glasshouse would produce not glass but disaster, for it would destroy pot and furnace. The glassmaker never possessed nor could possess the chemist's perfect control. His pots differed, his furnaces varied, his temperatures were not dependable, wind direction affected them, the quality of his fuel altered them and when both wind and fuel were favourable, an inattentive teazer could spoil all. Only long experience could teach him in what proportions he must mix his ingredients in these varying conditions. Being unable to adapt his pot and furnace to a mixture of strict proportions, he had to adapt the mixture to them. The use of cullet in the mixture, a normal practice, added difficulties, for the composition of this could vary considerably and could not be known, for the glassmakers would buy broken glass for cullet from any source. . .'

The trade secrets of Carré's Frenchmen may be related to this founding. Whether the small Weald glasshouses had a separate 'founder' is doubtful; in the small Early furnaces one skilled man probably built the furnace, fashioned the crucibles, was founder and 'gaffer.' Carré's *gentilhommes verriers* and the teams at the Late, and possibly larger, furnaces may have specialized more in their respective jobs.

The Two Types of Wealden Glass

There is no difficulty in providing fragments of typical Late Wealden glass for analysis because with few exceptions it is of uniformly good quality, hard, tough and unaffected by burial or the passage of time. The glassmakers of that period had

---

[25] *From Broad-glass to Cut Crystal* (1956), p. 41.

solved the problem which beset their predecessors, namely the very wide variation in quality – visual and actual – possibly almost from batch to batch. I have examined some thousands of fragments from all the Early Weald sites and the wide variation in quality alone suggests that selecting 'typical' fragments may be impossible, quite apart from the presence of cullet. An answer may well be in Agricola's description of mid-sixteenth century Venetian glassmaking technique. He says:

> 'Those who cook for one night only the materials for glassmaking and then proceed to make their glass articles, have a less pure and translucent result than those who first make a glassy mass and then recook fragments of it for two days and nights. For the goodness of glass consists not only of the materials from which it is made, but also in the cooking.'[26]

Whatever the technical causes may have been the effect is clear-cut and obvious: it is a turning point in English glassmaking.

The evidence from the furnace sites shows that there was a profound change and a great improvement in the quality and appearance of the Weald glass sometime in the latter half of the sixteenth century.

The characteristic Late glass can be broadly dated by the hard brown tiger ware found only in association with this Late glass.[27] It can be more closely dated from documentary sources. Jean Carré will be discussed later, but, very briefly, he stated in the summer of 1567 that he had erected two furnaces at 'Fernefol,' Sussex[28]. One of these can almost certainly be identified with a furnace (No. 25) found on Fernfold (now Barnfold) in 1934, which produced the characteristic Late glass.

The finding of what is perhaps Carré's furnace at Fernfold with its unmistakable Late glass, plus his stated importation of soda, had been accepted as being the reason for the sudden great improvement in the quality of Weald glass. It had been surmised that as he had probably reverted to the southern or Mediterranean soda glass in his London (crystal) glasshouse, soda might be the key to the dramatic change in the Weald from the primitive to the almost modern type of glass. This is not borne out by analysis of the two types which was done for me in 1950,[29] nor by later analysis. The theory is no longer tenable for forest glass.

---

[26] *Wealden Glass* (1933), appendix, p. 81.

[27] Fragments of this ware were kindly dated by Messrs J. G. Hurst and K. Barton. In 1965 Mr Hurst dated such ware from site No. 23 as the last quarter of the sixteenth century and from site No. 38 as the first half of the seventeenth century and it could be before 1618. In 1963 Mr Barton dated similar ware from site Nos. 14 and 32 as being from the last quarter of the sixteenth century. Three other Late sites can probably be dated by similar stone ware, Nos. 26 and 35 now lost, and No. 42 which was excavated by Mr E. S. Wood. The dating of Wealden glass is discussed in Chapter VI and the sites in Chapter IX.

[28] *See* Chapter IX, site No. 25. Three other sites, Nos. 36, 37 and 40 may possibly be dated from documentary sources.

[29] I am much indebted to Mr Jerome Strauss for arranging this.

Decomposition and Decay

Much has been written about this and I can contribute little that is new. The evidence from the Weald furnace sites is clear in one respect: good and very bad glass can occur in identical soil conditions and there seems no doubt that, excluding some particularly corrosive site such as may occur in a town, burying only accentuates its inherent defects. There is also a wide variation in the effect of wind and rain on ancient window glass, and the reason for both internal decay and external pitting or flaking,[30] must lie in faulty technique and incorrect proportions of materials in the original batch.

Some Early Weald glass is in a good state of preservation, probably little changed from the day it was made, but there is a very wide range of condition, from completely opaque crumbling disintegration like soft brittle toffee to good and stable, but cloudy, glass. The bulk of the Late glass is usually in excellent condition with only rarely some surface flaking.[31] and some, such as the Sidney Wood glass, with its burnished surfaces, appears to the unaided eye to be wholly unaffected by age or burial. I suggest the explanation may be that the Early glassmakers very rarely happened to hit the correct technique and mix but that, by constant experiment, the Late glassmen usually achieved the correct conditions.

There is some evidence that bad glass was not recognized at the time of glazing. Below the fifteenth century wall and east window of Kirdford church I found fragments of five different glazings, the latest being 1887 and two others, very thin, appear to be Late. It is unlikely that this ground has remained undisturbed but of what appear to be the two earliest glazings, one is thin ($\frac{1}{16}$ in.) and opaque, having decomposed on the surface, while the other ($\frac{1}{8}$ in.) is completely opaque and in an advanced state of crumbling decomposition. There is no doubt the seeds of decay were present when it left the furnace, and probably accounted for its removal from the window. These two glazings at least were probably of local manufacture.[32] The condition of our Early glass is not always related with its age.[33]

[30] The two types of decomposition, basic and superficial, are distinguished by W. B. Honey in his handbook *Glass* (Victoria and Albert Museum, 1946, p. 4, note 7) where he says: 'This diseased condition [due to faulty technique] is to be distinguished from decay due to burial, in which the surface only has been attacked by dissolved carbonic acid in the soil moisture; this has in the course of centuries drawn from the glass the alkali in its composition, leaving the distintegrated surface portion in a laminated condition commonly showing iridescence.'

[31] One Late furnace, Somersbury (No. 26), produced some poor glass showing heavy superficial flaking.

[32] The few fragments of contemporary glass, yellow-painted quarries, in the top of the two fifteenth-century windows of the north aisle of Kirdford church, are unlikely to be local glass. They were probably painted and fired in the London 'school.' That 'school' probably relied on the better imported window glass and used Weald glass only when trade with France was impossible. It is improbable that any Early Weald window glass now survives, judging by the condition of fragments found on furnace sites.

[33] Mr J. A. Knowles always considered that mid-fourteenth-century glass was of much poorer quality than that of earlier or later times, and attributed this to the effects of the Black Death. He thought that too high a content of alkali was used to make it melt at a lower temperature.

III

FUEL AND CRUCIBLES

Fuel

THERE is ample evidence from the three early writers (*see* p. 11) that dry wood was used. Theophilus (Book II, section V) says that after filling containers (crucibles) with frit (*see* p. 74) in the evening, 'throughout the whole night add dry wood to the fire so that the glass which liquifies from the frit, may be completely fused.' In sections IV, XIII, XVI, XXIII and XXX for various firing operations he specifies 'dry beechwood' or 'beechwood thoroughly dried in smoke' as fuel.

For melting the glass, Månnson (*c.*1530), said a fierce fire with dry wood must be kept up for two days and two nights; Agricola (*c.*1550), says that two boys must take turns night and day to feed the fire by putting dry logs on the hearth. The emphasis on dry wood was vital, because working close to a furnace with no chimney would be impossible with smoke from green wood and, in any case, dry wood gives a hotter flame.

The deeds of 1380 and 1385 relating to the Schurterre glasshouse (No. 12) in Kirdford (*see* p. 31) refer to 'underwood' and this appears to be the fuel. In the 1385 deed the underwood is mentioned as being cleaved, which suggests it was large. It may have been 15- or 20-year-old thinnings, probably beech and oak.

Possibly 'pollarding'[1] was also practised; it would provide excellent, easily hand-led fuel, when cut into lengths to fit the tiny individual fireboxes.

In 1557 Henry Strudwick of Kirdford, a yeoman farmer and glassmaker left to his sons 'the profyt of my Glasse Howse, withall the beches that I have bought, and half the beches in and upon Idehurst and Crofts,'[2] a combination which leaves little

---

[1] Carré in his letter to Lord Burleigh in 1567, asking for a licence to make glass (S.P. 12/43, No. 104, new calendar), said 'we do not mean to cut the actual trunks of good trees but only the branches, the trunks will produce branches [?] also in 8 or 9 years, &c. &c.' This suggests pollarding, but the interval is too short. There is a reference to pollarding oaks in Kirdford in 1766 (*S.A.C.*, vol. 93, p. 149). I asked the Forestry Commission Research station to comment on pollarding oak and beech and Mr N. Nimmo kindly replied: 'Both oak and beech may be pollarded successfully at intervals of about twenty years and would yield a good crop of small to medium sized firewood by such a system. Trees intended for pollarding should not be allowed to get too large before the first cut or the number of crops obtainable will be greatly reduced. In general oak will last longer than beech on such a cutting system. Coppicing will produce similar results but in this case the crop is cut close to the ground and the new shoots are therefore very subject to damage by grazing animals.'

[2] *S.R.S*, vol. 43, p. 72, and *S.N.Q.*, vol. 7, p. 171.

doubt that his fuel was beech billets. Until the coal fired glass furnace was invented early in the seventeenth century the fuel was invariably wood and, when available, it was probably beech. Today there are many fine beeches on Idehurst Hurst, a large area of woodland just south of Idehurst. If the woodlands of Croftes, 300 yards across the river from Idehurst north site refer, as they may well do, to a large area of woodland now called Jacksland Copse, and are added to the woodland on Idehurst, Henry had something well over a hundred acres of woodland, apart from the 'beches' he had bought.

I have suggested the forêt de Lyons fifteen miles east of Rouen as the most likely origin of the medieval glass industry in the Weald (*see* p. 12). The forêt is still celebrated for its beeches. Carré brought over the Hennezels, Thysacs and Thiétrys, glassmakers from the forêt de Darney, fifty miles south of Nancy. Vast forests of beech, measured in Lorraine in thousands of acres, are, and probably always have been, the main feature of both these districts. Here in the glassmaking parishes of the Weald, there are and were[3] some hundreds of acres of beech. It is not usually recognized by the botanists that on the Weald clay, given equal chances, beech thrives and will often swamp the oak, and make good, though not as fine trees as on the chalk.

There is little doubt that the attraction for glassmakers in all three cases was ample supplies of beech fuel, possibly in the Weald supplemented by oak. The relative merits of beech wood and coal as fuel were discussed by the late J. A. Knowles in a paper, 'Medieval processes of glass manufacture,'[4] where he quotes from Loysel[5] the result of lengthy experiments designed to compare the relative merits of fuels for glassmaking. The result showed that although a considerably greater weight of beech wood was needed this was broadly offset by the greater heating effect obtained. Wood also has the advantage that covered pots are not necessary such as are required for many kinds of glasses when coal is used. Our forest glassmakers certainly did not use charcoal as fuel; the furnaces would have had to be redesigned, as were the coal-fired ones of the early seventeenth century (*see* Fig. 20). Such charcoal as is found on the sites may be explained by the partial sealing up of the furnace flue at some stage in the melting. The wood billets would become charcoal which could be raked out.[6]

We have some valuable documentary evidence from Kent when John Lennard

---

[3] Lord Leconfield, *Petworth Manor in the Seventeenth Century* (O.U.P., 1954), p. 50. The 1557 survey of the manor of Petworth shows that in six woods in the northern part of the old parish, now North Chapel parish, largely on Weald clay, were 603 acres beech and oak. The details suggest that beech was at least as widely grown as oak. The entries are: 200 acres, beech and timber 140 years old thin set; 160 acres, most fair beech and some oaks; 76 acres, scrubbed oak and beech 300 years old; 39 acres, much fine timber, some great beeches 220 years old; 37 acres, mostly beech, 180 years old; 91 acres, old scrubbed oak and beeches, some 240 years old.

[4] J. A. Knowles, *Glass*, July to September 1927.

[5] Loysel, *L'Art de la verrerie*, p. 72.

[6] I have to thank Mr M. J. Lowe for this suggestion.

of Chevening, a bencher of Lincoln's Inn obtained a lease for some years of Knole about 1570. Some of his accounts and letters survive showing that he carried on the manufacture of glass,[7] possibly for the mansion house of Knole.[8] The accounts show that large amounts of fuel were used in a glasshouse at this time;[9] it is referred to as 'log wood' and 'clefte cords' which suggest that large timber was sometimes used. The evidence is not clear, but the fire-box of the working furnace was small, about 18 in. deep, two feet wide and about four feet long, and the amount of labour needed for cutting into short lengths and cleaving large timber trees suggests that 15- or 20-year-old thinnings or pollardings were much more likely. Between 7 June 1585 and 18 January 1586, 543 cords of wood were carried to the glasshouse. During a period of 226 days the glasshouse appears to have been working continuously. It is unlikely that they usually worked throughout the year; this is confirmed in Carré's letter to Lord Burleigh asking for a monopoly,[10] in which he says, 'at certain times of the year as at the height of summer the furnaces will be out for 8 or 10 weeks because during the great heat.' So that 700 cords a year for a large Elizabethan glasshouse may have been usual—as much as a medium-sized iron furnace[11] and more than many iron forges.

The two boys mentioned by Agricola as stokers would have to feed into the furnace nearly $2\frac{1}{2}$ cords of wood in the 24 hours. The price delivered at the glass house was 3s. 4d. a cord or, on the above basis, £146 a year. We do not know the wages of the four glassmakers named but Carré paid a principal workman 18s. a day (see p. 110). We do not know what expenses he had to meet out of this, nor how many days a year he worked. It was a very highly paid craft, because the rate for such skilled men as carpenters, masons and plumbers was only about 1s. a day at this time.

In a letter to John Lennard, 17 November 1587, Pulston says:

'Adams and George doe worke at the Painted gate and they do not sett upp the cords halfe so fast as they are caryed away, therefore yf you will have the glass-men to contynew at worke you must ether graunte that more woodcutters may be sett at worke or ells suffer to carry out of some other place in the parke, for all the clefte cords that were in hook wood are caryed to the glass-howse already.'

---

[7] T. Lennard Barrett, 'Glassmaking at Knole, Kent,' in *The Antiquary*, vol. 41 (1905), pp. 127–129.

[8] I know of no documentary evidence of temporary glass furnaces being built solely to glaze the vast and sometimes overglazed, Elizabethan mansions, but where there was ample woodland the practice has much to commend it. The tools were few and portable and the glasshouse could be built by two men in a few days.

[9] In a letter, November 1587, Lennard's manager, Roger Pulston, seems to imply there were two furnaces in the same glasshouse, but the wording is too ambiguous to be certain. The $7\frac{1}{2}$ month period is short but it is all the evidence we have.

[10] S.P. Dom., 12/43, No. 104 (new No.).

[11] The large Waldron iron furnace averaged over 14 years, 1646–59, 1,085 cords a year: E. Straker, *Wealden Iron* (1931), p. 124.

This looks as if the wood was being used green; if that was so the smoke must have been troublesome. Mrs E. S. Godfrey (*D.E.G.*, p. 350) comments that 'Once production was under way, the success of any glassmaking venture financially depended rather upon an adequate and reasonable supply of labour and fuel.'

The Knole fuel consumption was very large, and it may be typical of that period when the trade was booming. Judging by their scarcity, it is unlikely that there were usually more than one or two glasshouses working at one time in the Early period. With one exception, they are confined to the parishes of Chiddingfold, Hambledon and Kirdford, whose woodlands presumably supplied fuel for the industry for at least two hundred years. This alone is some indication of the smallness of the Wealden industry until the mid-sixteenth century.

During the Late boom period at least six (possibly nine) glasshouses are known to have operated in Wisborough Green, the centre of the Late Weald period, and this must have placed a strain on the local woodland, because there were also seven ironworks within a five-mile radius of Wisborough Green church operating during much the same time. The two industries must have provided winter work for many local men in the woodlands, and brought them some small prosperity. Mrs E. S. Godfrey makes it clear that

'The shortage of wood fuel, of course, affected not only glassmakers but many other industries and also the householder who was accustomed to burn wood. Mr Nef has already shown the extent of the timber crisis throughout England, particularly during the latter part of the reign of Elizabeth and the reign of James I. As a result the prices of firewood rose much faster than the average price of commodities in common use.[12] Glasshouses both contributed to the scarcity and were in turn affected by rising prices and short supply.'

A few glasshouses using 700 cords a year would place a great strain on fuel resources even of the Weald and some opposition to the glassmakers was aroused. The recurring apprehension about the possible diminution of the country's woodlands was a very different problem and it is often forgotten that woodland and copse simply provide long-term crops which may regenerate naturally. Furthermore there is evidence that the maximum production of the Wealden glass industry occurred in the last twenty years of its life (*see* p. 138). There is also evidence that the latest furnaces had to go further afield for their fuel (*see* p. 133) which suggests a temporary shortage only. By 1586 the shortage of fuel had become serious and Lutteri's furnace at Burgate was shut down (*see* p. 200), but there was discrimination because the local Peytowe family continued to make glass close by in Chiddingfold for at least another twenty-eight years. Three years later George Longe proposed moving most of the Weald glass industry to Ireland largely to reduce the fuel demands (*see* p. 143). The greatly increased competition for available fuel within the few

[12] J. U. Nef, *The Rise of the British Coal Industry* (London, 1932), vol. I, pp. 156–164, quoted in *D.E.G.*, p. 84.

parishes was real enough, but it was used to drive Lutteri, a stranger, out of the area, as it was used thirty years later to establish Mansell's monopoly by forcing Isaac Bungar and the Henseys out of business. The unsuccessful Jamestown (Va.) venture of 1608 was started by London merchants for the same reasons as the proposed move to Ireland.[13] 'By 1612, possibly by 1611, the technical changes permitting the use of coal solved the problem of fuel and sent the British industry far in advance of the French for many generations.'[14] Coal was a much cheaper fuel and better quality glass could be produced with it; so the drift of surplus Lorrainers from the Weald, which had been going on for twenty years and more, was accelerated and concentrated on the coal districts of the Midlands and Tyneside.[15] But as Mrs Godfrey shows it was another six or seven years before the 'truculent' Bungar, after a long and bitter struggle, was forced to shut down his Weald glasshouse in 1618. The move was also hastened by a Royal Proclamation of 23 May 1615 prohibiting the use of timber or wood as fuel for glass furnaces and, in 1618, by Mansell's determined enforcement of his monopoly. Mrs. E. S. Godfrey says,

> 'It can hardly be over-stressed that the change from wood to coal fuel, was the most significant occurrence in the English glass industry during the century under consideration [1560–1640]. Without the change and with a diminishing wood supply, production would of necessity either have remained stationary or more probably would have fallen gradually to lower levels.'[16]

All these factors contributed to the decline of the Weald industry and by 1618 the last furnace had probably been abandoned never to be re-occupied and such was the end of the forest glass industry in England.

Crucibles

Fragments of crucible found in the Weald are unmistakable, unlike any other pottery and if found in quantity are conclusive evidence of a glass furnace nearby. Glazed brick or stone which recur at the many lime and brick-kilns in the Weald, or stray fragments of glass without crucible are usually of little significance, but crucible seldom occurs more than a few hundred yards from a furnace and a concentration of fragments, with glass adhering, in a few square yards usually indicates a furnace. In the Weald these pots (Fig. 1) varied from a large breakfast cup size and shape to very large bucket-shaped pots holding 2 cwt. and more.[17] A usual pot appears to have held about 2–3 gallons with a base of 10–12 in. in diameter and about

[13] D.E.G., p. 94.   [14] D.E.G., p. 102.

[15] Mrs Godfrey comments (D.E.G., p. 153), 'Since seven or eight tons of coal at the very least were required to produce a ton of window glass, it was clearly more economical to ship the finished product than the fuel to the London area.'

[16] D.E.G., p. 102.

[17] A possible very large crucible from site No. 14 is discussed in Chapter IX. A reconstruction of crucible fragments found at Woodchester (see Chapter X) was approximately 24 in. high, with a diameter at the base of 16 in. and at the top of 18½ in.

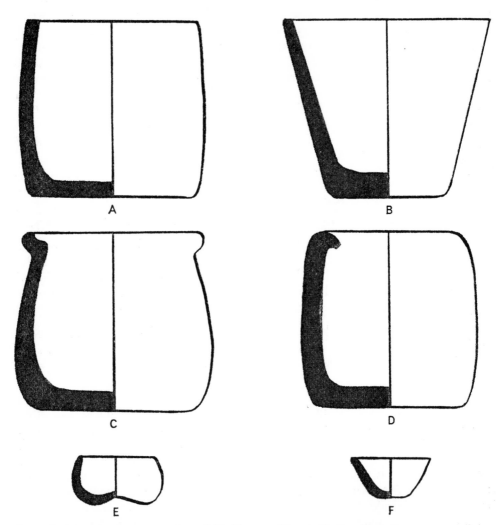

Fig. 1. Some suggested reconstructions of Wealden crucibles. A. Bucket shape, the commonest form. See *W.G.*, p. 54. B. Bucket shape with flared sides, a common form. From No. 29. *See* Plate V. C. Barrel shape with unusual rim. Found only at No. 33. D. Heavily inturned rim found only at No. 32. E. Small, from No. 4. *See* Plate III. F. Small, unusual. The only complete crucible found. From No. 38. *See* Plate IV. The exact sizes of only E and F are known. The others are shown in approximate relative proportion.

the same height, some straight-sided, some bowed and some tapering outwards. The thickness varies with the size but 1 in. sides and a slightly thicker base is common.[18] Occasionally, mainly on the Late sites, fragments of thin crucible walls are found only $\frac{1}{2}$–$\frac{3}{4}$ in. thick. The texture and colour varies with a few yellow and pink specimens,[19] but the great bulk have a muddy-grey centre with an off-white surface. Apart from the Blunden's Wood crucibles which appear to be unique in the Weald, both in thinness of walls and shape of rims, there is no difference in the crucible fragments from Early or Late sites. Of the Blunden's Wood crucibles Mr Wood says:

'A large number of fragments of crucible was recovered from the site, both among the stones of the kilns, in the magma which blocked the flue of kiln A and strewn on the ground. The inference is that the breakage of crucible during the glass-making process was considerable. They were presumably not fired quite hard enough to withstand the pressure of the boiling glass, whose rate of expansion was greater than that of the earthenware.

The crucible is not made from the local clay. Many pieces were coated with glass, which was not, however, the remains of glaze. This adhering glass appears as greenish, yellowish or brownish, but this may well simply be due to impurities, weathering or patchy colouring of the crucibles showing through.

The crucibles are of greyish or buff paste, coarse and granular. Many show whitish exterior and darker interior. The fractures are often jagged. A few are pink, a colouration due to high firing temperature.

They fall into two classes and three thicknesses of wall; *bucket* - and *barrel* - shaped, and walls of about 1 in., $\frac{1}{2}$ in. and $\frac{1}{4}$ in thick.

I. The *bucket*-shaped pots are straight-sided, or curve in slightly at the top. No rims were found, but from Winbolt's illustration they appear to have had plain rims (i.e. none at all). They are about 12–15 in. high, 14–15 in. in diameter at the top, and 11–12 in. at the base; walls $\frac{3}{4}$–1 in. thick, base $1\frac{3}{4}$–2 in. thick. This is the commonest type found on most recorded glass sites, and was in use throughout up to the seventeenth century.

II. The commonest type however at Blunden's Wood is the *barrel*-shaped pot, which bellies out below a pronounced and distinctive rim . . . These fall into two sizes (a) diameter at top about 12 in. walls $\frac{1}{2}$ in. thick; (b) diameter at top about 10–11 in. walls $\frac{1}{4}$–$\frac{5}{16}$ in. thick.'

As Mr Wood says crucible rims vary very widely,

'but the Blunden's Wood rims are so homogeneous and distinctive that they seem to bear the signature of three individual potters. This is not unlikely, in view of the short life of the glasshouse. But whether they all worked at the same pottery

[18] The late Rev. T. S. Cooper's few dimensions, found in his loose notes, broadly agree with this. He says he found large quantities of crucible fragments, as we did.

[19] There are fragments of large pink pottery jars the bases of which at first sight look like crucible bases; these can be readily identified because their texture is soft and crumbly.

cannot be stated. The regular potting, however, seems to indicate professional manufacture; local manufacture would imply a potter at Blunden's Wood, which is not probable. One wonders whether thicker walls would have been less liable to breakage, but after all, breaking of pots is a problem which has always beset glassworkers.'

Mr Wood discusses the origin of the crucible clay and crucible glazing and decides that the clay was not local and that 'the unnecessary application of glaze seems highly improbable.'

Merret records that the 'clay ground to a fine powder mixed with water is trod with bare feet till it comes to a good consistence, fit to mould, which they do with their hands and when fashioned, dry them in a convenient place, and afterwards anneal them in or over the furnace.'[20] Mr J. C. Harrington says the pots were formed by moulding them by hand from coils of clay, and without the aid of a potter's wheel.[21] This was probably the usual method but some in the Weald appear to have been made on a wheel. Mr R. J. Charleston has assembled the recorded descriptions of crucibles and the origins of the clay for making them.[22] Most, but not all, of the Wealden crucibles were fine, very hard pots which could have been made only with good quality fire clay which is not found locally.

Some sites produced only a few fragments and some had a few hundred. Three sizes and shapes are illustrated, Plates III, IV and V. The small one (Plate IV) came from Sidney Wood (No. 38) and is the only complete specimen I know. It has a small quantity of glass or frit inside. It is roughly made and resembles half an ostrich's egg. It has a round bottom, is about $2\frac{1}{2}$ in. high and $4\frac{1}{2}$ in. across the top. All measurements are outside. The Chaleshurst (No. 4) crucible (Plate III) is larger with an approximate base diameter of $5\frac{1}{2}$ in. with slightly bowed sides and probably the same diameter across the top. It is 2·4 in. high, with a slightly concave base, and resembles a saucepan without a handle, not unlike some of the Jamestown pots; it was probably wheel-turned. The colour is the common shade of muddy buff. It is made up from three fragments which appear to be from one pot, but the right-hand portion had about $\frac{1}{4}$ in. thick of 'sealing-wax' ruby glass still adhering (this shows in the photograph) whereas the centre portion has no glass inside and the left hand portion has a thin coating of apparently good green glass. The base appears to marry up with about $\frac{1}{2}$ in. of clinkery material sticking to the bottom where it sat on the siege.

The Malhamashfold (No. 29) crucible (Plate V) is the largest surviving single fragment and is now in Haslemere Museum.[23] I consider it is a much more usual

---

[20] pp. 245–246, ex Mr R. J. Charleston's notes (unpublished) for his History of Technology paper. Merrett translated, in 1662, Neri's *L'Arte Vetraria* of 1612.

[21] *Glassmaking at Jamestown*, p. 38.

[22] 'Ancient Glass-Making Methods,' Circle of Glass Collectors, Duplicated paper No. 124, March 1961 (issued for private circulation to members only).

[23] Winbolt, *W.G.*, p. 67, says the largest [fragment] he had seen was 'about 15 in. across the mouth.' It came significantly from a Late site (No. 4).

form in shape, size and thickness than the other two. The base diameter is 11 in., the walls taper outwards like a bucket and may have been over 13 in. high. The walls about half way up are $\frac{3}{4}$ in. thick. It has some glass remaining in the bottom, but has no glazing inside or out. The texture is unusual, being a fairly uniform grey right through, whereas the great majority of Wealden crucibles have off-white surfaces inside and out, and are of harder and better quality. It has some glass and scum sticking to the base, which shows it sat on top of the siege and not in a hole in the siege, as suggested by Theophilus. I can recollect no evidence from many crucible fragments, that the pots were inside holes in the siege. They all stood on top.[24] The round base of the tiny crucible described above, may have sat in a small flue hole for some special purpose but it is probably a freak.

I am not satisfied that there was more than a very general size and form for the industry as a whole. Glazed or unglazed, inturned (usually) or out-turned rims (see Fig. 1) large or small seem to have been used at any period, but any very heavy large pot is likely to belong to the last fifty years of the industry. One site, Woodhouse Farm (No. 32) had most unusual heavily inturned rims (see Fig. 2). This furnace was one of the last to be abandoned, but it is unlikely that such rims had anything to do with experiments in coal firing. The whole furnace design was different and the cost of carting coal to the Weald would have been prohibitive.

Some pots have simple incised wavy lines below the rim and one fragment is heavily ribbed down the outside (see Fig. 3). Some crucibles appear to have had a glaze before use, either inside or out or on both surfaces. A brown glaze is not uncommon. Mr E. S. Wood, who discusses crucible glazing fully in his paper on the Blunden's Wood glasshouse[25] thinks a glaze could be due to some constituent in the clay being brought to the surface by heat; therefore the glaze may not have been intentional.

Crucibles had to withstand high temperatures, probably about 1200°C.; if they cracked or collapsed the furnace was put out of action and damaged, so great care had to be used in selecting the clay, in the making of the crucibles and in the rigid inspection and discarding before re-use if they showed any sign of failures. Even so, the turnover was probably high, because molten glass slowly dissolves its container. Crucible making was a specialist job and particularly in the Late period when upwards of a dozen furnaces may have been working; it is likely that there was a crucible maker for this district. The only evidence as to where crucibles were made comes from the valuable Knole glass furnace documents and accounts.[26] Under February 1586 is an item 'ii lode pot clay for makyng XII pots.' This suggests that the pots were made in or near the glasshouse, unhappily it does not say where the clay came from and its price is grouped with thirteen other items. Assuming a load was a cart load, the pots must have been large.

[24] The Blunden's Wood crucibles were in slight depressions in the siege, but not in holes; see p. 60.

[25] Sy.A.C., vol. 62, p. 72.   [26] See 'Glassmaking at Knole, Kent.'

One great problem is the provenance of the clay. A member of the recent Geological Survey of this area knew of no sources of fireclay for crucibles in the Weald clay series. It may have come from Purbeck, Nonsuch (Ewell) or Stourbridge. Merret writing in 1662 says that the crystal glass pots were made from Purbeck clay but the green (or poorer quality) glassmakers in London used clay from Nonsuch mixed with a different clay brought from Worcestershire. This would almost certainly be Stourbridge, about 150 miles away from our centre. Nonsuch is about 25 miles. Purbeck was easily accessible by sea from Arundel and by smaller boat up the Arun to Greatham about ten miles from the centre of our industry. What appears to be a fragment of a 'mavering' slab of Purbeck marble was found on a furnace site at Idehurst, so there was some communication. This is confirmed by the use of the marble in Sussex churches from Norman times. Mr N. P. Bridgewater, in his admirable paper on the St Weonards (Herefordshire)[27] glasshouse which is the same date as our Late sites, goes into this question very fully. He had detailed analyses made of his crucibles and of the varied fireclays of the Forest of Dean and Stourbridge. He says that 'in view of the wide variation in their chemical composition it cannot be asserted that either district was the source of our fireclay. Nevertheless, there are two of the Stourbridge clays whose composition is similar to that of our crucible sample. Apart from this, there are reasons on general grounds, for identifying Stourbridge as the source.' He sums up: 'It is therefore suggested that our crucible pots came from Stourbridge in their manufactured form.' Stourbridge is about 50 miles from his site. The St. Weonards crucible cannot be exactly matched in appearance by any Weald pots. The former is slightly better quality than the latter and its faint pink shade is unknown in Sussex. The variation in fireclays and in Weald pots suggests that any analysis would be a large and possibly inconclusive exercise. After Mansell started to make glass in Newcastle upon Tyne, c.1616, so important was the clay that for a time it was brought at great expense from Staffordshire to Newcastle.[28]

The three early writers provide some information, Theophilus[29] being the most useful. He says:

'Meanwhile, take some of the white clay from which crucibles are made, dry it and grind it carefully. Add water, beat vigorously with a piece of wood and make your vessels. These should be wide above and narrow below, and have a small inward curving lip round the mouth. When they are dry, lift them up with the tongs and place them in the red hot kiln in the holes made for this purpose. With a shovel, take up the frit and fill the containers in the evening. Then

---

[27] *Woolhope Naturalists' Field Club Transactions*, vol. 37 (1963). The walls of the St Weonard's crucibles varied from $\frac{1}{2}$ in to $1\frac{1}{2}$ in. and were thus similar to the Weald pots, although slightly heavier.

[28] S.P. 14/162, No. 231B, ex *D.E.G.*, p. 155.

[29] These details are taken from Theophilus, *De Diversis Artibus*, edited by C. R. Dodwell (1961) Book II, Section V.

throughout the whole night, add dry wood to the fire so that the glass, which liquifies from the frit, may be completely fused.'

Månnson and Agricola describe sixteenth-century Venetian practice.[30] By our standards the pots they describe are large and, in Agricola's case, of a shape unknown in the Weald. Månnson says the pots were heated for a day before the frit was put in. Agricola seems to suggest that crucibles were not matured,[31] because he describes how the pots are heated under a slow fire so that they give off their moisture and then under a fiercer heat so that they turn reddish; if they show no cracks they are put in the working furnace.

Pape[32] has this to say about the North Staffordshire crucibles:

'Judged by the amount of fragments of crucibles at all the sites there is no doubt that the pots were continually being broken and their renewal must have been a very expensive item in the making of glass. At the Bishop's Wood there were so many pieces that some belonging to the four bases cemented into the platforms were able to be picked out, and so reconstructions in part were able to be carried out. The crucibles varied considerably in texture, size and thickness [as they do in the Weald]. The texture was generally a dull white or a dark grey, glazed inside and out with a thin layer of glass. By the curvature of the base fragments and the rims, the larger crucibles, which were in abundance, had round flat bases twelve inches in diameter and they curved barrel-shaped to an open top eleven inches or slightly more in diameter. Perhaps their height was twelve inches. The rims of nearly all the crucibles were rounded in section showing a half circle, but occasionally a fragmentary rim showed the curve on the inside, then flattened out on top and came down straight on the outside. The thickness of the walls of the crucibles showed great variety. The bases varied from $1\frac{1}{2}$ to 3 in. and the walls from $1\frac{3}{8}$ to $\frac{1}{2}$ in.; the average wall thickness was perhaps not quite an inch.'

The drawings (Figs. 2, 3 and 3a) show a range of rims and bases.[33] It is perhaps impossible to date crucible by size, shape or texture, though it may be that larger pots were used in the Late period.[34] The heavily inturned rims shown from Woodhouse Farm (No. 32) were found only at that site. It is seldom possible to reconstruct crucibles as the fragments are too scattered. I agree with Winbolt that the dimensions are about 12 in. high with a base and lip outside diameter of 10 to 12 in.; but I think his thickness is too great. He gives the thickness of the wall at its thinnest as 1 to $1\frac{1}{4}$ in.

[30] These details are taken from the valuable appendices in *W.G.*
[31] Today Messrs Powell mature their crucibles in a controlled atmosphere for a year.
[32] Pape, p. 36.
[33] The specimen with flanges inside and out came from Malhamashfold, site No. 29.
[34] Mr N. P. Bridgewater notes that the St Weonards crucibles were larger than those found on Wealden sites.

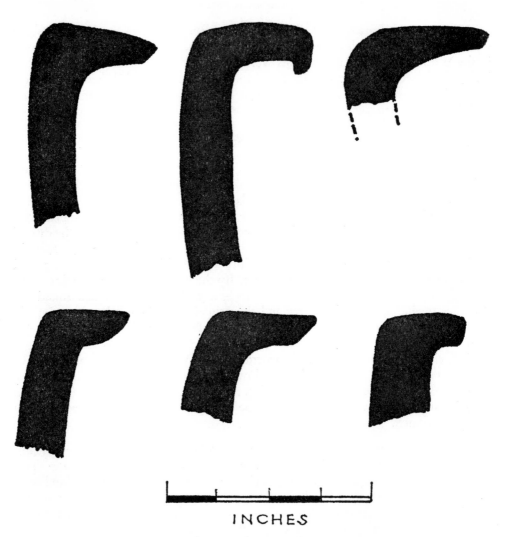

INCHES

Fig. 2. Heavily inturned rims peculiar to No. 32.

INCHES.

Fig. 3. Crucible rims from Wealden furnaces.

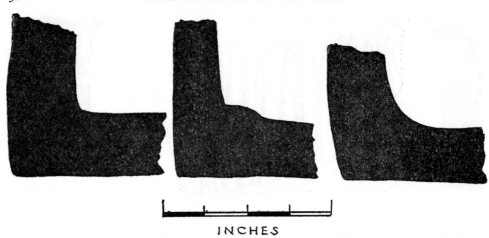

INCHES

Fig. 3a. Crucible bases from Wealden furnaces.

and at the angle between wall and base about $2\frac{1}{8}$ to $2\frac{1}{2}$ in. These, I think, were the upper limits and many were thinner. Cooper gives dimensions of two pots,[35] neither from known sites, as 12 in. high, and $1\frac{1}{2}$ to $2\frac{1}{2}$ in. thick at base, one with an outside base diameter of $10\frac{5}{8}$ in. and the other of $8\frac{3}{8}$ in.; the former had a mouth diameter[36] of the same and the latter of 11 in., in other words it was bucket shaped, which seems very usual.

[35] The dimensions of these two pots given in V.C.H. *Sy*, vol. II, p. 295, do not agree with his notes.

[36] Attempting to assess the diameter at the mouth from a fragment of crucible rim can be wholly misleading because some crucibles had one flat side with a straight rim, others were ovoid. The bases are probably more reliable.

IV

THE GLASSHOUSE AND ITS FURNACES

Throughout this book the word 'glasshouse' means the whole factory shed covering the working, fritting and annealing furnaces and, if not prefixed, the word 'furnace' means the working furnace in which the glass was melted. The Blunden's Wood site in Surrey is the only forest glasshouse in England known of in 1965 to have been completely excavated, described and illustrated;[1] this chapter has been transformed by the inclusion of the structural part of Mr Wood's admirable paper on his excavation of this site. He very kindly allowed me to make full use of his paper before its publication. This chapter also includes descriptions and plans of the working furnaces at Bishop's Wood (Staffs.) and Jamestown (Va.), with a plan of the complete glasshouse at the latter (Fig. 9) and descriptions by various authorities, to show how these small furnaces operated.

Blunden's Wood, Hambledon, Glasshouse

The Blunden's Wood glasshouse was a rare survival which remained untouched since it was abandoned. Being close to the stone of the Greensand ridge it probably did not attract the usual stone robbers and it was partially fossilized in its own spilled glass, making demolition difficult. It lay awaiting all the benefits of modern scientific archaeology which Mr Wood brought to bear on its problems.[2] His resulting paper provides a model for any future excavations. It was a rare combination of the right man in the right place at the right time, because the site was demolished shortly after the dig was completed. Being expendable nothing escaped examination.[3] We now know in some detail what a fourteenth-century forest glasshouse in the Weald was like. Ample datable pottery was found which together with the magnetic dating of the kiln enabled Mr Wood to give an authoritative date for the glasshouse within the 2nd quarter of the fourteenth century, and probably around 1330. I have with Mr Wood's kind permission copied his description, and used some of his plates and drawings of the glasshouse and also his section on the function of the Blunden's

---

[1] At Fernfold, Vann and Bishop's Wood the working furnaces only were examined. The Woodchester glasshouse (*see* Chapter X) may have been completely excavated but only a small plan survives. This is printed in Mr J. S. Daniels's *The Woodchester Glasshouse* (1950). The plans of Fernfold and Vann working furnaces are in Chapter IX and the Bishop's Wood furnace plan follows in this chapter.

[2] Mr E. S. Wood is the author of *Collins Field Guide to Archaeology* (1963).

[3] A large area surrounding the glasshouse was later stripped by a bulldozer showing that the complete installation had been examined. Sites are not always expendable, and on one copse site we were forbidden to cut any roots.

Wood ovens.[4] Particular details have been selected as the paper is readily accessible to the specialist who wants the full discussion of the pottery and magnetic dating or the analysis of the crucibles.

Mr. Wood writes:

'*The site as found*. The mound as found was some 16 ft. across and some 1 ft. 6 in. (south side) to 2 ft. 6 in. (west side) high. It was littered with glass waste, burnt clay and sandstone, and crucible. When the area was cleared for excavation a smaller mound, 10 ft. across and 1 ft. high, was seen about 6 ft. to the west of the large mound, but had not previously been visible in the undergrowth.[5]

THE MAIN KILN (A). The large squarish mound covered a sub-rectangular kiln, consisting of a straight central flue with fireplaces at each end (lying NW–SE), and stone banks on each side, each with two sieges. The structure as excavated stood some 2 ft. high, and this was approximately the original height of the basal parts of the kiln, the structure being held rigid by the very unyielding mass of hardened scum (*see* below). Of the roof no coherent evidence remained. The kiln was 11 ft. long and, as excavated, had slightly bowed walls, being 10 ft. wide at the west end, 11 ft. in the centre, and 8 ft. (the original width) at the east end.

The kiln may conveniently be described in the order of the original construction; *see* plan [my Figs. 4 and 7] and sections [my Figs. 6 and 7].

The Sieges. The first parts to be built were the two benches on which the crucibles for melting the glass stood. These were roughly 8 ft. long by 2 ft. 3 in. wide, and 2 ft. high. They were made of chunky pieces of local sandstone, mostly about 6–9 in. across, built up in dry-wall construction (there was no trace of mortar anywhere on the site). There were no foundations – the structure rested on the surface of the natural clay (from which the topsoil only had presumably been removed). In these structures two circular emplacements slightly depressed for the crucibles had been made, consisting of spaces in the stonework filled with clay resting on flat stones. These were 3–6 in. from the ends of the banks, 1 ft. 3 in. in diameter, and 4 in. from the edge of the flue and the wall cavities. The stones surrounding the sieges was spattered with glass.

The Flue was next to be finished. The builders of the walls of the pot-banks had trampled the soil into a hard surface, which showed a deeper red in section. On this was spread a layer of clay 3 in. thick, which had hardened in the heat into a bricky layer, purplish-red inside and blue outside. At each end the fires were kindled, producing black patches some 3 feet by 1 ft. 2 in. The flue as first seen was a narrow channel (1 ft.–1 ft. 10 in. wide by 10 ft. 6 in. long) in a thick

---

[4] From *Sy.A.C.*, vol. 62 (1965). I am much obliged to the editor, Mr E. E. Harrison, for his permission and help.

[5] I have not reprinted all Mr Wood's illustrations because they are easily accessible. Those omitted are therefore not included in this transcription of his text. [G.H.K.]

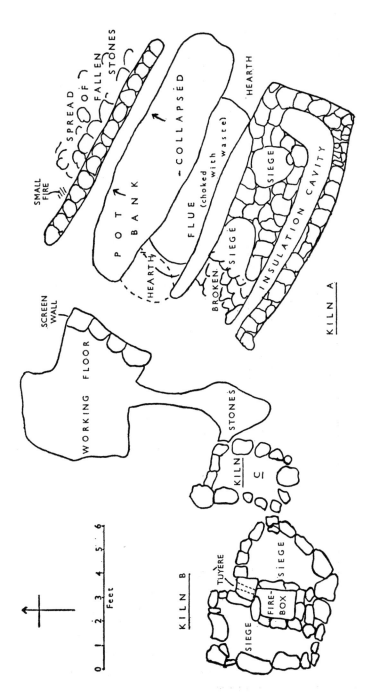

Fig. 4. Blunden's Wood. General excavation plan.

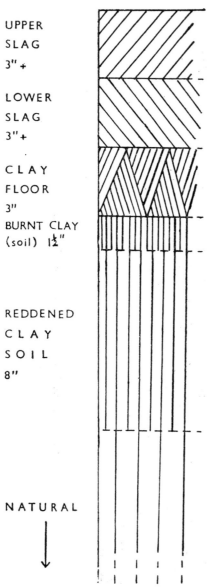

UPPER
SLAG
3" +

LOWER
SLAG
3" +

CLAY
FLOOR
3"

BURNT CLAY
(soil) 1½"

REDDENED
CLAY
SOIL
8"

NATURAL

Fig. 5. Blunden's Wood, Kiln A. Section of
east end of flue.

layer of a grey substance, the edges of which rose over the lips of the pot-banks, and humping in the middle nearly to the top of the flue. This was a puzzle until it was realized that the material was not the hardened clay flue-floor, but glass scum which had over-flowed from the boiling and often broken crucibles into the flue, finally blocking it to the point of obstruction of the draught, and giving the reason for the abandonment of the kiln. This scum, which contained pieces of stone and crucible, was hard enough to resist the pick. It seems to have collected in two separate layers, representing a break in the use of the kiln [my Fig. 5].

The Walls. At about a foot from the central structure a stone wall 8 in. wide was built all round the kiln to the height of the siege-banks. The cavity between the two (*c.*11 in. wide), was filled with clay, which contained some fallen stones. The walls ran round the corners (where the cavity was larger) and across the ends of the kiln in a curve, to contain the hearths [my Plate VII]. The northern pot-bank and outer wall had collapsed outwards, but the southern side provided enough evidence for a reconstruction. The entire site was strewn with stones fallen from the roof, and with burnt clay. The heat of the kiln had reddened the soil for 2–3 ft. all round, and under the flue for a foot down. The walls and roof were no doubt set in or plastered with clay for rigidity and thermal efficiency.

The remains of a small fire, apparently lit for some casual purpose, were found in the shelter on the N. wall of the kiln.

The flue at Blunden's Wood appeared narrower than at other sites; those at Fernfold and Jamestown were 2 ft. wide; but this is probably deceptive, and due to irregular sagging of the walls. A width of 2 ft. is in fact to be assumed here also.

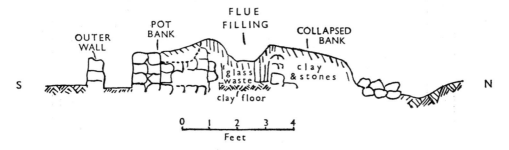

Fig. 6. Blunden's Wood, Kiln A. Cross section.

The Roof. Although no direct evidence was found, an attempt must be made to conjecture its nature. Medieval engravings show a barrel-vault, but this necessitates wedge-shaped stones, which were not found on this site (unless they had been robbed). The suggestion of Mr Harrington, for Jamestown, Virginia, of rough stones embedded in thick clay is more feasible, but difficult to imagine holding up until fired hard, unless it was supported on a timber frame which burnt away. In any case the weight of such a roof would need a strong support if it is not to spread and collapse, and the double walls of this kiln may have been made to take the thrust of the roof, which would rest on the inside skin, with a batter of clay joining it to the outside wall over the clay-filled cavity. But this is theoretical, and I can find no direct evidence of it in medieval building practice. On the other hand, the cavities in the walls need not have been filled with clay originally, but could have been filled later in the decay of the structure.[6] Indeed, contemporary filling would presumably have hardened, and shrunk away from the walls, which was not the case. On this view one must postulate a mass of stones and clay, forming the walls and roof, being fired over a wooden frame until it reached a degree of homogeneity where the thrust would be vertical and not oblique. In this case the roof could rest on the outside walls, and the cavities be empty, as an insulation space.

Of course, the cavities may represent the spaces in which the frame was erected, if such was the case. A conjecture which appeals to me strongly is that the siege-banks were built first; a frame was then erected outside them, against and over which the walls and roof were laid. The cavities would then be left free when the kiln was fired and the frame burnt away, and would have a secondary use for insulation. These cavities in any event seem to be a feature

[6] This is supported by the fallen stones, as well as clay, found in the cavity.

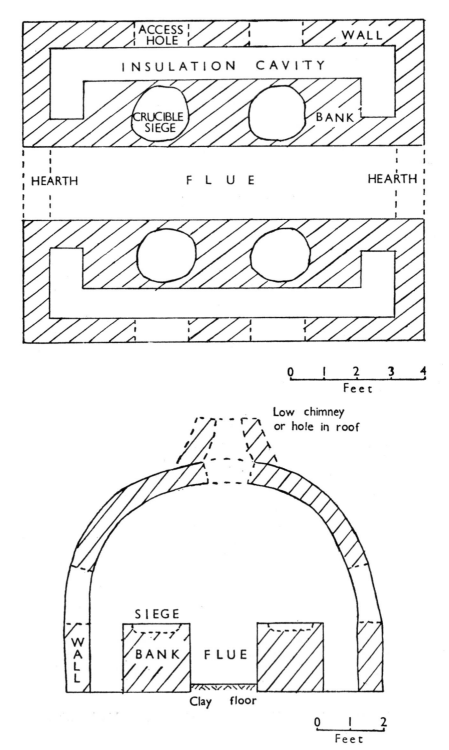

ACCESS HOLE

WALL

INSULATION CAVITY

CRUCIBLE SIEGE

BANK

HEARTH   FLUE   HEARTH

0 1 2 3 4
Feet

Low chimney
or hole in roof

SIEGE

WALL

BANK   FLUE

Clay floor

0 1 2
Feet

Fig. 7. Blunden's Wood, Kiln A. Reconstruction plan and section.

unique to Blunden's Wood.[7] Unless a forced draught were used, for which evidence is lacking, there must have been a chimney, however small.

THE ROUND KILN (B). Seven feet west of the large kiln was a low mound, which covered a low heap of stones, some 8 ft. by 4 ft. 6 in. When excavated this turned out to be another kiln, roundish or heart-shaped, the roof of which, beehive by analogy with early descriptions was founded on very large stones (some 9 in. across) round the outside of the kiln. Inside, in the centre, was a well-defined square cavity (a fireplace) filled with burnt clay (1 ft. 1 in. by 1 ft. 3 in.), with a passage, 4 in. wide, curved in a dog-leg (each leg 7 in. long), and covered by a flat stone, leading to the outside, no doubt a bellows-tuyere, implying the use of forced draught. On either side of this, in the lobes of the heart, were long cavities, one 4 ft. by 1 ft. 6 in., the other 3 ft. by 2 ft., filled with burnt earth, but having also hard floors of reddish (burnt) clay on which were laid thin slabs of stone. The left-hand (east) cavity was spattered with glass.

A large number of crucible fragments, most of the glass and pottery sherds, and the horseshoe, came from among the stones of this kiln and its vicinity.

THE SMALL OVEN (C). Between kilns A and B was a small round oven (C) 2 ft. 6 in. by 1 ft. 6 in. represented by an irregular oval of large stones surrounding blackened soil.

THE WORKING FLOOR. Two feet west of the end of kiln A was a low wall of large stones, still standing three courses high. This was about 4 ft. long, and curved gently outwards in the middle, away from the hearth. Its purpose was no doubt to shield the legs of the workers from the heat of the fire, because just beyond it was a floor of smallish stones. The area paved in this way was some 5 ft. by 5 ft. 6 in. with a narrow trail running from it towards the east side of Kiln C, where it broadened into a paved strip some 2 ft. across. It may be supposed that this floor had originally been larger and more continuous, but the presence of the screen wall indicates that the main working area may have been in that part of the site.

A general plan of the structures as excavated is in [my Fig. 4].

OTHER FEATURES. No refuse heap, or store of cullet, was found, although search was made. Nor was there a surrounding ditch. No trace was found either of the shed which normally covered a glasshouse, whether by way of postholes or otherwise.[8]

This could be explained by the removal of the posts supporting the shed

[7] Four lines omitted here because Mr Harrington, writing in May 1966, says of Plate VII in this present book, 'Unfortunately that particular photograph suggests a double wall, but the stonework was continuous. It just so happens that the portion adjacent to the fire-chamber was a little higher and the shadows make it appear to be a double wall.' [G.H.K.]

[8] At Jamestown the presence of such a shed was inferred from the clearly defined edges of the working floor, but this was not the case at Blunden's Wood. Only four out of twenty-five known Weald glasshouses have ditches surviving. [No. 42 brings the total to twenty-six.]

entire when the kilns were abandoned, leaving no stumps in the ground to rot, but only holes which quickly filled with earth and become unnoticeable.

LATER FINDS. The site was visited again a few weeks later, in May 1960. By then the entire area had been cleared of trees and undergrowth, and the bulldozers had left nothing but a wide space of bare churned clay several hundreds of yards long by about 200 yards wide, from the stream nearly to the track. The kiln site had been completely destroyed. This gave a good opportunity to see (a) whether the site as excavated was the whole installation, (b) whether the glasshouse was the only one in the immediate area. Both these points could readily be settled in the affirmative. No ditch or subsidiary structure, or other kiln, appeared. The site in fact showed as three patches of burnt reddened clay, the largest (representing Kiln A) extending over some 21 ft. by 11 ft. the two smaller ones being closely comparable in size and position to Kilns B and C as excavated. The burnt area of Kiln A thus extends up to over 4 ft. round the actual structure, which gives an idea of the heat generated inside it when working. The mass of overflowed glass waste blocking the flue, which had resisted the excavators' picks, was hard enough to resist the bulldozers also, and huge unbroken masses of it were strewn about the neighbourhood of the kiln.

The proximity of the kiln to the edge of the bank was also revealed; this was no more than ten feet away. The edge here was quite sharp, and the bank fell steeply down to the stream after a slope 30 ft. long.

In August 1961 the Brick Company informed us that further bulldozing had revealed another kiln some distance away from the one excavated, and that the whole area would be removed for brick-making clay within a week. An emergency search of the area revealed that in fact there had been a misapprehension of the terrain, and that the discoloration seen by the Brick Company was in fact the traces of the excavated kilns, and that there were no others. This was in a way disappointing, although it bore out the results of the earlier search, because a second kiln would not have been unexpected in the light of Wealden practice. Such a kiln may exist to be discovered in the part of the wood still unreached by the bulldozers.

The earth-moving machines had shifted a considerable amount of soil from the site of the kilns, and had piled it up in heaps some 20 ft. to the north, over the edge of the bank. Search in these heaps revealed considerable quantities of glass, and some pottery (including pieces of the large thumbed-base jug), all quite consistent with what was in the excavation. It appeared indeed as though the cullet or waste heap of the kiln, not located in spite of search at the time of the excavation, had been turned over. Alternatively, the fragments could have been in the soil outside the excavated area. This was a fortunate chance indeed.

The glass fragments fell into a number of categories, and although these may not be complete, in view of the necessarily cursory search, in the short time available, yet they supplement the meagre harvest of the excavation in a way which probably gives a true picture of the workings of the kiln.'

Mr Wood comments on the glass: 'This was all pale-green uncoloured glass of the Early type, made before 1567. It is mostly of good quality. The colour in fact varies from nearly clear, to pale milky, to a fresh yellowish or sometimes faintly bluish green. There could have been no consistency between melts.' The glass compares favourably with samples from other Early sites and is more plentiful than on most.

Mr Wood continues:

'*Functions of the Blunden's Wood Ovens.* There is, it is clear, much variation from site to site. But with this in mind, and from the evidence at Blunden's Wood, I am inclined to suggest the following scheme:

> Small oven (C) – for preheating pots
> Round oven (B) – left side, for fritting
> Main oven (A) – for melting
> Round oven (B) – right side, for annealing.

From the mass of waste glass in the flue of Kiln A, there is no doubt of its use as a melting furnace; but there is no evidence whether annealing was also carried out in an upper stage of this kiln. The left-hand siege of Kiln B was spattered with glass, and fritting seems a reasonable explanation of this. The right-hand side was free of glass, but the whole oven was littered with broken crucible and pieces of finished glass. Kiln C was also free of spilt glass. It is not impossible that the suggested functions of B (right) and C could be reversed, but on the whole the scheme proposed seems reasonable.

There are, of course, other possible alternatives. If, for example, as Professor Turner did not rule out, annealing was done over the roof of the melting furnace (A), then Kilns B and C, would be restricted to preheating pots and fritting. But the Jamestown evidence shows that a separate oven was used, in this type of glasshouse, for annealing.

Complete certainty is not to be had, and the question must be left open.

Jamestown, Virginia,[9] offers a number of interesting parallels to Blunden's Wood. Although not built until 1608, the colonists were reduced to the simplest construction and equipment, and the conjectural restoration shows a surprisingly medieval-looking glasshouse. The kilns were made of stones set in clay, and the evidence shed much light on the processes used. Jamestown had a working furnace with room for four pots; a small kiln for firing new pots or for preheating pots; a fritting furnace and an annealing furnace, these two joined together in one structure with ovens each end.' [*see* p. 72].

---

[9] J. C. Harrington, *Glassmaking at Jamestown* (1952).

Discussing actual glass sites Mr Wood comments (his p. 64) that 'evidence from continental sites does not add to the picture.'[10] Mr Wood discusses the pottery and magnetic dating in detail and gives a most convincing date of *c*.1330 for the glasshouse. Of the magnetic dating he says: 'The substantial structure of the large kiln (A) at Blunden's Wood, and its undisturbed condition since its abandonment, offered a very suitable opportunity for a magnetic dating test to be made.[11] Mr Wood's summary:

> 'This paper describes the results of excavation of a hitherto unknown glasshouse at Blunden's Wood, Hambledon, Surrey. This consisted of a group of three kilns, with a working floor and store of cullet. It is dated by associated pottery (supported by magnetic dating) to the second quarter of the fourteenth century A.D. The products were crown glass and probably vessel as well. It has certain unusual features, and is in any case of interest as being one of the few undisturbed and relatively complete glasshouses so far discovered. The material is in Guildford museum.'

In the Pilkington Museum at St Helens, which was opened in November 1964, there is a conjectural reconstruction of a medieval glasshouse based on the evidence from the Blunden's Wood excavation and on medieval and later prints. The reconstruction was designed by Mr James Gardner, the organizer of displays at the Museum. Mr Wood (p. 65) says, 'This is a remarkable achievement on Mr Gardner's part and gives a broadly accurate impression of what a medieval glasshouse must have looked like.'

We also have a good idea of the appearance of a Late forest glass furnace from Mr T. Pape's remarkable find at Bishop's Wood, Staffs. (Plate VI), and Mr J. C. Harrington's plan and conjectural reconstruction of the Jamestown (Va.) furnace in 1608 (Plate VIII). The fine early fifteenth-century Mandeville drawing in the British Museum (*see* Plate X) provides an invaluable general guide for the appearance of a forest glasshouse. It is unlikely there was any standard size, some glasshouses might be run with two men and a boy; others, particularly in the booming Late period, producing mainly window glass, may have had upwards of six men working. The glass furnace at Knole, Kent, clearly had five or six men working there (*see* Chapter X).

Bishop's Wood Furnace

The Bishop's Wood furnace is particularly valuable because, apart from the roof having collapsed, much of the furnace survived intact, with bases of round-shaped

---

[10] The best documented is the Carolingian oven in the Forêt d'Anlier, Belgium (C. Dubois, in *Annales de l'Inst. Arch. du Luxembourg*, vol. 46 (1911), p. 355; more accessibly in H. Arbman, *Schweden und das karolingische Reich* (1937), p. 83, and R. Chambon, *L'Histoire de la Verrerie en Belgique* (1955), p. 47). This had a round oven with three tiers. (These references are owed to Mr R. J. Charleston.)

[11] The principles and method are described in *Archaeometry*, I, II and III (1959, 1960, 1961).

crucibles cemented in position on the small siege platform (*see* Plate VI). The tiny stoke hole can be seen in the top photograph of Plate VI, and as a dark hole in the lower picture, which shows a small rough stone kiln. Its discovery was due to Mr T. Pape finding entries in the Eccleshall P. R. between 1600 to 1604 of four different names of glassmakers connected with Blore Park (Bishop's Wood). Three large overgrown mounds with glass fragments close by were found near the eastern edge of the wood. The smallest mound covered a circular sandstone floor at ground level, showing no signs of firing. The second mound had a large tree growing out of it and contained a glass furnace, crushed out of all shape by the growing roots, and this could only be removed piecemeal, much as at Brookland (No. 23). But 'in the centre of the largest mound, which was six feet high and eleven feet in diameter, nearly three feet up from the ground level, the woodmen came across a glass furnace built up from very thick sandstones glazed on the inside'.[12] The furnace was excavated and examined in 1931 and 1932 (*see* Fig. 8).

Mr Pape describes it:

'The furnace had been built up solidly from large squared local sandstones. The western side for about two feet six inches up was fairly complete and the greater part was three feet two inches in thickness. Right through the centre from west to east was a fire trench twenty inches wide and the blow-hole on the western side was complete, though the sandstone arch on the inside was broken and would have fallen in if all the supporting soil had been cleared away.

This was left in position so that the loose glazed stones inside could be easily restored by the careful use of cement. Although the eastern side was nearly all broken and the arch of the central blow-hole had been destroyed, yet the two corners were well defined, and the curved central glazed sandstones of the arch along with slag and fragments of some thick green glass vessel were found at the bottom of the trench. The lower part of the furnace is rectangular, four feet five inches long from north to south and two feet ten inches in width; the sides are not perpendicular but slope gradually outwards. At the north and south ends are platforms raised up one foot from the central fire trench, each sixteen and a half inches in width and, of course, two feet ten inches in length. On each of them firmly fixed are the bases of two circular crucibles or siege-pots, each a foot in diameter. Also, between the two crucibles on the south, the base of a small round pot is cemented into the green glazed surface of the platform.'

Mr Pape added that 'only one length of blow pipe, much corroded, was found, $3\frac{1}{2}$ in. long with $\frac{7}{10}$ in. diameter, of which the hole measured $\frac{3}{10}$ in.' From the flints found at the furnace sites he suggests they were most likely used for marking lines of fracture. Practically no restoration was carried out, but only preservation, and Mr Pape succeeded in 1933 in getting this unique survival covered by a rustic lock-up shed.

[12] Pape, p. 27.

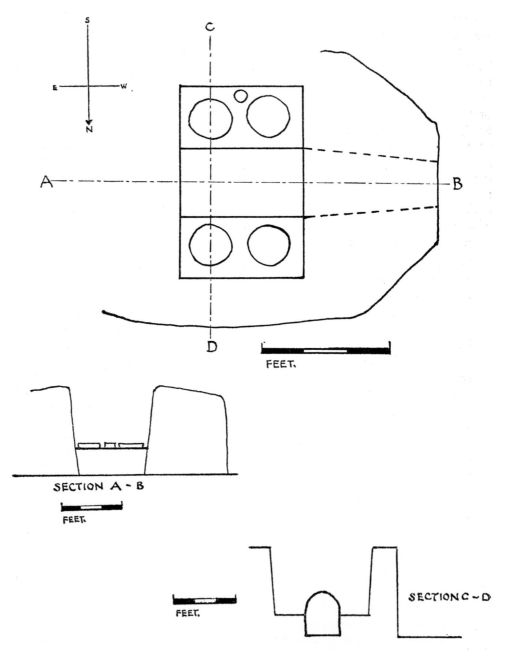

Fig. 8. Bishop's Wood. Plan and section of furnace.

Winbolt (*W.G.*, p. 21) notes that the furnace was built well above ground level, that no bricks were used in its construction and that the sandstone floor was found extending 6 ft. outwards from the furnace. He commented on the glass which Mr Pape sent to him that it was precisely similar to the Sidney Wood glass and that vessel and window (both disc and muff) were produced there. Mr Pape says of the six North Staffordshire glass furnaces on four sites which he examined

'no doubt all the furnaces were rectangular in shape, most likely with two platforms for the crucibles as was the case with the well preserved one in Bishop's Wood. From the platforms for at least two feet up the rectangular walls sloped slightly outwards, but how they were roofed in we do not know, nor do we know where the openings were for gaining access to the molten metal in the crucibles.'

He suggests the dates for the North Staffs. glasshouses as being 'from about 1580 to a period not later than about half way through the reign of James I, about twenty years in all.' He has five interesting pages on the families engaged in glassmaking and their movements; the Henzeys figure prominently. At another glasshouse site about one mile north of the one in Bishop's Wood he found it 'had been so much disturbed that its measurements could not be taken with any approach to accuracy and all that one could say was that it had been oblong originally.' At another site about one mile and a quarter south of the Bishop's Wood furnace, Mr Pape found four or five broken bricks, the only site 'where any bricks had been used.' With the Weald sites, it is a matter of chance what the stone robbers happen to leave.

The Bishop's Wood furnace, worked by members of the same glassmaking families who made glass in the Weald, provides a very useful guide to the dimensions of our Late furnaces.
1. Its fire chamber width of 20 in. is probably a minimum, anything less would make stoking with wood billets difficult.
2. Its two siege platforms 2 ft. 10 in. long and 16½ in. wide and 1 ft. above the fire chamber floor, with their four crucibles, would easily accommodate four normal sized crucibles.
3. Its furnace walls were 1 ft. thick, possibly a minimum to conserve heat.
The sum of 1, 2 and 3, gives an overall width of 6 ft. 5 in., which is probably near the minimum for this type of furnace. The hearth tunnels at Bishop's Wood appear to have tapered, whereas those at Fernfold and Vann had parallel sides; at Vann they were the same width as the fire chamber and at Fernfold they were slightly less.

Jamestown Glasshouse

The Jamestown furnace (Plate VII) had only one hearth tunnel. With the introduction of coal firing, after the industry had left the forest, the furnaces had four flues or hearth tunnels (*see* Chapter X). Mr J. C. Harrington's conjectural restoration of the furnace at Jamestown (*see* Plate VIII), shows the lay-out which he says does involve some guesswork, but 'is probably very close to the original.' He says,

> 'from the overall size and shape of the Jamestown ruins, we can assume that the interior construction was similar to the Bishop's Wood furnace. Externally, the furnace would have had the general appearance of an Eskimo igloo. ... The available evidence indicates that the entire structure was built of boulders imbedded in clay. ... There was no chimney in the furnace, for it was important that the flames and combustion gases be drawn around and over the melting pots.[13] The working holes would have served as the principal draft flues. ... The problem of replacing broken pots was solved as it was in the Bishop's Wood furnace, by providing a large opening at the back of the furnace.'

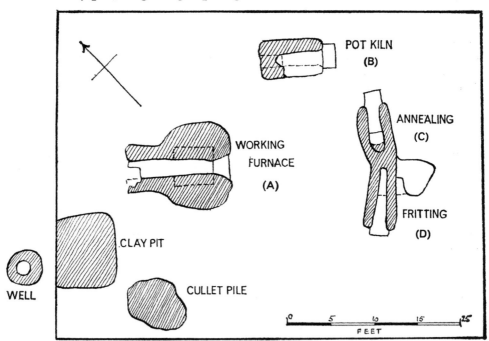

Fig. 9. Plan of the Jamestown Glasshouse.

This access is shown as clay and rubble on the plan. Mr Harrington examined a large area and determined the limits of the glasshouse, his plan of the complete lay-out is shown in Fig. 9. Writing to me fourteen years after the publication of his booklet *Glassmaking at Jamestown*, Mr Harrington said 'the main revision I would suggest over my early interpretation is to omit any special fritting and make the backed-up small furnace [(C) and (D) in my Fig. 9] simply a pair of lehrs [annealing ovens].

[13] *See* also p. 78 [G.H.K.]

Then I would forget the matter of intentionally adding lime, and let the wood ashes take care of that problem' [*see* also Chapter II, p. 36]. Commenting on the pair of lehrs he says

'To operate a simple glasshouse of this type continuously would have required either a tall or larger melting furnace which would also have served as a lehr, or else some separate furnace which would allow for daily replenishment. By using a pair of lehrs, one could be loaded and sealed off on a given day, the other one used the next day while unloading the previous days' product from the other section.'

The unsatisfactory plan of Buckholt furnace made in 1860 is included in Chapter X, p. 216 (*see* Fig. 20) with some comments. The crucial differences between a wood and a coal fired furnace are shown on the same page.

The Mandeville Glasshouse Sketch

There is a beautiful detailed coloured drawing of a northern forest glasshouse in *Sir John Mandeville's Travels*, painted early in the fifteenth century, probably in Bohemia (*see* Plate X).[14]

All round there is forest, with a man carrying fuel in a basket, two others carrying ash in sacks, one man digging sand from a hill with a stream at its foot, and another carrying the sand to the furnace in a shoulder hod. Below is the glasshouse, a kiln with a rough shingle-roofed open shed having its stoke hole[15] entrance roofed with wood billets drying on a heavy timber frame. The furnace appears to be rectangular having rounded and domed corners with a circular flue on top, possibly controlled by a large sliding tile.[16] The furnace may have had four crucibles, two each side; the annealing furnace is built on at the end. Vessel glass is being made. The master, in a hat, inspects a jug; a workman is taking a vessel out to finish its annealing in a large storage jar. Two skilled glassmakers, wearing sweat rags, are shown, one is blowing and shaping a vessel on a mavering slab and the other gathering glass from the crucible on his long wooden handled blowpipe. The boy stoker is raking out ash or pushing wood billets into the fire-box. The stream in the background suggests a need for water, for washing the sand, mixing the ash and possibly preparing the crucible clay. The whole lively scene, with its emphasis on the temporary

[14] B. M. Add. MS. 24188, f. 16; there is no description with it. This picture was first used by Dr L. F. Salzman in his *Medieval English Industries* (O.U.P. 1923). Mr R. J. Charleston says it is the earliest representation of a northern furnace which we possess.

[15] The furnace appears to have a stoke hole and hearth tunnel at each end. Theophilus (*see* p. 11 above) in his section on frit, says, 'When these preparations [the building of the working furnace] have been made, take some beechwood logs, thoroughly dried in smoke, and light a large fire at both ends of the larger kiln.' If this refers to the working furnace, and it is not clear that it does, Theophilus' furnace had two hearth tunnels, as Vann and Fernfold had.

[16] The important point is that the heart of the furnace was rectangular even if as at Jamestown the exterior was rounded.

woodland shack, rings true. It is packed with authentic information about a northern medieval forest glasshouse. The five men shown on the lines of communication as keeping one small glasshouse and its three or four glassmen in action, very probably provide an accurate picture of the balance of labour. At the height of the boom period, *c*.1600, with about eight possibly larger glasshouses working in the Weald, there may have been forty or more men cutting and carting fuel and collecting sand for perhaps nine months of the year. There would also be a few local glasscarriers. For at least a generation this small industry may have brought some welcome cash to a rather poor farming district.

The reconstruction of Theophilus' glass furnace (*see* Plate IX), I find less useful because I think it is larger than anything known in the Weald until possibly in the Late period.

The Process of Glassmaking

Mrs E. S. Godfrey describes the Late forest furnaces in her thesis. She says: 'Glassmaking as practised in the sixteenth and early seventeenth centuries required the application of heat in three distinct stages, which involved either three separate furnaces or separate parts of one or two furnaces.'[17] The three stages were in the fritting, working and annealing furnaces, each

> 'requiring different degrees of heat and different sorts of containers to hold the metal in various stages of fusion. If they were to be done in the same furnace they either had to be done successively which involved long delays, or in separate compartments so that the heat varied with the distance from the flue.'

She cites the Jamestown lay-out as using three separate furnaces. Blunden's Wood small oven (C) is the only fritting furnace known in the Weald. Mr Harrington shows separate fritting[18] and annealing furnaces at Jamestown (*see* Fig. 9).

The first two stages and the temperatures involved were discussed by the late Professor W. E. S. Turner:[19] 'The melting process was carried out in two stages, first a comparatively low temperature operation whereby the sand and the ash (or soda) was converted into a frit, the second in which the frit was converted to glass in crucibles in the melting furnace.' He says that frit remains a powder below 700°C. and only assumes a fritted condition above 750°C. He says that

> 'From our knowledge of the construction and operation of glass-making furnaces it is highly doubtful if temperatures as high as 1200°C. were normally attained before the second half of the eighteenth century. . . . The diagrams available of tenth to sixteenth century A.D. furnaces, in conjunction with observations on wood-fired furnaces seen at Murano, would not lead me to anticipate the likeli-

[17] *D.E.G.*, pp. 263 and 265.
[18] For Mr Harrington's recent interpretation, *see* p. 72.
[19] *S.A.G.T.*, pp. 293–298.

hood of exceeding 1200°C.[20] ... The need to scum the surface of the molten glass before working it continued throughout the nineteenth century &c. ... The day of a chemical industry making standardized products had yet to come. And if, after many trials and errors, when using available materials, an ancient glassmaker succeeded in working out procedures for making good glass is it surprising that he should be secretive? Who shall say that he was not justified.'[21]

He examined the efficiency of Theophilus' glass furnace:[22]

'The furnace temperature and fuel consumption of Theophilus' glass furnace is estimated from the reconstruction by Theobald. These are compared with performance figures from a modern pot furnace. The flame temperature is estimated to have been between 1400°–1500°C. The fuel consumption per weight of glass must have been about 20x that of modern normal pot furnaces.'

Professor Turner writing to me in 1955 about the Jamestown furnace, said he was puzzled how adequate air is to be provided to keep the fire burning at the intensity needed.[23]

The third stage, annealing, might be carried out in a separate kiln or, where it was part of the main furnace as in the Mandeville drawing, that part of the furnace might have been gradually cooled off to remove the stresses from the finished glass. It is possible our 'double furnaces' may have been an attempt to make the process more continuous. But why 50 yards apart?

Furnace Routine

Mr J. C. Harrington[24] gives a good description of the glassmaking cycle and says the logical starting point

'is the day after the glass had been worked out of the pots and the furnace had been allowed to cool down slightly, preparatory to recharging the pots and getting ready for the next run. We can assume that this interruption has not been long enough for the heavy stonework to have cooled off materially, but it has provided a chance to rake out the ashes, to make any necessary minor repairs to the furnace, and to replace damaged pots.

Now the fire is started up again and the desired combination of "frit" and "cullet" placed in the pots. As the "batch" begins to melt, more ingredients are

---

[20] This is remarkably close to the temperatures reported by Dr S. C. Waterton for the Blunden's Wood glass which melted at 1200°C., which implies that it was probably originally founded at about 1200°–1250°C. See *Sy.A.C.*, vol. 62. [G.H.K.]

[21] There no doubt was and is ceaseless experiment and there are still secrets today in the glass industry. [G.H.K.]

[22] *S.A.G.T.*, p. 162.

[23] There is no evidence that forest furnaces had chimneys or bellows.

[24] *Glassmaking at Jamestown*, p. 41.

added, until finally, after about a full working day, the pots are fully charged. During this early stage of melting, the material is stirred with a special iron rake.

At first there is only a sticky mass in the pots, but gradually the material liquifies and takes on the appearance of molten glass. Impurities rise to the surface causing a white spongy scum to accumulate. This "sand gall," or "sandever," is removed immediately with an iron ladle.[25] As Merret says, the master work-man has "to scum the Sandever, and dross, from the pot wherein he worketh."

Gradually the heat of the furnace is increased until finally, after another day, vitrification is complete and a true glass has been achieved. The fire is then slackened just enough so that the molten mass is at the right temperature for working when the crew comes on next day. The glass has been tested from time to time by dipping out a small amount and letting it string out into a thread. Many fragments of such testing threads were found in the excavations. In addi-tion to firing the working furnace, fires have also been started in the annealing furnaces so that they will be ready to receive the completed glass.'

The Working Furnace

Until the development in England in 1611 of a coal-fired glass furnace, with its grate bars, underground flues and high conical chimney, almost all post-Conquest English glass was produced in woodland country in primitive furnaces based in general on four flame-heated crucibles sitting on two small siege platforms with one or two hearth tunnels and a probably low barrel-vaulted roof.[26] With one excep-tion, Woodchester, all the forest working furnaces known in England were rect-angular[27] after the French pattern. Woodchester was circular, and probably tiered, after the Venetian pattern.

The sections through five rectangular forest furnaces are shown opposite; and the dimensions of their essential parts are summarized here for comparison in Fig. 10. The basic design seems to have remained unchanged for upwards of three centuries, from the earliest to the latest known datable sites, but the dimensions varied considerably. Starting with the core of the furnaces, the fire chamber was about 2 ft. wide and could be fed from either or both ends through hearth tunnels of that width but varying lengths. Each side of the fire chamber was a raised plat-form about 1 ft. high and 1 or 2 ft. wide of varying lengths from about 3–6 ft. long,[28] on which stood two open crucibles, making a total of four. Plate VI shows the in-terior of such a furnace. The total siege space of Vann furnace was very small, being

[25] It is probably the commonest form of waste dross and is likely to occur on most sites. It is in heavy, tough, cellular cakes. Other forms of dross appear to be lumps of frit and at Blunden's Wood a vitreous type was found not unlike Tudor iron slag. None of these can be compared with fragments of crucible as simple, unmistakable evidence of a glasshouse site. [G.H.K.]

[26] *See* Fig. 18 and note 28 below.

[27] By this I mean the core of the furnace was rectangular whatever the outside shape.

[28] It is not always possible to decide where the hearth tunnels end and the fire chamber and 'siege' platform begin, the dimensions given in Fig. 10 are therefore approximate only.

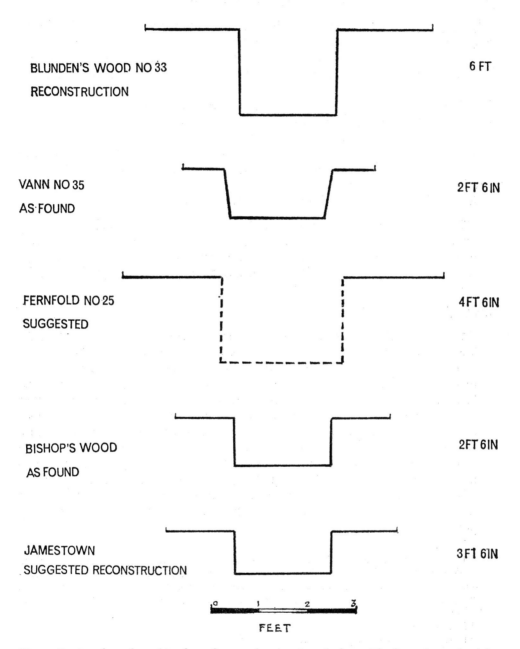

BLUNDEN'S WOOD NO 33
RECONSTRUCTION
6 FT

VANN NO 35
AS FOUND
2FT 6IN

FERNFOLD NO 25
SUGGESTED
4FT 6IN

BISHOP'S WOOD
AS FOUND
2FT 6IN

JAMESTOWN
SUGGESTED RECONSTRUCTION
3FT 6IN

FEET

Fig. 10. Sections through working forest furnaces showing siege platforms. The dimensions at the right-hand side are the approximate lengths of the platforms. In Nos. 33 and 25 allowance has been made for the end walls.

only 2 sq. ft., and its crucibles must have been smaller than usual, possibly being designed for vessel glass only.[29] The Jamestown interior reconstruction was partly based on the known dimensions of the Bishop's Wood furnace (*see* p. 69) so their siege spaces are similar at 4–5 sq. ft. Fernfold at about 8½ sq. ft. is about twice that size and could have accommodated more than the usual four crucibles. Blunden's Wood was larger still at about 13½ sq. ft., but the slightly depressed emplacements show that it housed only four crucibles. The furnace walls varied in thickness from about 12–21 in. plus possibly an outer casing of clay, for additional insulation, which has disappeared. The Blunden's Wood fourteenth-century furnace was a primitive affair of undressed stone embedded in clay, whereas the Late Wealden furnaces, Fernfold and Vann, had interiors more carefully built of brick.

Mrs Godfrey completes a description of such a furnace:

'The crown of the furnace was a low arch which kept the flames and gases beating upon the pots.[30] There was no chimney, but there were openings on either side made large enough for the placement and removal of the pots. These openings were filled in with a removable cover containing a small working hole about the size of the palm of a man's hand.'[31]

Mrs Godfrey also says:[32]

'More highly skilled operations required more men per furnace opening. At least two working as a team at a single pot were necessary to make Norman or "Crown" glass by the pricked bubble method, while three were required to make broad glass by the Lorraine method. The contract of Carré with the Hennezell brothers makes clear the latter were to bring with them 4 other gentilhommes verriers so that they could work in teams of 3 at each of two ovens.[33] Anything but the simplest vessel glass also required a group called a "chair" consisting of from 2 to 5, but normally of 3 skilled workmen at a single furnace opening, each with his own specialized part in the process. The glass-makers themselves constituted a group apart. Next to them in skill was the "founder"[34] or consore, who prepared and mixed the ingredients, watched over the "fritting" or pre-heating and tended the final batch until a proper working point was reached.'

[29] There is a reference in Carré's will, 1572 (*see* p. 122) to 'the little furnace of the small glass.' Small glass, 'petite verre,' was vessel glass, and different from 'grande verre,' the large muffs or discs of window glass. Possibly specialist window glass furnaces were larger than those making mainly vessel.

[30] Tapered firebricks were found on Late sites Nos. 23 and 32. They could have been parts of an arch. [G.H.K.]

[31] Merret, p. 242.

[32] I have quoted from her pp. 325 and 326. [G.H.K.]

[33] Lansdown MS. 59, No. 74, enclosure Ap. 17, 1568.

[34] *See* site No. 37. The term was used in the Weald in 1612–13 when Laurence Fryer 'glasse fownder of Ewhurst, Surrey' is mentioned. [G.H.K.]

Mrs Godfrey estimates that Bungar may have produced 400 cases of window glass or over 40 tons a year.[35] She comments that 'this would seem to be about normal on a yearly basis for one glassmaking team of 2 or 3.' But she qualifies this by saying that we 'cannot assume a 50 week year.' As to the total output she estimates that 'about 1590 when there were perhaps 15 or 16 glasshouses in England, some of which made green drinking glasses and apothecaries wares, there could have been no more than 15 or 16 teams making window glass.' From this she goes on to estimate something 'under 700 tons of window glass for all of England' in a year.

Apart from Blunden's Wood (No. 33), discussed at the beginning of this chapter, there are only two sites in the Weald which have provided the sizes of their working furnace, Fernfold (No. 25) and Vann (No. 35). Winbolt's plan of Fernfold (Fig. 16) shows the furnace with its hearths (but excludes the stoking platforms) as being 15 ft. 6 in. long and 7 ft. wide excluding his ramps of clay. Winbolt's dimensions of Vann, without its wings, 12 ft. × 5 ft. 6 in., are discussed in Chapter IX and the width is shown to be very narrow. An original coating of plaster and clay may have disappeared and could bring the overall width to over 6 ft.—a more likely figure.

Three other sites (Nos. 5, 23 and 29) have provided rectangular burnt areas which could be measured, and we assumed they were the furnace floors. In two cases, Nos. 5 and 23,[36] they may be, but I have little doubt the measurements include stoking platforms and possibly some surround of the actual kiln. In the case of No. 29 the area of burnt sandstone covered the whole of the small area 15 ft. 10 in. × 10 ft. 10 in. tightly enclosed by ditch on three sides and a steep bank on the fourth. Clearly this must have been one complete unit of a glasshouse, because of the ditches. The kiln in its centre is unlikely to have been more than 8 ft. × 5 ft., smaller than the kiln at Bishop's Wood (Staffs.), which was approximately 8 ft. 10 in. × 6 ft. 6 in.[37] Its size is surmise as nothing remained of the structure, which was built on top of the sandstone floor.[38]

Four sites in copses, all Early, had their surrounding ditches more or less intact. They must represent not furnaces but glasshouses or separate sheds of a glasshouse. They measure inside the ditches:

[35] Her estimate for the Ballynegery furnace in Ireland early in the seventeenth century was 43 tons a year.

[36] Winbolt in his amended copy of W.G. describes No. 5 as having a red-clay floor 18 ft. × 15 ft. in the centre of slight ditches whose measurements he does not give. At No. 23, the burnt area measured 14 ft. × 10 ft. similar to No. 29. At No. 18 only one side of the burnt area survived, 16 ft. long.

[37] It had two sieges about 3 ft. long and 16 in. wide carrying two pots each side of a fire-box 20 in. wide.

[38] This appears to have been a working furnace because of the amount of broken glass and crucible in the surrounding ditch.

No. 5   18 ft. × 15 ft.[39]
No. 7   42 ft. × 20 ft.   There may have been two sheds on this site.[40]
No. 21 22 ft. × 16 ft.
No. 29 15 ft. 10 in. × 10 ft. 10 in. (*see* above).

Winbolt's plan of No. 7 (*see* Fig. 15) suggests that it may have included the furnace floor which he says was 15 ft. × 10 ft., the [glass] house floor about 25 ft. × 20 ft. and also a [?] annealing furnace shown inside the ditch. At Sidney Wood (No. 38) Winbolt conjectures that the glasshouse was 30 to 40 ft. × 15 ft. to 20 ft., and at Petworth Park (No. 40) about 27 ft. × 18 ft. All these six sites (Nos. 5, 7, 18, 21, 23 and 29) appear to have included the working furnace because they all had fragments of local glass and crucible on the site, but with no structural remains it is not certain.

There is so far no trace in the Weald of a true circular working furnace; *i.e.*, circular inside. Nine sites (Nos. 5, 7, 14, 21, 23, 25, 29, 33 and 35) had sufficient remains to show the furnaces were rectangular, three others Nos. 18, 38 and 40 probably were. Fernfold and Vann, both Late, appear to have been built largely of brick,[41] and the Early furnaces may have been built of stones embedded in clay as was No. 33. At the Northiam site (*see* p. 210) Mr Oliver says 'The dimensions of the shed floor on which the furnace stood were found to be about 20 ft. by 11 ft, the long axis running east and west.'

In the Weald I would expect the working furnace alone, to be roughly 10 ft. long and 6 ft. wide with a surround about 3 ft. wide of burnt clay[42] covered in some cases with a brick floor, making in all about 16 ft. by 12 ft. for that unit of the glass-house. Our glassmakers were probably always working near the limit of thermal capacity of their furnaces and possibly tended to try their own ideas. In some cases the working furnace, possibly incorporating an annealing furnace, may have had its separate shed from the fritting furnace; only extensive excavation such as was carried out at Blunden's Wood and Jamestown is likely to reveal a complete lay-out,[43] a task far beyond our resources of thirty years ago, and impossible, without root damage, in a growing copse. I know of no evidence in the Weald to suggest what our glasshouses looked like. They probably were timber-framed structures roofed with

[39] This site is Early. Winbolt describes the floors of the furnace as 18 ft. × 15 ft. 'in the centre of a mound surrounded by slight ditches.'

[40] Provisionally Early.

[41] Four Late sites, Nos. 23, 25, 32 and 35, provided evidence of fire-bricks, having a texture and appearance similar to that of crucibles.

[42] At Blunden's Wood, Mr Wood found that 'The heat of the kiln had reddened the soil for 2–3 ft. all round and under the flue for about a foot down.' (*See* pp. 62, 147.)

[43] Mr J. C. Harrington's preliminary and most interesting report of 47 pages includes a full account of the glasshouse covering the working furnace and what may have been the fritting and annealing furnaces; an area of 1,850 sq. ft., but *see* p. 72 for his recent interpretation. No actual remains survived of the covering shed. To ensure that nothing was missed, test trenches were extended out from the furnace ruins, exploring the surrounding area for a distance of 100 ft. in every direction.

tiles, which were found on some sites. The shingles, shown in the Mandeville draw-ing, or thatch, seem less likely because of the fire risk. Four furnaces in the Weald are sited with their long axis east and west (Nos. 5, 7, 29 and 35) and if Winbolt's drawing of No. 38 is correctly orientated, three (Nos. 21, 23 and 38) have their long axis north and south. Two others (Nos. 18 and 25) do not fit into either orientation. Again it appears to be a matter of individual choice.

Double Furnaces

The question of how many kilns, ovens or furnaces there were on a site is not easy to determine, nor can I suggest why in some cases there were two working fur-naces 50 yards apart and, from the glass evidence, apparently operating at about the same time. Upper and Lower Chaleshurst (Nos. 3 and 4) are 40 yards apart and ap-pear to have been worked at different periods, Upper being Early and Lower Late. Winbolt says of Fromes (No. 5) that there may have been another furnace a few yards away to the north-west. Mr R. S. Porter tells me that he suspects there is another furnace 22 yards south of No. 7. Winbolt suggested a separate annealing furnace on the original Cooper site. At the Glasshouse Lane site (No. 14) there was a second furnace 50 yards from the first one found. Both produced identical glass. Brookland (No. 23) had two furnaces, 50 yards apart, producing identical glass. Winbolt says of Fernfold (No. 25) 'it is virtually certain though we have not dug them out, that there were two others [furnaces] aligned with [his] Fernfold.' I am not entirely satisfied about this. At Malhamashfold (No. 29) there may have been two furnaces the second one being destroyed when stone was being dug; it would be about 20 yards away and under a separate shed. Examining the ground again after thirty years I doubt that there was a third, strung out in line over about 50 yards, as suggested by Winbolt[44] There may be three furnace sites at Woodhouse Farm (No. 32) spread over 70 yards. At Sidney Wood (No. 38) Winbolt conjectured that the glass-house was rectangular, 30 to 40 ft. long and 15 to 20 ft. wide. If this was so it must have covered more than one furnace.

I simply note, but cannot explain, that at three sites, Chaleshurst, Glasshouse Lane and Brookland, there certainly were two furnaces 40 to 50 yards apart; at two others, Malhamashfold and Woodhouse Farm, I suspect there were two or three furnaces and there is a possibility at Nos. 5 and 7 of there having been a second furnace. At the first three sites the finding of the second furnace was pure chance and it clearly is not worth while trenching outwards in every direction for 50 yards on the off-chance of finding a second furnace, even if the landowner allowed it. The practice of having double furnaces was not confined to one period as there were three or four double furnaces on both Early and Late sites.

[44] *S.C.M.,* vol. 9, p. 791.

V

WINDOW, COLOURED AND VESSEL GLASS

Window Glass

Owing to the confusion caused by the use of 'cullet' (*see* p. 18), it is impossible to say from the site evidence how important was window glass. But with one late exception (No. 4), window and vessel glass was made at all the Wealden sites where a sufficient quantity of blown glass fragments survived to provide good evidence of the products. The only documentary evidence of an Early glasshouse in the Weald shows that both window and vessel were made in 1380 (*see* p. 31). The only convincing accounts surviving for Early window glass from the Weald concern the glazing of a Royal Palace Chapel in 1351.[1]

Dr D. B. Harden, discussing the use of domestic window glass in medieval England says: 'Thus by the beginning of the sixteenth century glass must have been normal, not only in palaces but in most houses of any pretension, including town dwelling-houses.'[2] It is not known what proportion of medieval window glass was imported, but it was probably high (*see* p. 105).

After the Reformation and in particular in the last half of the sixteenth century, there was a burst of activity in domestic building, bringing with it a greatly increased demand for window glass. This demand was probably met in the Weald by Frenchmen brought over by Jean Carré in 1567 (*see* p. 120) and carried on after his death in 1572 by those glassmakers from Lorraine and Normandy together with at least two local families, the Strudwicks and Peytowes, to the end of the wood-fired forest industry, c.1618. The question of continuity is interesting and not easy to answer. There is recorded evidence of uncoloured window glass production in England during the late fourteenth and fifteenth centuries. From 1380 the dates from various sources[3] are: 1397, 1418, 1447, 1449, 1469, 1471. These refer to the country as a whole, but it is unlikely that the only district in England[4] where Early furnace sites have been found was not producing window.

There is no recorded or archaeological evidence so far known, of glassmaking in the Weald between 1385 (*see* p. 31) and 1495, when land in Chiddingfold was

---

[1] *See* p. 27.

[2] 'Domestic Window Glass: Roman, Saxon and Medieval,' in E. M. Jope (ed.), *Studies in Building History* (London, 1961), p. 57.

[3] *B.E.S.*, p. 183.

[4] There may be a medieval glasshouse at Kingswood, Cheshire; *see* p. 220.

conveyed to Henry Ropley 'glasscarrier' (*see* p. 29). This gap may have been bridged by unrecorded members of the Schurterre and Peytowe families.

The next reference is in 1536 when John Peytowe's will was proved. He left to his son John his tools and moulds belonging to his glasshouse.[5] He could have over-lapped with Henry Ropley the glasscarrier of 1495. The next recorded Peytowe was Thomas, whose will was proved in 1562.[5] His son, William, and grandson, John, who died in 1616, appear to have carried on the trade.[5] From 1536 until the end of the Weald industry there are known to have been eight Peytowes making glass.[5] One Early site, Broomfield Hanger, producing window glass, may have been worked by them.[5]

There was a Richard Mose of Kyrdeforde, glassmaker, in 1547[6] and evidence that a glassmaker, apparently producing only vessel glass, worked at Chiddingfold in 1557.[7]

Something is known of the state of glassmaking in England on 7 August 1565 when Armigail Waade, clerk of the Council, wrote to Sir William Cecil on behalf of one Cornelius de Lannoy, who had apparently undertaken to improve the English manufacture of glass and pottery: 'All our glasse makers cannot facyon him one glasse tho' he stoode by them to teach them. . . . The potters cannot make him one pot [possibly crucible] to content him. They know not howe to seasson their stuff to make the same to systeyne the force of his great fyers.' Waade further writes 'I would he wear putt in some generall cumfort of some place to be provided for him here in England, he liketh marvelously well the syte of Guldeford.'[8] No more is known of de Lannoy and his undertaking, so that we may conclude that it failed.[9] The reference to the maturing of possible crucibles is interesting.

---

[5] *See* p. 160.   [6] *See* Lyons Farm, Chapter IX (p. 179).

[7] 'As for glassmakers, they be scant in this land,
Yet one there is as I do understand
And in Sussex is now his habitation.
At Chiddingfold he works of his occupation.
To go to him it is necessary and meete,
Or sende a servant that is discreete,
And desire him in most humble wise
To blow thee a glass after thy devise:
It were worth many an Arme or a Legge.
He could shape it like to an Egge;
To open and close as close as a haire;
If thou have such a one thou needest not fear.
Yet if thou hadst a number into store
It is the better for store is no sore.'
from T. Charnock's *Breviary of Natural Philosophy*, 1557, printed in the *Theatrum Chemicum* of Elias Ashmole, published 1651; *see* Hartshorne, p. 150, from which both Cooper and Winbolt probably quoted. It is possible, as Winbolt says, *W.G.* (p. 12), that he was a Peytowe of Lower Chaleshurst, who produced apparently mainly Late vessel. It is much less likely he was a Peytowe of Broomfield Hanger which produced Early window.

[8] S.P. Dom. Eliz. xxxvii, 3, ex V.C.H., *Surrey*, vol. 2, p. 297.

[9] A. Nesbitt, *Glass*, p. 126, ex V.C.H., *Surrey*, vol. 2, p. 297.

About two years later we have Carré's well-known petition to Cecil which relates how he enquired 'of one of the masters of furnaces' at Chiddingfold, who said he could make only 'such little works as primitive bottles and other small things.'[10] Carré was hoping to get a licence to produce window glass and was anxious to show that no English window glassmaker would be displaced. This was the statement of only one native glassmaker.

There is very little doubt that at least one other glasshouse was working in the Weald when Carré called at Chiddingfold in 1567. In 1557 Henry Strudwick of Idehurst, Kirdford, bequeathed to his two sons, his glasshouse, ovens, irons, etc. Two furnace sites have been found on Idehurst, both produced Transitional type glass.[11] Between 1557 and 1614 six Kirdford Strudwicks have so far been traced as glassmakers and one as a glasscarrier.[12]

The only other Transitional site, Frithfold Copse, also produced window glass. Mrs E. S. Godfrey discusses the rise of Isaac Bungar, possibly the most important glassmaker in the Weald after Carré, and a formidable opponent of Mansell's monopoly; she notes that at an Enquiry, Bongar stated that his forebears came from Normandy 'to teach the English to make window glass.'[13]

'In the map of England dated 1566 painted on the walls of the Guardaroba in the Palazzo Vecchio at Florence, besides Guildford the capital no other place is marked in Surrey but Chiddingfold.'[14] This place was clearly known abroad for its glassmaking and it seems unlikely that such fame rested on one or two glassmakers who could make only vessel glass.

I share the late Mr Giuseppi's doubt that the making of window glass had died out at a time of greatly increased demand.[15] Furthermore I know of no Early or Transitional site, where any quantity of glass survived, which did not produce evidence of window glass manufacture. So the doubt remains, Mr E. Wyndham Hulme notwithstanding.[16] The survival of medieval records is so much a matter of

[10] S.P. Dom. 12/43, No. 43. N.D. but probably in 1567 (New Cal. No. 104). *See* also p. 121. Phials and drug bottles were the lowest level of the glassmakers' art. Speaking generally, Honey says, 'But throughout the Middle Ages glass vessel-making was a minor art compared with the making of window-glass which flourished from the twelfth century onwards' (*Glass*, 1946, p. 14).

[11] Idehurst, south, No. 17 (*see* p. 177), provided a quantity of glass fragments of little interest except that most of them were window glass, which can be fairly safely dated *c*.1557.

[12] *See* Chapters I and VIII.   [13] S.P. 14/162, No. 231A; *see* D.E.G., p. 96.

[14] V.C.H., *Surrey*, vol. 2, p. 298.   [15] V.C.H., *Surrey*, vol. 2, p. 298.

[16] There are five short papers in *The Antiquary*, vols. 30, 31, by an authority, the late E. Wyndham Hulme, on 'English Glassmaking in the sixteenth and seventeenth centuries.' In vol. 30, p. 210, he said: 'To the latter cause [lack of technical skill] must be assigned the disappearance of the native window-glass manufacture, which enjoyed a precarious existence in the fifteenth century.' Hulme appears to have relied on Carré's petition and on Isaac Bungar's statement many years later, that his forebears came from Normandy to teach the English to make window glass (*see* p. 131). Hulme strongly criticizes Hartshorne (*Old English Glasses*, 1897) for not accepting the evidence of Carré and Bungar (*The Antiquary*, vol. 34, p. 112). I realize that the site evidence, though significant (*see* Introduction, p. 5), is by no means always conclusive, due to cullet and close dating difficulties, and I am inclined to leave this question unsolved.

chance, that too much weight should not be placed on the absence of references in the fifteenth century. The entries of the migratory French glassmaking families, such as the Bungars, Henezells and Titterys, in the Wisborough Green P.R., for example, between the dates 1567 and 1617 is good evidence for continuous glassmaking there for the last fifty years of the industry. All of which, though far from definite, suggests that glassmaking in the Weald may have been continuous from the start until its end in c.1618, that the industry was at a very low ebb in the mid-sixteenth century when, possibly, the art of making window glass may have been temporarily lost.

The two common methods of manufacturing window glass, 'crown' and 'muff' are described by Dr D. B. Harden in his paper, 'Domestic Window Glass: Roman, Saxon and Medieval.'[17] Very briefly, the more simple but wasteful crown or disc method involved blowing and spinning a flat disc, while muff or broad glass was made by blowing a cylinder, splitting it down the side by cutting it while still hot and opening it out on a flat bed.

When examining a fragment of Wealden window glass I have taken the most useful distinguishing features of 'muff' and 'crown' window glass to be:

Muff

1. A slightly thickened 'thumb' edge from the top or bottom of the cylinder. This edge is straight.
2. One side may be slightly rough and therefore more opaque, where the opened cylinder had been laid out to flatten.
3. The fragments are not always quite flat.

Crown

1. Fragments from the circumference have a heat sealed edge which is curved and provides some idea of the diameter of the disc or crown.
2. There is a variation in thickness from the centre of the disc outwards.
3. The surface is sometimes rippled and one side burnished where held towards the fire.
4. Centre 'bull's eye' sometimes found.

I have found the evidence of bubbles, supposedly parallel in muff and in spirals in crown to be uncommon and unsatisfactory; much Early glass is too corroded to see the bubbles and they are not obvious even in Late fragments. It is generally supposed that the Lorraine glassmakers brought over by Carré used the muff process which had been used in the Weald at least from the fourteenth century (*see* Chapter I, p. 31), and that the Normans used the crown method.

Dr D. B. Harden in his paper quoted above says (p. 42):

'Panes made by the cylinder process can in theory be readily recognized, since any bubbles and other impurities they contain should appear in parallel and

[17] Chapter 3 in *Studies in Building History*, ed. by E. M. Jope (London, 1961); *see* also Guttery p. 45.

elongated, not in spiral formation like those in crown glass. In practice this criterion does not always work effectively, since glass is a wayward substance and does not always flow to pattern.'

Owing to the confusion caused by the use of cullet (*see* p. 18), any assessments from the site evidence as to the relative amounts of window made by the muff or crown methods are difficult and rarely valid. Cooper noted that 'the great bulk of fragments found are muff,'[18] a remark based on three prolific Chiddingfold sites. I endorse this general impression based on glass from all the known sites, and thirty years ago I regarded crown as so rare that I saved and noted it. I do not agree with Winbolt (*W.G.*, p. 69), that 'on most sites muff and crown were about equally common,' or accept two or three bits of indisputable crown which may be cullet, on a site, providing mainly muff, as evidence that both methods were used there. If a sufficient quantity of only one type is found on a site, as at Blunden's Wood (No. 33), and at Glasshouse Lane (No. 14),[19] the evidence is probably valid.

Winbolt says (*W.G.*, p. 41), of Somersbury (No. 37) that 'nearly all the glass is thin, spun window glass.' Of Sidney Wood (No. 38), he says two bull's eyes were found and at Petworth Park (No. 40) 'some window was made in discs.' These sites must be mentioned but the amounts of window from Nos. 38 and 40 are too small to afford a reliable conclusion. Crown glass was certainly made at Knightons (No. 42), whether solely must await the full report.

To sum up, although the amount of valid site evidence is small, it points to both methods being used in the Early and Late periods, and that a glassmaker may have specialized (*see* p. 174) in one method only as one would expect.

Mrs E. S. Godfrey has much of interest to say about the window glassmaker Isaac Bungar of Wisborough Green and Billingshurst, 1600–18, which will be found in Chapter VIII.

On the organization of glassworks, Mrs E. S. Godfrey says (p. 323), 'The production of window glass on any considerable scale necessitated a more elaborate division of labour, as Carré's contract shows.[20] Each of the Hennezell brothers was to be the chief of a unit of 3 skilled workmen who were to make every day in each of the 2 ovens 30 bundles of glass,' and (p. 324), 'The 6 glassmakers were to produce a total of 60 bundles of broad glass per day.'[21]

Mr R. J. Charleston in a letter (1965) said he thought the term 'broad glass'

'was normally used for the muff process (which after all, is spread out in breadth, whereas the circular crown really has no "breadth" in any direction), even though it was sometimes extended to mean simply window-glass of any kind. I am far

[18] He excavated the Roman villa at Chiddingfold in 1888 and noted that the window glass was of muff type (*see* his loose notes at Haslemere Museum).
[19] No. 33 was Early and No. 14 was Late; they produced crown and muff respectively.
[20] Lansdowne MS. 59, No. 76 enclosure.   [21] *op. cit.*

from convinced that just anybody could make either kind of window-glass. Especially in the eighteenth century, when both the muffs and the crowns became so large, it was a very specialized business. I suspect this specialization was traditional.'

The earliest reference to broad glass in the Weald is in 1380 (*see* p. 31), and the term continued in use in Stourbridge and Newcastle upon Tyne well into the eighteenth century. In 1616 the Norman Isaac Bungar and the Lorrainer Edward Hensey were described as 'broad glassmakers in the Counties of Surrey and Sussex' (*see* p. 132). Possibly, in the main, the term 'broad' relates to 'muff.' There is no trace of heavy plate or mirror glass on any Wealden glasshouse site, Early or Late.

Cutting

It is unlikely that diamond cutters were used in England until the sixteenth century, when they may have been introduced from Germany. In 1622 a Petworth glazier bequeathed to his son-in-law, his 'diaman' – presumably for glass cutting.[22]

I am inclined to accept the late Mrs B. Halahan's belief that the small shaped flints found on some Early glasshouse sites were used for cutting or marking glass, but there is no proof until the latter part of the sixteenth century that window glass was cut and shaped at the glasshouse (*see* site No. 14, p. 173).

Quarrels or Quarries

Dr L. F. Salzman says of this type of window glass, 'In domestic glazing the Tudor period saw the establishment of the diamond lattice which is still a pleasing feature of so many of our older houses'; he gives 1505 as the earliest recorded reference to them.[23]

Fragments of quarrels found in quantity on two Late sites, Nos. 14 and 37 (both probably working into the seventeenth century) vary little in size, having sides between 3 and $3\frac{1}{2}$ in.; the tip angle is about 65°. Many are about $\frac{1}{32}$ in. thick and sometimes less. They are fragile but may still occasionally be seen in windows of late sixteenth- or early seventeenth-century date. The glass is not transparent by our standards, and was perhaps made very thin to allow more light to come through, but being so thin it had to have the support of lattice work lead. It would be lighter to transport and probably cheaper than quarrels of over $\frac{1}{16}$ in.

Late quarrels may have been 'cut' at the glasshouse because judging by the extreme thinness of some, the glass could not have been transported in larger sheets. The 'cutting' at the glasshouse would provide plenty of the essential cullet. Until

[22] *S.A.C.*, vol. 98, p. 84.
[23] *B.E.S.*, p. 177. They were used earlier in churches and castles. There is a thick, small ($1\frac{3}{4}$ in. sides) red-painted green quarry from Bramber Castle said to be late fourteenth century, and it well might be, in Barbican House Museum, Lewes. The late J. A. Knowles told me that quarries in church glass were common in the thirteenth century.

this standardization, it is unlikely that the thicker, Early glass was 'cut' on site more than enough to make it portable; it was probably 'cut' and shaped at glaziers' town workshops.

Coloured Glass

There is no evidence from the furnace sites that coloured glass was made in the Weald except at Nos. 4 (Late) and 29 (Early) where ruby was certainly produced.[24] At No. 4 it appears to have been used for vessel decoration and at No. 29 for flashing on to the local window glass, but it may not have been more than experimental. Some of the Late sites, notably No. 32, produced intense blue-green glass, some lumps of which appear to be a beautiful blue, but whether this is real blue glass or simply appears to be blue due to slight devitrification is uncertain. The wide range of coloured fragments, largely from the Chiddingfold sites, is probably imported cullet.

There is no documentary proof of coloured glass having been made in England on a commercial scale until long after the forest industry shut down. The late Mr J. A. Knowles says that the first definite evidence of such manufacture is to be found in Dr Pococke's *Travels through England*. In 1751 Pococke found coloured glass being made at Stourbridge.[25] There is no evidence that the well-known John Utynam patent of 1449 was taken up or developed; Knowles comments that it does not seem to have been a success.[26]

Cooper produces no evidence that coloured glass was made at his few sites, except the interesting crucible containing ruby glass from Lower Chaleshurst (No. 4). The two scraps of blue he mentions from Schurterreshurst and Gostrode were almost certainly cullet. His window in Chiddingfold church must have taken most of the colour his family found from sites Nos. 2, 6 and 7. Winbolt and I never found anything like that quantity and the fragments in the window in Kirdford church took a great deal of finding: one piece of ruby came from site No. 15 and most of the rest from No. 29. Outside Chiddingfold, very little coloured glass was found except at No. 29 and much of that was fragmentary as found at No. 5. Knowles doubted if a small amount of coloured glass would matter if mixed in the cullet, and it is possible that at the three Cooper sites mentioned above there was some broken thirteenth-century window with too much colour and it had been thrown out.

Glass Prices in the Seventeenth Century

Some information on glass prices in Petworth are in a glazier's inventory of 1629. Two of the Petworth glaziers, William Seamer who died in 1622, and Isaac Mills who died in 1629, very probably sold glass from the glasshouses in Petworth Park, Kirdford and Wisborough.[27] At least one of these was working as late as 1614.[28]

---

[24] 'Red molten glass' was also found in one of the crucible fragments from the Kingswood (possible) glasshouse site, Delamere, Cheshire. Its date is not known; *see* p. 221.

[25] *Glass*, June 1926, p. 296: 'The source of the coloured glass used in medieval stained glass windows.'

[26] *Glass*, March 1926, p. 157.   [27] *S.A.C.*, vol. 98, p. 108.

[28] Inventory of H. Strudwick, glasscarrier, 1614, *S.A.C.*, vol. 93, p. 135.

Isaac Mills' will directed that he should be buried at 'Green' (Wisborough Green); he obviously had a close connection there and left 5s. to the poor of Loxwood and Wisborough Green where at least three glasshouses may have been working after 1600. Perhaps Mills kept a small shop in Midhurst because his goods include 'glass and other implements at Midhurst, 5s.' His stock at Petworth included 39 drinking glasses at 3d. each and window glass at 3d. a [square] foot. Inventory values are not reliable but, unlike farm stock or furniture, the retail price of drinking glasses was probably fairly standardized. Window glass value can be roughly checked with contemporary records: thus the estimates for 9732 square feet of glass in 242 windows, for the 9th Earl of Northumberland's proposed 'New House at Petworth' in 1615 was 6d. a square foot.[29] In 1627 at St Saviour's Southwark, now the cathedral, 8 ft. of new glass was charged to the churchwardens at 6d. a foot.[30] In both cases the glass may have been of finer quality and heavier, and the price appears to include fixing, so that 3d. a foot for Mills' window glass is not far out.

Glass, window and probably vessel, though still by our standard very costly, was within the resources of at least half the people of Petworth early in the seventeenth century.

Vessel Glass

The careful collection of cullet and its remarkable fragmentation into its scraps, have resulted in vessel glass remains in the Weald being very disappointing indeed.[31] Only six sites, Nos. 5, 7, 12, 14, 23 and 38, produced some vessel scraps of interest. Most of the material from the three Early sites (Nos. 5, 7 and 12) cannot now be identified and some is shown as 'Chiddingfold' glass, but the best scraps from the three Late sites (Nos. 14, 23 and 38) are shown by their site name in Plates XIV and XVI. On Early sites the fragmentation might be partly explained by much of the glass being of poor quality, but it is curious that Late vessel scraps are so small; possibly some of this glass was too thin, and some was crushed by earlier investigators. When examining sites I was particularly careful to grasp any chance of reconstructing fragments, but this scarcely ever occurred; the poverty of evidence is great. The few fragments illustrated in Plates XII, XIII, XIV and XVI and Figs. 11–13 make this clear and they are the best of thousands of scraps. There is no doubt that fine quality vessel was made in the Late period, notably at Sidney Wood (No. 38) but though there are hints of decoration, little is known of the forms. For Winbolt's description of the vessel scraps he found there *see* Chapter IX site No. 38.

---

[29] *See* 'Notes and Documents on Petworth House, 1574–1632,' by G. Batho in *S.A.C.*, vol. 96, pp. 115, 124. This palace was never started.

[30] I am indebted to Miss A. Reeve for sending me this reference. The churchwardens' accounts are on loan to the G.L.C.; the reference is P/92/S/684.

[31] At the Blunden's Wood glasshouse Mr Wood found very few vessel scraps of any significance apart from the bases of unusually small hanging lamps. See *Sy. A.C.*, vol. 62, p. 65.

The bases of hanging lamps[32] and fragments of the wide rimmed necks of urinal flasks[33] were found on Early sites only, or made of Early glass. Fragments of small phials and bottles, round and hexagonal, vessels with wrythen pattern necks, drinking glasses with flat and high-kick hemmed rim bases were found on both Early and Late sites.[34] Various moulded designs[35] and applied ornament, rods and tubes, handled jugs or mugs occurred, more particularly on the Late sites. Confined to Late sites were fragments showing honeycomb moulding, knopped stems from drinking glasses, the small bowl or dish shown in Fig. 11, possibly retorts, which may have needed a quality of glass not attained by the Early glassmakers, posset cups (see Fig. 11) and linen smoothers; a possible handle of such a tool is shown in Plate XVI. We found no evidence of the making of hour glasses.

The total site evidence in the Weald, suggests that with one exception, window and vessel glass was produced at all the glasshouses. Some of the Late sites appear to have a preponderance of one or the other; e.g., No. 37 may have produced largely window and No. 38 largely vessel glass. With the possible exception of site No. 4 which may have produced vessel only, I am not persuaded that any known site confined its production to either window or vessel glass alone.[36]

Apart from the few examples mentioned above, there is no possibility, at present, of dating Wealden vessel glass by its form alone.[37] There is, however, no doubt that the Early vessel, apart from its quality, is generally much cruder in appearance than the Late, some of which must have been of great beauty, but the complete form of this is usually tantalizingly out of our reach.

The difference in quality between the Early and the Late Wealden glass is clearly illustrated in Plates XII and XIV. The Early is cloudy and slightly corroded, the Late

[32] See W. A. Thorpe, English Glass (2nd edn., 1949), Plate XIV (b) and (d), my Plate XIV and also p. 96.

[33] They had to be very thin to be nearly transparent so very little survives. See Thorpe, Plate XIV(a).

[34] Hemmed-base fragments are common on Late sites but were found on only two Early sites, Nos. 2 and 12, both of which could be late in the Early period; i.e., in the first half of the sixteenth century. This cannot be confirmed because neither site had any documentary or pottery evidence.

[35] John Peytowe in 1536 left to his son John his 'tools and moulds,' see p. 117.

[36] The confusion of evidence caused by the use of cullet is discussed on p. 18. The more reliable documentary evidence is scarce. Both window and vessel glass was made at Schurterre's glasshouse in 1380 (see p. 31). In 1618 Paul Vinion (who was born at Wisborough Green) and Peter Comely said they made green drinking glasses with wood fuel in Sussex before and after 1615 (see p. 139); this suggests some specialization which is rarely confirmed by site evidence.

[37] Finds of medieval glass vessels are rare partly because, unlike pottery, glass was probably not in common use and because, also unlike pottery, it was mostly thin, fragile and liable to collapse. Some has probably completely decomposed. In the London Museum Medieval Catalogue (1st ed., 1940), there are only two fragments of Syrian glass vessel discussed in six lines, in a book of 298 pages. Honey, in Glass (1946), p. 107, note 6, says 'It is remarkable that broken glass, especially of the seventeenth century date and later, is found but rarely in London excavations, while fragments of pottery and porcelain are found in quantity.' He blames cullet collection 'since old and broken glass has an intrinsic value for use in this way.' The rarity of fine quality Late vessel is largely due to its fragility and also to the difficulty in distinguishing some of it from modern intrusions. See p. 97.

is clear, burnished and usually with no corrosion. Sidney Wood glasshouse produced the finest quality glass in the Weald and probably in the whole English forest glass industry.

The misfortune of fragmentation is emphasized by the broken vessel base in Plate XVI which was part of a drinking glass of fine and delicate quality. The vessel mouldings shown in the same Plate (Nos. 4 and 5) were fairly common at Sidney Wood; No. 6 from Brookland shows some surface corrosion unusual from Late sites.

The drawings of Late vessel fragments and a reconstruction in Fig. 11 include the most beautiful and fairly complete vessel fragment found in the Weald; its site may be dated to c.1615. It was found before the last war, but unhappily got broken and thrown out while the owner was away. Below in Fig. 11 is a fragment (c) found by Winbolt at Fernfold; it is now in Lewes Museum.

Both fragments shown in Fig. 12 are of good quality glass showing fine workmanship.

The large hemmed-rim base of a (faulty) bowl (Fig. 13), probably from the Glasshouse Lane site, is part of the largest glass vessel I know of from the Weald. It appears to be the base of a thin bowl which might have had a diameter of upwards of 12 in.

There are vague hints from tiny fragments[38] that the range and variety from some of our Late sites extended beyond drinking glasses and assorted bottles. The small dish (Fig. 11) from site No. 14 is an example, and mugs or jugs were certainly made because fragments of handles are found (see Fig. 12).

The possibility of finding fragments which could be reconstructed was the spur on a number of most unrewarding sites. It scarcely ever became a reality. Mr J. C. Harrington at Jamestown says 'the keenest disappointment was that none of the glass fragments were large enough to show what the original objects had been.'[39]

There is no evidence, but the forms found at Woodchester may have been made by members of the foreign families who started their English careers in the Weald under Carré and carried on the forms they knew.[40] The fragments from Wood-

[38] Mr B. P. Marmont in a paper read to the Woolhope Naturalists' Field Club in 1922, said that he found at Woodchester glasshouse 'scores of fragments of various shaped drinking glasses, bottles, etc., many of them large enough to have exact reproductions made, some of which are very graceful and coincide with original specimens in the Museums of Antwerp and Brussels'; see J. S. Daniels, The Woodchester Glass House (Gloucester, 1950), p. 19. We found nothing to compare remotely in tough survival with the Woodchester vessel glass. Woodchester is the only known circular tiered-type furnace in England and may have provided more efficient annealing.

[39] Glassmaking at Jamestown (1952), p. 15. On p. 29 Harrington says 'Practically no specimens of the plain utilitarian wares from that period are to be found today, or, at least none that are recognizable as such.'

[40] Woodchester is the only known round furnace in the English Forest industry. Thorpe, English Glass (2nd edn., 1949), says of it 'there are strong reasons for believing that this furnace was not French, but worked by one of the Flemish glassmakers who had been brought to England in Carré's time.' It is not known if any Fleming worked in the Weald, but there is a Mr Berry, glassmaker, stranger, in the Kirdford P.R. in 1589. This may be an Anglicized form of Buré, a Flemish glassmaker mentioned by Thorpe on p. 88, note 2.

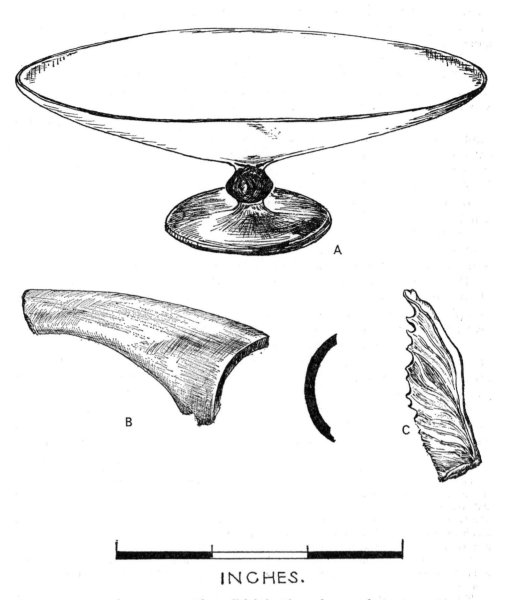

INCHES.

Fig. 11. A. Conjectural reconstruction of a small dish, based on a fragment from No. 14. B. Fragment of a ?posset cup spout from No. 14. C. Applied decoration in the form of a ?bird's wing from No. 25.

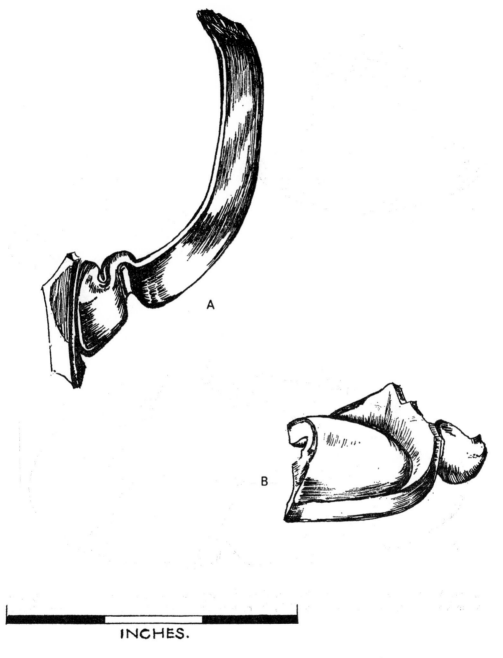

INCHES.

Fig. 12. A. Mug or jug handle. B. Small handled vessel base. Both from No. 23.

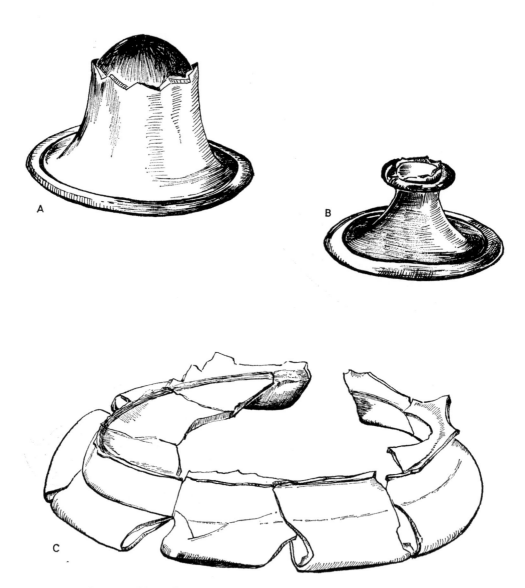

Fig. 13. A and B. Vessel bases from No. 38. These drawings, without scale, are from a photograph by the Rev. F. W. Cobb, in *W.G.*, p. 39. C. Faulty base (approx. $5\frac{1}{2}$ in. diameter) of a Late period bowl.

chester and suggested reconstructions (Plate XIX)[41] made by Messrs. Powell about 1920 probably provide some idea of the Late period Weald vessel forms.

Discussing the vessel fragments from Woodchester, Blore Park (Staffs.) and Sidney Wood (No. 38) Mr W. A. Thorpe says: 'If we had the green beakers entire I suspect they would take a place beside Verzelini's 'Venice glasses,' a different but not inferior art.[42] Some scraps of Late vessel from Sidney Wood show honeycomb mouldings, and ribbing oblique and vertical; they are very thin and of fine quality, and amply justify Mr Thorpe's comment.

Mr R. J. Charleston[43] says:

'This industry, situated in the well-wooded country of the Weald which supplied it with all the timber needed for its furnaces, was mainly devoted to the making of window-glass. The blowers, however, were certainly also capable of blowing simple vessels; and fragments of such vessels, of thin green glass, have been found on the Wealden glasshouse sites. Impure green glass of this sort, however, was probably restricted to humble domestic roles, being made into lamps, bottles, urinals and the like.'

To these may be added drinking beakers. Fragments of bases, the strongest part, are common on Late sites and were found on at least two Early sites.[44] but their exact date cannot yet be established. Commenting on the Woodchester glasses which I suggest are comparable with Sidney Wood forms, Mr Charleston says:

'The glasses made at Woodchester fall into two main classes – drinking glasses and bottles. The drinking-glasses were tall tumbler-like beakers of two types. The first kind were straight-sided and almost perfectly cylindrical, being made stable by the addition of a coil of glass round the foot and by the pushing-in of the base in a slight conical "kick". The second of the taller beaker shapes was made by pushing in the bottom of the vesicle of glass whilst still soft, and thus making a low pedestal of double thickness, above which the body of the glass rose in the form of a slightly everted cylinder.[45]

This method of fashioning the foot, which was characteristic of French glass-making was also used in making goblets, the second main group of drinking glasses . . . The bottles made at Woodchester were quite small (the only intact example measures $5\frac{1}{2}$ in. in height), and were normally hexagonal in section. One exceptional fragment, however, came from a flattened spherical bottle of

[41] These are illustrated in *The Woodchester Glass House*. Most of the material and fourteen of the Powell reconstructions are in Gloucester Museum. The Powell reconstructions were of necessity tentative; future finds may adduce fresh evidence. Some are shown in Plate XIX. The Woodchester glasshouse is discussed in Chapter X, p. 218.

[42] Thorpe, *op. cit.*, p. 93.

[43] *The Connoisseur Period Guides. Tudor Period: Pottery, Porcelain and Glass* p. 84. This guide includes five drawings of the Powell Woodchester reconstructions.

[44] *See p. 90, note 34.*

[45] Plate XIX shows these types of glasses. [G.H.K.]

German type, decorated with ribs blown in a mould and then "wrythen" to produce diagonal patterning.

Mould-blowing, indeed, was the most favoured method of decorating the glass found on this site.[46] The moulds imparted either a honeycomb pattern[47] or a design of vertical ribs which could be twisted on withdrawal from the mould, to give the "wrythen" effect described above.

Another favoured decoration was a trail of glass laid round and round the glass, either in a spiral or in a series of horizontal bands. In the latter case, the trails were sometimes combined with small applied blobs of glass stamped with a design like the pips of a raspberry. Similar "prunts" were worked, whilst still plastic, into the form of rosettes . . .[48]

Although the bottle fragments at Woodchester were not so numerous as those of beakers, there must have been in the late sixteenth and early seventeenth centuries a vast output of small green bottles for a variety of purposes.'

As it is the thickest part of any vessel which survives, with the hanging or bracket lamps it is the bases which can be found on most Early sites. A fine specimen of one of these glass lamps found at Winchester is illustrated in Plate XV.[49]

Mr R. J. Charleston has this to say about glass lamps.[50]

'Of the many other domestic uses to which glass was put, lighting was undoubtedly one. Green glass fragments of what were certainly lamps are not infrequently found in the excavations of English cities, and probably date from the later Middle Ages. The form was that of a cylindrical cup suddenly tapering below into a long point.[51] This lamp was intended primarily for suspension. There is no evidence to show what sort of lamps were used in Tudor England, but that they could be of glass seems evident from an observation of Thomas Platter's in 1599. In Whitehall he saw an emblem of "a glass full of oil and a light burning in it".'

In an interesting section on Lighting in the *London Museum Medieval Catalogue* (1940) p. 174,[52] the writer says:

'The commonest form of artificial lighting during the early medieval period was

---

[46] In the Weald moulds appear to have been used on most of the Early sites also. [G.H.K.]

[47] *See* Plates XVI and XVIII. [G.H.K.]

[48] Winbolt found parts of prunts at sites Nos. 26 and 35. I can recollect no other 'prunts' in the Weald, but otherwise all this comment applies to the Weald glass. [G.H.K.]

[49] I am much indebted to Mr G. C. Dunning, and to Mr F. Cottrill, Curator of the Winchester Museum, for their help in getting a copy of this photograph.

[50] *Connoisseur Period Guide*, p. 88.

[51] It is these points, or cup bases, which survive on our Early sites. They were referred to as 'palm glasses' in *W.G.* but later Winbolt agreed they were lamp bases. Mr Wood found fragments of these lamps at Blunden's Wood, *c.*1330. [G.H.K.]

[52] I am much indebted to Mr G. C. Dunning for this reference.

the open cresset-lamp. This took the form either of a bowl standing on some form of foot, or of a funnel-shaped bowl with a downward projection, for insertion in a bracket or for hanging in a loop from the ceiling.

In French and English manuscripts and sculpture the commonest type is the hanging lamp[53] ... Hanging lamps are normally shewn in an ecclesiastical context. Examples do, however, sometimes appear in scenes of civil life ... and there are a number of surviving specimens of a purely domestic nature. It would seem, therefore, that the emphasis on ecclesiastical use is due rather to the character of the scenes usually depicted than to any restriction of actual usage.'

With the catalogue illustration of such a hanging lamp, *c.*1200, may be compared the sketch (Fig. 14) of a beautiful twelfth-century panel at Chartres[54] which shows such a lamp hanging over the manger.

These funnel-shaped lamps were also made in pottery and the catalogue illustrates a thirteenth-century specimen. There is no evidence of such lamps being made in the Weald after the Early periods. This suggests that they may have gone out of use before then.

From our site evidence I suspect the furnace sites are the last places to find fragments of vessel sufficient to make reconstructions. More rewarding is the collection of green glass vessel found on bombed sites in the City of London and now in the Guildhall Museum, which may be of the same date as our latest sites. It provided some interesting forms. I have twice examined this collection[55] and I am not satisfied that any of it originated in the Weald. The glass is only slightly different from any Weald glass I know, but it *is* different. The difference is impossible to describe but having examined the glass from Woodchester which is probably, after Sidney Wood, the finest English green forest glass, I think all the Guildhall green glass vessel was probably imported. It is not easy to be definite but I consider the finest glass from Sidney Wood is of appreciably better quality than the glass in this Guildhall collection.

The very poor type of old small cottage formerly on the site of my house was the humblest form of dwelling hereabouts, and yet its occupiers used Early Wealden glass vessel. The position is about ½ mile from site No. 18. Fragments of six bottle necks, one unusually heavy, and five bases, are illustrated (Plate XVII). They are crude and roughly made, only the tiny square phial base and the hemmed-rim beaker base being fairly good. They were better preserved than fragments on a furnace site because, having been broken in the cottage, thrown out and gradually buried,

[53] Such funnel-shaped, hanging lamps appear in three late twelfth-century illuminated MSS. now in the B.M., but it is impossible to be certain whether they are of glass. I am much indebted to Miss V. Smith for these references: Cotton MS. Caligula, A.VII, f. 8b and f. 5, and Royal MS. 2 A.XXII, f. 13b. [G.H.K.]

[54] It is the bottom right-hand panel of the large central lancet at the west end of the nave. The Virgin's face and figure of Joseph are unskilful nineteenth-century restorations: *see* J. S. Johnson, *The Radiance of Chartres* (London, 1964), p. 69.

[55] I am indebted to Mr A. H. Oswald and Mr N. C. Cook for their help.

Fig. 14. A twelfth-century glass panel in Chartres Cathedral showing a hanging lamp.

they lay undisturbed by searchers for cullet or stone. Some fragments of Late vessel were also found, all of which suggests that glass vessel was used in the humblest homes in this district from perhaps the fourteenth century onwards. There is no evidence that the well-known seventeenth-century squat wine bottles were made at our Late sites. They were probably not made until *c.*1650, and are crude wares compared with the suggestion of beautiful form, fine quality and relatively clear glass found at Sidney Wood.

Bottle necks and hemmed-rim bases of the Early and Late period, possibly the strongest and most durable part of the glass vessel in use, were the commonest fragments in the garden. From our earliest date, bottles probably were the commonest glass vessel used among the ordinary country homes.

A few details of vessel scraps are included in the site descriptions in Chapter IX.

It is, as yet, impossible to date closely Early Wealden glass by its appearance only. Though some of the Early vessel glass is thin and has an attractive appearance, is not without quality and shows considerable skill in fashioning, in general it tends to corrode, is much cruder than the Late vessel, and cannot be compared with the finest from Sidney Wood.

I surmise some of the humble Early vessel, such as small phials and urinal flasks, could have travelled as far as London. Possibly some of the fine quality Late vessel may have gone further, but in my opinion the forest glass production was small until after the mid-sixteenth century and it is not surprising that little of it is found in town rubbish pits earlier than the seventeenth century.

Glass vessel, often thin and fragile, was undoubtedly used in the houses of the wealthy but until the end of the sixteenth century it was probably largely imported.

It is very doubtful if Early Wealden glass, window or vessel, has any definable visual quality to distinguish it from green forest glass produced anywhere in northern Europe between c.1200 and the mid-sixteenth century. But any surviving medieval window glass, particularly if it is coloured, is almost certain to have been imported (see p. 105). One might hazard a guess as to the origin[56] of glass apparently made after the mid-sixteenth century, especially if one knew where it had turned up, but any label 'Weald Glass' on a specimen found outside this small district should be viewed with great suspicion.

Unlike pottery, Wealden glass is not a product that holds out much promise of classification or definition beyond the three types suggested.

[56] See p. 97 re Guildhall collection.

VI

TYPES OF WEALDEN GLASS

Apart from decayed glass, there appear to be two types of finished glass fragments[1] found in the Weald, each having characteristics which can be defined.
The two types are usually quite distinct and at only one site, No. 42 (*see* p.
208), was there substantial mixing not clearly attributable either to scraps of cullet
brought in or to the less likely re-use of the site.[2]

The necessity for cullet collection not only creates a scarcity of waste glass at the
site but its haphazard dispersal confuses the evidence of glass type.

The three suggested Transitional sites may be ignored for the moment, and the
two basic types, which may be called X and Y, examined. Their most outstanding
characteristics are:

X is uniformly of good quality and at its best, at Sidney Wood (No. 38) is not
always easy to distinguish from modern glass. Y is very variable in quality and at
a given site, some glass may be fairly good, whereas some in exactly the same
context, is completely decayed into a dark brown crumbling fudge-like condition, unrecognizable as glass.

Good quality in type X, means broadly, the normal glassy characteristics of
durability and transparency as opposed to type Y which is more perishable and
only translucent. The types are described after making some allowance for their
context and any weathering.

X is hard with a sharp fracture, tough, often with burnished surfaces, usually
having little if any, superficial corrosion and no decay under any conditions in
the Weald, though the glass from Nos. 37 and 42 showed some flaking, considerable weathering and some surface pitting. The decayed glass at No. 42 may be
imported cullet or simply due to bad workmanship. It is often almost transparent
and has a small colour range—usually dark green with blue or olive shades.

Type Y is easily scratched and has no sharp fracture, is fairly easily broken and
often has a rough surface due to corrosion and unrelated to soil conditions. The
two types can often be separated simply by the feel of their surface. Type Y is

---

[1] Lumps of unblown glass can be very misleading in appearance for type dating purposes. In
general they are almost useless and the only reliable evidence must be taken from fragments of blown
or finished glass.

[2] Winbolt says he found blue-green glass at site No. 7 which I have called type Y provisional.
This site is the only one which I think might have been re-used. (*See* p. 107.)

usually, and possibly always was, translucent only. It has a characteristic, not large, range of colour, the bulk of which is pale milky green.

Not surprisingly the best glass is the latest and at some date, probably in the mid-sixteenth century, the bane of the early forest glassmakers, namely the great variation between the batches, was overcome. The dating can be demonstrated because at two-thirds of the Weald sites where type X is found, either pottery or records survive to place it as after the mid-sixteenth century.[3]

Type X glass was found on Carré's Fernfold site, probably worked by the Frenchmen he brought over in 1567–8, at a time when English window glass making appears to have been at a very low ebb. The Frenchmen were understandably very secretive about their methods and it is not unreasonable to credit them with the introduction of a good and rigidly practised technique which resulted in this uniformly good X type glass. They and their descendants remained leaders of the Wealden glass industry until its end in 1618.

The Wealden industry is known from documentary sources to have ended in 1618 so that type X can be placed between the mid sixteenth-century and 1618. Outside the Weald this X type glass occurs on datable sites in E. Sussex in 1581, in Hampshire in 1576 and in Staffordshire in c.1584–1604. It is found on two other sites at Woodchester (Glos.) and St Weonards (Herefordshire) which probably belong to the latter part of the sixteenth century. As far as I know, no pottery was found at any of these sites, except at Bagot's Park in 1966.

The dating of type Y is less satisfactory because of the shortage of dated sites on which it is found.[4] Only one type Y site, No. 33, can be dated by pottery,[5] and one, No. 15, just possibly by record; both are fourteenth century. Type Y can be matched in datable, painted, church window glass and this is invariably medieval. Church window glass is not a wholly satisfactory dating medium because its origin is unknown. Though type Y glass is found as cullet on type X sites, which can be dated as mid-sixteenth century–1618, type X glass is not found on type Y sites and so quite apart from type Y being poorer and more variable in quality, it is reasonable to assume that type Y preceded the good, uniform type X. All this suggests that type Y may be dated as from early in the fourteenth to the middle of the sixteenth century. It is, as yet, impossible to date type Y glass closer than pre mid-sixteenth century, though earlier workers attempted to do so. We have seen in Chapter II that analysis

---

[3] Pottery at Nos. 14, 23, 26, 32, 35, 38 and 42. Records of No. 25 in 1567–8. Nos. 36 and 37 probably c.1612. No. 40 possibly c.1604; see Chapter IX.

[4] See Introduction, p. 8, note 29.

[5] The oldest glasshouse site in the Weald so far known is No. 33, dated by pottery and supported by magnetic dating as within the second quarter of the fourteenth century, probably around 1330 (see Chapter IV). The glass is unmistakably type Y. Site No. 7 had a fragment of pot which is probably fourteenth century but this site might have been re-used and the evidence, Cooper's, Winbolt's, and my own does not agree, so I have not used it; see Chapter IX and p. 107.

is unlikely to help, though the total alkali content of the few samples of type Y is markedly higher than that of type X.

To sum up, I have for convenience, and I trust accuracy, called type X 'Late' and type Y 'Early.' The great change,[6] almost certainly permanently established by Carré's Frenchmen, was probably due not to any change in chemical composition, such as the introduction of barilla, but rather to a new discipline or technique.[7] These two points on chemical composition and manufacturing technique are included in a valuable appendix in Mr Bridgewater's paper on the St Weonard's glasshouse.[8] One point relevant to this dating hypothesis remains in Mr Bridgewater's statement; he says: 'Colour differences are influenced by the quantity of iron or other salts in the raw materials, and cannot be used as a criterion of glass type, except in the sense that a glassmaker would insist on obtaining a particular kind of sand.'

Colour alone would certainly be an unreliable criterion of glass type but in the Weald the two basic types, Early and Late, for whatever reason, and it may be fortuitous, do have an obvious, constant and definable difference of colour and should be included along with Mr Bridgewater's warning, to complete the picture. If it is easy to state the observed characteristics of the two types of glass, it is difficult to explain those characteristics. There is much variation in individual batches from Early glasshouse sites but apparently no evidence of any basic and lasting change from the beginning of the industry in the fourteenth century or earlier until after the middle of the sixteenth century.[9] Type dating seems to be the simple answer to the fundamental query: Is the glasshouse pre- or post- mid-sixteenth century? It is important because, apart from Blunden's Wood and the Late sites on which pottery fragments were found (*see* p. 101) or for which there is documentary evidence, it may be the only means of broadly dating the glass and the site.

Glass from only two sites, both Late, does not conform to the characteristics outlined. One, mentioned, on p. 208 is Knightons (No. 42) where the range of glass appearance and quality is considerable and unlike any other Late site. Some glass is unmistakably Late and the pottery evidence confirms this, but there is, for a Late site, a curious lack of uniformity in the glass fragments, some being poor quality and semi-opaque and, with the vessel fragments more characteristic of crude Early glass. Some has decayed, a feature hitherto unknown on Late sites. The site is being

---

[6] *See* Chapter II.

[7] 'A whole range of technological aspects might be involved in moving from one type of glass to the other,' is the suggestion made by Dr Thorpe of the British Glass Industry Research Association in 1963; *see* Chapter II, p. 41. I am indebted to Mr R. J. Charleston for this investigation.

[8] N. P. Bridgewater, 'Glasshouse Farm, St Weonards: A Small Glassworking site,' in *Transactions of the Woolhope Naturalists' Field Club*, vol. 37 (1963), pp. 300-313.

[9] There may have been other attempts in the mid-sixteenth century to revive English glassmaking, and some Late type glass of moderate quality may ante-date Carré by a few years, but there is no evidence, as yet, that any attempts were sustained until Jean Carré's importation of French glassmakers in 1567-8.

fully excavated by Mr E. S. Wood and this interesting problem will no doubt be solved in due course.

The other site which does not conform is Somersbury (No. 37), and here the glass though uniform, has flaked badly. The site was dug over in the nineteenth century and is in a damp place, but so are other sites; neither fact explains the pronounced weathering. It seems that on this site the glassmaker omitted some vital detail from the batch or the process.

In four cases, Nos. 20, 28, 39 and 41, there was not enough finished glass evidence to suggest a type of glass; in another six cases there was only just enough to make an attempt and I have added 'provisional' to the types given. They are Nos. 6, 7, 8, 9, 11 and 35, three probably being Early and three Late, but further evidence may alter the type. Five of the six are in Chiddingfold. All the sites and their details are described in Chapter IX.

There remains some glass with characteristics of both Early and Late types for which I have provisionally suggested the name Transitional. Two of the three sites (Nos. 13, 16 and 17) where this type of glass is found can be dated from documentary sources as working c.1557, which fits the suggestion. Both sites were worked by a local yeoman family, the Strudwicks, who remained in glassmaking until at least 1597, and it is possible that although they continued to work the glasshouses which they owned until after the coming of Carré's Frenchmen only part of the new technique was shared. It is also possible that the finest quality Late glass belongs to the early years of the seventeenth century.

Owing to the curious fragmentation on all Wealden sites, Early and Late, too little is known at present to use vessel form as a means of dating, except in the few instances considered in Chapter V. There are no fragments of knopped stems, honeycomb moulding, or possible retorts, posset cups and linen smoothers of Early glass, or any fragments of urinal flasks or lamp bases of Late glass.[10] Such lamps are probably medieval and fragments of the bases are not uncommon on Early sites. There is nothing in the Weald (in 1965) to compare with the Woodchester fragments for tough quality and significance. This is unfortunate because the Late site in Sidney Wood probably produced the finest and most delicate vessel glass in the forest industry so far known in England, but it was crushed into insignificance by stone hunters and earlier excavators. There is no doubt that Early vessel form was much cruder than the delicate and diverse Late vessel but it is very difficult to provide examples to support this generalization.

The earliest satisfactory documentary evidence of glassmaking in the Weald is in 1351[11] (see Chapter I), but the earliest archaeological evidence is about twenty years earlier (see Chapter IV). The latest documentary evidence is in 1618 (see Chapter

---

[10] I purposely do not say on Early or Late sites because it is possible to find Early glass cullet in various vessel forms on Late sites.

[11] Glass may have been produced in the Weald in the thirteenth century (see Chapter I).

VIII, p. 135). The industry lasted at least three hundred years. The great change from Early to Late type glass dates from the middle of the sixteenth century, so the Early period lasted about 250 years and the Late about fifty years, with some possible Transitional glass in the middle of the sixteenth century (see also Introduction, p.17).

I know of no means of closely dating fragments of unpainted glass, from our sites by its appearance except, as has been suggested, into Early and Late, with possibly some Transitional. The photographs (Plates XII and XIV) of glass in Guildford Museum from the Chiddingfold sites and from Sidney Wood show some of this difference between the Early and the Late types of Weald glass.

Both Cooper and Winbolt naturally were much concerned with dating the local glass. They were well aware of the value of associated pottery and Cooper, in particular, of the importance of records. But where there is no such evidence (*see* p. 9) both men attempted to date the glass by its appearance. Cooper with the experience of only two or three sites and guided by the writing of Winston attempted to date window glass very closely to within ten or twenty years by its thickness. Winbolt, with wider experience mentioned at least three types, modified Cooper's idea and added to it the degree of corrosion, but did not attempt limits closer than a given century. I would go part of the way with his dating of our local product, because if I was shown a piece of window glass upwards of $\frac{1}{4}$ in. thick, pale cloudy-green and badly pitted, I would guess, and I emphasize guess, from some experience of ancient and datable painted church glass that it is unlikely to be later than the fourteenth century. The amount of corrosion can be misleading as the Early glass seems to have varied from batch to batch. Perhaps we were incorrect in placing the most corroded glass as the earliest; it may belong to after the Black Death period which is known to have produced very inferior glass (*see* p. 44, note 33).

At the other end of the scale, a piece of window glass $\frac{1}{16}$ in. thick or less, darker green, shiny, uncorroded and relatively clear could safely be dated as not earlier than the mid-sixteenth or early seventeenth century because glass of this type is found only on sites which can be dated by Rhenish stoneware or by records as belonging to that period. Those are the extremes, anything in between is much less certain and close dating by appearance only is, as yet, unreliable. Dating by chemical analysis has already been discussed (*see* p. 43); for a variety of reasons it holds little promise.[12] The very wide range of quality on most Early sites, quite apart from the cullet problem, might require a large number of analyses from a given site to produce any useful result. The uniform Late glass may prove relatively simple when a new technique for dating is available.[13]

As most sites have been thoroughly disturbed, ploughed up, robbed for stone or dug over by cullet hunters from later sites there is usually little, if any, stratification. Medieval pottery dating has made great advances in the last few years and, coupled

---

[12] *See* Chapter II. Both Early and Late were potash-lime glass.
[13] I would not rule out a 'crush' test, to reinforce appearance and quality.

with magnetic dating, may in future give an impressively close date for the rare untouched glasshouse site, as Mr E. S. Wood showed at Blunden's Wood.[14]

There is a wide variation in the amount of glass surviving on the sites, generally the Early sites have very much less,[15] possibly they had been carefully stripped of cullet, some of them providing only a few scraps. The Transitional and Late sites with few exceptions provided an adequate amount and on some, notably Nos. 14, 23, 37 and 38, a gallon or more of fragments survived. It cannot be explained why a lot of lumps of unblown glass were found at No. 32 but very few finished blown glass fragments. But all five sites may well have been among the latest furnaces to shut down and no one bothered to clear up the waste from the final batches as they had no successors. This theory is supported by the probable date of Somersbury (No. 37, see p. 201).

I am satisfied that thirteen[16] of our sites which I have described as Early were working before c.1550 but how many of those may be medieval in origin it is impossible to say. An industry which over at least two centuries has so far provided only thirteen sites is unlikely to have had more than one or two glasshouses working at a given date. Probably only about ten or twelve glasshouses are known to have been working in the Weald in medieval times. No other known medieval sites have so far been found in England, though the site at Delamere in Cheshire (see Chapter II) may be one of them. The number is so trifling compared to the 168 known medieval sites in France[17] that it is difficult to avoid the conclusion that before the middle of the sixteenth century our native glass industry was small and unimportant. Judging by the glass found on the Early Weald sites, the quality is generally poor and it is unlikely that much English medieval window glass now survives. The close dating of Northern European glasshouses for some centuries prior to the mid-sixteenth, by their products alone, unless it is painted window, does not look promising.

So far, Early vessel glass is a much less reliable guide than window; there is insufficient surviving to make any useful detailed comments. Thickness has little significance as some of the Early vessel is very thin.

Thirteen sites were Early and sixteen were Late[18] so that if the Wealden industry began c.1330 there were possibly five times the number of glasshouses working in the last fifty years, which points clearly to a boom in the trade.

It is this boom together with the revival of an almost dead industry, coupled with the great and sustained improvement in quality and vessel form after the mid-

[14] Sy. A.C., vol. 62.

[15] This statement is based on my own experience, and where we followed Cooper it may be incorrect. It is difficult to know what he meant when he says of No. 3 he found an 'immense quantity of window glass,' of No. 7 that 'innumerable fragments' were found. No. 5, seen after he died, was fairly productive. His collection does not provide much evidence for Nos. 3 and 7.

[16] Including three provisional. See p. 152.

[17] J. Barrelet, La Verrerie en France (Larousse, 1953), p. 153.

[18] Subject to the 'provisional' qualification, see p. 152.

sixteenth century which is the most important and interesting happening to the glass industry in the Weald and probably in the English forest industry.[19] There are records of quarrels, patents and parish registers providing some life and valuable evidence during the Late period. The industry had become significant.

It will be shown that Wisborough Green was the centre of the Late Wealden glass making. Carré started here at 'Fernefol' in 1567 and it cannot be a coincidence that no specified 'French' families appear in the P.R. until 1567 and these as suddenly disappear from the registers in 1617. They were Lorraine and Norman immigrants brought in to staff the glasshouses and when the industry died out they moved elsewhere. There is nothing unusual in finding 'stray' Frenchmen in sixteenth-century parish registers, even away from the ports, but our men have the names of well known glassmaking families and their dates fit exactly (*See* Chapter VIII, p. 137

The Re-use of Sites

The re-use of furnace sites, a controversial matter, must be discussed under dating. It could depend, to some extent, on whether the glassmakers owned the woodland or, more likely, bought the growing timber or underwood on it, as is customary today for other woodland trades. The only relevant early deed, 1385 (*see* p. 31), makes it clear that the glassmakers Pikeboussh and Shertere bought the growing 'underwood' only, from the agent of the Abbot of Séez, and that they built a 'Glashous' in that woodland. They were tenants.[20] The agreement was flexible and gave them about thirteen months to 'cut down, cleeve and expend' the timber. It appears to follow an earlier agreement of unknown length. But the building of a 'glashous' was evidently a temporary arrangement for as long as the 'underwood' lasted.

If 'underwood' or 'pollardings' were the usual fuel, presumably they might possibly return when it had grown again. But if beech billets from timber trees were the fuel, as the 1557 will of Henry Strudwick suggests (*see* p. 119), it could be 150 years before a glassmaker owner or tenant would return.

We do not know whether 'underwood' or trees were normally used, but the fact that the 1385 agreement mentions cleaving suggests that the 'underwood' was large, twenty or more years old. The glassmakers certainly could, and probably did, move round very easily, when readily accessible fuel was exhausted. The few tools and any small surplus of sand, ash or cullet could be carted to the next site. The building presented no difficulty, a rough shed with its small furnace could be built by two men

---

[19] Outside the Weald the forest industry expanded between *c.*1570 and 1618 from possibly one or two (unknown) glasshouses in Staffordshire to about twenty. In addition there were two in Gloucestershire, and one each in East Sussex, West Sussex outside the Weald, Kent, Hampshire and Herefordshire, making a provisional total known in England of forty-three glasshouses during the last fifty years, where only about fourteen are known in the previous two or three centuries. Forest glass production may have increased more than ten times.

[20] *See also* p. 109, note 4 and p. 214, note 15, for an agreement between Richard Bagot and Ambrose Hensey in 1585.

in a few days. To follow their fuel like charcoal burners was a much less costly procedure than carting it far.

It is pure guesswork to say how long glassmakers stayed in one place; we do not know if the Early glassmakers worked continuously, but judging by the large quantity of fuel consumed at the Knole glasshouse in 1585–6, it is unlikely they could remain in one place for long, possibly no more than five years.

Whether they returned to old sites is also not known. If the gap was twenty-five years the primitive glasshouse and kiln shown in the Mandeville drawing would have fallen down and the furnace would be useless. They might return to the same area, but it would be simpler to start afresh than to make use of a ruin. It is highly improbable anything remained, it would soon be 'quarried.' If the cycle was 150 years there would probably be nothing left to use and in any case it would be a different glassmaker with his own ideas. I have seen little evidence to support the idea that these sites were re-used. In this stoneless country the glassmakers may have stripped the site and moved any waste stone from the abandoned kiln to fresh woodland. This could explain the disappointing lack of significant remains.

While not rejecting the idea that some sites were re-used, I am less enthusiastic about it than Winbolt who thought there were two or more periods at such sites as Nos. 2, 5, 7 and 35. I do not consider the evidence is convincing for the first two and the last, and am doubtful about No. 7 – the most likely – because as it had been so disturbed by the Cooper family's digging, the stratification is suspect. The characteristics of a glasshouse site have been discussed and while all four are good sites, almost any other spot would do as well.

In his prelude to the description of glasshouse sites Winbolt, *W.G.*, p. 29, says 'some seem to have had long lives, their furnaces being rebuilt many times, when woodlands had recovered and there was a renewed local demand for glass.' Describing Fromes site (No. 5) he says 'During the century and a half of its intermittent use there must have been many furnaces erected on this site.' Apart from its being Early, there is no evidence when and for how long No. 5 was working.

VII

ADMINISTRATION

UNTIL the arrival of Carré in 1567 very little is known about the administrative side of this small forest industry. Two deeds, 1380 and 1385, and a few entries of window glass purchases between 1351 and 1378 are quoted in Chapter I. After the middle of the sixteenth century there was a marked increase in the quality and scale of the industry and some agreements, leases and patents have survived.

The two local families who combined farming with glassmaking, the Peytowes of Chiddingfold and the Strudwicks of Kirdford, were landowners on a scale sufficient to provide some, at least, of their fuel requirements. The Peytowes owned about 1500 acres and the Strudwicks of Idehurst alone owned 350 acres; other members of the family at least doubled this amount. The proportion of woodland on a good Kirdford farm in 1627 is known (see *S.A.C.*, vol. 93, p. 101); it was twenty-six per cent. Henry Strudwick in 1557 had bought beech trees at Crofts in addition to his own beeches, almost certainly fuel for his glasshouse (*see* p. 119). This 'landowner' type of arrangement may have applied at three or four of the Chiddingfold sites and three or four at Kirdford.

This chapter owes a great deal to Mrs E. S. Godfrey who says of Carré's arrangements:

'Carré's original glasshouses, operating under a royal monopoly, naturally had stronger backing than some of his immediate successors. The amount invested is never stated, nor do we know the legal nature of the "fellowship" or "company" which financed the venture. It must have been some form of partnership, for there is no indication that it was a true joint stock company with limited liability. It is clear, however, that the "company" was to bear all charges,[1] subject to one exception, as well for capital investment in buildings, for running expenses such as wages, and for further supplies and marketing costs. The exception is in the peculiar arrangement with the Hennezell brothers. By the terms of their contract with Carré's company,[1] these men, who were workmen and managers, seem to have supplied half the necessary capital. In return, after all expenses, including the Hennezell's own salaries as workmen, were paid, the profits were to be divided equally between the Hennezells on the one hand and Carré's company on the other. In the Norman factory the Bungars and the other workmen were not part

---

[1] Lansdowne MS. 59, No. 76, enclosure.

owners but were on a straight salary, though a very much higher one.[2] There is less information about Carré's other factories, but they seem to have followed the pattern of the Norman factory. Carré's company, composed of himself, Chevalier, Briet, Appel and possibly others, represented largely merchant capital. Although ownership of the Norman factory eventually passed to the Bungars and the crystal factory to Verzelini, the company continued to exist after Carré's death, for in 1576 Briet and Appel were still concerned with the manufacture of glass.[3]

All the men known to have invested in Carré's patent were aliens or denizens. As the Huguenots migrated throughout England, the financing of their small furnaces was generally shared jointly by the glassmakers themselves [providing the skill] and members of the local gentry, who sometimes supplied capital directly and almost always supplied credit for fuel to be repaid either in cash or in finished glass.[4] The glasshouse near Knole House in Kent supplies the clearest example of this sort of arrangement.[5] The chief workmen, Onely and Ferris, seem to have owned the furnace and equipment, though this is not clearly stated. They arranged for wood from Knole Park on credit, to be paid for in finished glass, and accounts were kept by a steward of the Knole estates, who went every day to the glasshouse to represent the interests of his master. Since a small glasshouse and furnace similar to this could have been erected for between £12 and £20[5] whereas 30 cords of wood costing £5 was consumed on an average every 10 days[6] the importance of the credit for fuel as opposed to the necessity of help in the original investment in furnace and buildings can be clearly seen. A month's fuel was likely to cost as much as the entire furnace.

That such agreements were common throughout the period [1560-1640] is indicated by the career of Abraham Bigo.

Having secured from Mansell the right to make green glass on payment of £100 a year, he persuaded Sir William Clavell of Purbeck to supply him – "with a howse Roome a ffurnace & coales for making greene glasse," all to be paid for in finished glass.'[7]

[2] *Ibid*. No. 76, 1st document. [Unhappily we do not know for certain which glasshouses the Hennezells worked, but Fernfold is almost certain, with Nos. 30 and 32 as possibilities. We have only a vague hint of the Bungar sites; one might be No. 41. G.H.K.]

[3] Lansdown MS. 22, No. 6. [Appel was probably Peter Appel, Carré's son-in-law. *See* Chapter VIII, p. 123. G.H.K.]

[4] This type of agreement was used for a glasshouse in Bagot's Park, Staffs., in 1585. It is printed in *Glass Notes*, No. 15, 1955 (*see* p. 139, note 110), and is discussed in the forthcoming volume of the V.C.H., *Staffordshire*. I am much obliged to Mr J. G. Jenkins for this information and for kindly sending me his draft copy of this section. See also *S.A.C.*, vol. 99, p. 106. [G.H.K.]

[5] T. Barrett Lennard, 'Glassmaking at Knole, Kent', in *The Antiquary*, vol. 41 (1905), pp. 127–129.

[6] Westropp, p. 25. The manuscript gives the costs of the Ballynegery glasshouse with a wood-burning furnace apparently similar to the Knole House one.

[7] Lennard, p. 127. [*See also* my note, p. 221, on the Bigo/Clavell glasshouse in 1618. G.H.K.]

Mrs E. S. Godfrey comments that

'The arrangements among the glassmakers themselves as to financial responsibility and divisions of labour and profits, must have been of the most informal kind. Where ties of blood prevailed, as they did among the Henzeys, Tysacks and Titterys, patriarchal status no doubt determined the mastership of the glasshouse. In enterprises such as the one at Knole where the men were not related or even of the same nationality, we hear of quarrels and also of times when "they agree very well, God be praysed." '

During the Late period, Carré and his Frenchmen and the two local families did not control all the glasshouses in the Weald as Miss G. M. A. Beck has shown in an interesting short paper on 'Ogniabene Luteri: A Surrey Glassmaker.'[8] Luteri worked a furnace at Burgate, which may be the Vann site (No. 35), in 1586 (*see* Chapter IX, p. 199). Luteri appears to have been operating on his own, with a backer who probably put up the money for him to buy some growing timber and set up his glasshouse in it. He represents a third type of organization, the single skilled glassmaker. A variation of this is found in the agreement that Edward Hensey had for his glasshouse at Bagot's Park (*see* p. 214, note 15). Yet another variation is found at Knole (*see* p. 219).

Wages

Mrs E. S. Godfrey examined the question of wages closely and she says (pp. 351–3): 'For the larger concerns, especially those operating under monopoly grants, labour was always a serious concern, and for them we have some information as to actual wages paid as well as to their difficulties in keeping a staff. Carré, the first recipient of a patent, negotiated separate contracts on different terms with the Lorrainers and with the Normans.

The Hennezell brothers from Lorraine who were part owners of their plant said they were to receive "two hundred crownes every yere that is to say from six months to six months for recompense for our thirde of the glass" in addition to half the profits of the enterprise when all expenses had been paid.[9] The wording seems slightly ambiguous but if this statement means that 200 crowns (or £50) was to be paid to both men, not to each, annually, then on a basis of a 50 week year each man received only 10/- weekly as wage. This was remarkably little and can only be accounted for on the basis that they were also to receive half the profits of the enterprise, which were expected to be large.

The Normans employed by the same firm were not owners, but their wages were astonishingly high. Becku, Carré's co-patentee, complained to Cecil thus: "Their wages be greate, for the principall workemen hathe XVIII s daylie and

---

[8] *Sy.A.C.*, vol. 52, p. 90.
[9] Lansdowne MS. 59, No. 76, enclosure: contract between Carré and the Hennezells.

for that he is bounde to make iii cases of glass which is of his parte not accomplished, and yet paid for."[10]

The other workmen, he added, also received very high daily wages, though the amounts are not specified. That the glassmaker was far above the ranks of the ordinary workmen can be seen easily from a comparison with the average wages of other skilled craftsmen. In 1583 a carpenter, a mason and a plumber each received an average wage of 1s. a day.[11] The difference is comprehensible when we remember that the "principall workeman" who received 18s. a day from Carré was undoubtedly Pierre de Bongar,[12] a man whose family was of noble rank and had owned glasshouses for generations. The high wage is also understandable when one realizes that Bongar was to produce each day 3 cases of Norman glass which could sell for about 30s. per case. Since the cost of fuel scarcely ever exceeded the cost of labour and since the cost of the other ingredients was very low, the industry could well afford to pay handsomely for the scarcest necessary item – the skill involved in fashioning the product.'

Transport

The earliest known reference to a glass carrier in the Weald comes in 1495, when Henry Ropley a member of a Chiddingfold family is so described.[13] Production was evidently sufficient to keep at least one man so employed. During the Late period there are six references to glass carriers, some of whom were local men and others who were travelling pedlars. In 1575 George Strudwick of Kirdford, glass carrier, appears as a witness in the Deposition books of the Consistory Court of Chichester.[14] The other five occur between 1609 and 1618. It is very unlikely that this is chance, because out of the twenty-six references to French families in the Wisborough Green P.R. between 1567 and 1617, no less than sixteen occur in the last twenty years. The Wealden glass trade was booming, right up to its closing down.

Three of the glass carriers appear in the Chiddingfold parish registers. Cesar Parisee buried in 1610,[15] William Evans of 'Minmouthshire', buried 1611-2, and the daughter of John Phillips of 'Rumsee' in Hampshire buried 1615-6. In the Elstead (Surrey) P.R. in 1609 the son of Peter Barton 'a travayling glass carrier' appears,[16] as baptized and two weeks later buried. His wife evidently travelled with him.

---

[10] *Ibid.*, Becku to Cecil, 1569.   [11] J. E. T. Rogers.

[12] This is probably the Pero Bungar, a Frenchman, of Wisborough Green, who on 17 October 1579 was licenced to minister and serve in French. *W.G.*, p. 17, ex C.C.C. diary, vol. C, fol. 22 *v*, now in the Diocesan Record Office, Chichester (ref. W. D. Peckham). [G.H.K.]

[13] *See* Chapter I, p. 29. This is the only known evidence for glassmaking in the Weald in the fifteenth century.

[14] I am indebted to Dr L. F. Salzman for this reference. B. M. Add. MSS. 39, 437.

[15] Cooper mentions a possible Frenchman in the P.R. in 1595 as John Lue, who is referred to again in 1602 as John Parasie *alias* Lue. He mentions William Duke *alias* Cressell, carrier, buried 1613.

[16] I am indebted to Miss G. M. A. Beck for this reference.

The fifth glass carrier at the end of the Late period is the most interesting because his inventory has survived.[17] He was Henry Strudwick *alias* Deane, buried in 1614. The gross value of his inventory was £33. He had some small comfort, sheets, tablecloths, pewter, etc. and a short sword valued at 5s. His six small nags or mares with cart and harness were valued at £13 8s. 4d. The 'nags' may have been pack-animals possibly carrying 200 to 300 lbs., but their mention with a cart and harness makes it possible though unlikely, with no proper roads, that both methods of car-riage were used. His net debts amounted to £22 of which £6 10s. was due to 'William Strudwick his master.' A William Strudwick of Idehurst was buried in 1615 (Kird-ford P.R.) but there is no evidence the family was still making glass there.

Like many of the small tradesmen Henry was also a small holder; he had 2 kine with a sucking calf and 2 'twelvemontheinges' valued at £7, 5 small hogs valued at £1, 1 plough, 1 harrow, 1 bill, 1 axe, 1 spitter, 1 shovel and all other implements of husbandry valued at 13s. 4d., oats in the barn and soil (dung) about the house, valued at 10s., 2 bushels of rye valued at 5s., 5 hens and a cock and all other lumber about the house valued at 6s. 8d. No doubt he carried glass when his holding did not demand his presence.

Glass carriers cannot have had an easy time in the early seventeenth century.

> 'By the Statute of 39 Eliz. cap 4. Pedlars and Chapman are adjudged Rogues and Vagabonds, but glass men of good behaviour may travel in the country only having a licence from three justices of the peace. But in the statute of 1 James 1. cap 7. the said licence for glass pedlars is repealed, because under cover of this liberty, rogues, vagabonds, etc. followed their trade in this way, and it is enacted that all such persons as shall wander up and down to sell glasses shall be treated as rogues and vagabonds and dealt with accordingly.'[18]

Our glass carriers probably did peddle their wares around this district as well as acting as pure carriers. Such a pedlar is illustrated in Plate XI.[19]

Inland water transport for Wealden glass going north to the Thames by the river Wey, or south to the coast, by the Arun, may appear promising, but the river Wey was not made navigable from Guildford to the Thames until 1653[20] some time after the forest industry had shut down, and the Arun was only 'cleared about the beginning of Elizabeth's reign by Henry Fitzalan for the conveyance of timber by barge from Pallingham [at the southern end of Wisborough Green parish] to

---

[17] *See* also *S.A.C.*, vol. 93, p. 135.

[18] A. L. Howard, *The Worshipful Company of Glass Sellers of London* (1943), p. 24. I am much indebted to Miss A. Reeve for this information.

[19] This Plate XI is of a coloured print of the first half of the sixteenth century in Anciens cris de Paris, Print No. 264, fol. 30, Bibl. de l'Arsenal, and is reproduced by kind permission of the Conservator-in-chief. It was printed in J. Barrelet, *La Verrerie en France* (Larousse, 1953), pl. XXXII.

[20] P. A. L. Vine, *London's Lost Route to the Sea* (London, 1965), p. 22, quoting from *The High Stream of Arundel*, ed. by J. Fowler (1929), pp. 20–21.

Arundel,[21] Mr Vine commenting on this says: 'Navigation, however, above the tidal limit at Houghton must have been extremely slow and hazardous.' Possibly the 'clearing' was useful for the great weight and relatively low value of timber but less suitable for the more costly glass which was probably normally carried by packhorse.

In the Port Books there are some references to the transport by sea of English glass. The glass, probably largely window, was almost certainly produced in the Weald and at the Beckley and Northiam glasshouses. English glass was shipped from Arundel with Littlehampton: in October 1574, fifty-five cases went to a London merchant, William Sherington, and later in the same month thirty-eight cases and one chest of English glass were shipped to him.[22] The two consignments probably amounted to nearly five tons.[23] In February 1589, seven loads were shipped to London[24] and in November 1592, two loads went to Poole; in December 1592, three cases to Dartmouth; in July 1593, one load to Weymouth and in August 1593, thirty-two cases were shipped to Southampton.[25] There do not appear to be any further shipments of English glass after this date. Glass was still being imported and in 1604–5 there is an entry into Arundel, among a mixed cargo, of 'two groce drinking glasses,'[26] from Roane, France.

In April 1574 twenty-four cases of English glass were shipped to London from Rye[27] and in February and March 1580 there are two entries of unspecified amounts of English glass also shipped to London from Rye.[28] There are sixteen entries of shipments of glass from Rye between April 1574 and December 1581, but only the three above are specified as English. Between the years 1575 and 1585 there are six entries of glass being imported from 'overseas,' one from Rotterdam, one from France and one 'Norman glass from overseas,' so that unless the glass is named as English any exports may be only re-exports. The English glass from Rye in 1581 almost certainly came from the Northiam glasshouse, only six miles away, and in 1574, from an earlier glasshouse in the neighbouring parish of Beckley (see Chapter X, p. 210).

Marketing

We have seen in Chapter I that, in the fourteenth century, Alemayne, who may have been a glassmaker and Holmere, who appears to have been a dealer, were paid

[21] Vine, *op. cit.*, p. 11.

[22] Port Books of Arundel and Littlehampton, P.R.O. E.190, 740/22.

[23] Dr L. F. Salzman (*B.E.S.*, p. 184) says 'from these various entries it would appear that the case, chest or cradle of glass was equivalent to the seam of 120 lb . . .'

[24] Port Books, E.190, 745/20.

[25] All four entries in Port Books, E.190, 748/3.

[26] *op. cit.*, 754/5.

[27] *S.R.S.*, vol. 64, *The Port Books of Rye. See* also p. 18, note 65.

[28] What may be the same ship, the *Christopher* of London, of 12 tons, was used; if so the round trip on this occasion took about a month (see *S.R.S.*, vol. 64, p. 55).

direct for Chiddingfold window glass, by the Clerk of the Works for glass used at
St Stephen's and St George's Chapels. Mrs E. S. Godfrey[29] says there is very little
information about the marketing of glass in the early years of her period [1560–1640].
She goes on to differentiate between the Glass Sellers Company of London who
dealt in imported vessel glass and probably also in home produced vessel, and the
Glaziers Company, a much older Company with origins in the Middle Ages, who
generally speaking, in the sixteenth and seventeenth centuries, were men who bought
window glass wholesale and with it fitted and leaded new window openings and
repaired old ones.

[29] *D.E.G.*, p. 334.

VIII

GLASSMAKING FAMILIES

General

THERE is very little documentary proof of the glassmakers in the Weald until the sixteenth century. The possible thirteenth-century references are dealt with in Chapter I; a much repeated, but inconclusive, story has grown up from very slender evidence. With the fourteenth century, however, we are on solid ground and written records are supported by the earliest archaeological evidence for the industry from the glasshouse in Blunden's Wood which has been dated as *c.*1330. Briefly, all that can safely be said is that glass was being made in the Weald in 1351, probably by John de Alemayne, who presumably came from what is now Germany, and certainly by the Schurterre family from *c.*1367 to *c.*1400. The origin of the Schurterres is not known, but they were by 1367 established small landowners in Chiddingfold and not travelling glassmakers. Nothing is known of fifteenth-century Wealden glassmakers, and it is not until the sixteenth century with the arrival of Carré's named French glassmakers that a lasting link with France can be established, though Normandy was probably the place of the origin of the industry (*see* p. 12). In the sixteenth and early seventeenth century members of at least two long established local yeoman families were making glass: the Peytowes of Chiddingfold for at least eighty years and the Strudwicks of Kirdford for at least forty years. The evidence points strongly to the leaders of the industry in its final fifty years being the glassmakers from Lorraine and Normandy, principally the Henseys and the Bungars. Fifteen other glassmaking families are mentioned.

The Schurterres

The Schurterres were the earliest indisputable glassmakers who had glasshouses in this district. John ate Schurte, who may have belonged to the same family, held land in Dunsfold in 1298 (C) and William le Shurtare was assessed at Witley, for the Fifteenth and Tenth of 1332.[1] Richard le Shurtere was a member of one of the Chiddingfold tithings at a view of frankpledge in 1343,[2] so the family appears to have been established in the neighbourhood for some time before the first mention of a 'glasier' among them – John Schurterre in 1367.[3] He died *c.*1379, and in 1380 his widow brought in John Glazewryth not from France but from Staffordshire, presumably another glassmaking district, to work and share her glass furnace in

[1] *See* Chapter I, p. 25, note 6, *Surrey Taxation Returns* (Surrey Record Society), Pt. 1, p. 9.
[2] Loseley MSS, 197.   [3] GMR., 105/1/110.

Sherewode, 'Kueredeforde' (*see* p. 31). John Schurterre's son was another John, 'glasier,' who in 1385 also had a glasshouse in Kirdford (*see* p. 32). This might be No. 12 on the schedule. This is the earliest specific mention of a 'glasshouse' in the Weald and, as far as I know, in England.[4] Three Schurterres were described as 'glasiers,' the two Johns just mentioned, who were certainly actual makers of glass, and Peter, nephew of John, junior, who is mentioned in a 1391 deed.[5] He may be the Peter Shortere who supplied glass to Westminster in 1400 (*see* p. 29) and he also may have worked in Kirdford. It is worth noting that there is no mention of glass-makers among the many trades named in the Chiddingfold assessment for the 1380 Poll Tax (C). Dr L. F. Salzman says, however, that these assessments may be incomplete. The Kirdford Poll Tax list for 1380 has not survived in readable condition.

So we have three generations of Schurterre glassmakers known to have been working over a period of at least 33 years. The family was in Chiddingfold for at least 267 years but no other connections with glassmaking are known. There was a John Schurterre who was a common brewer in 'Chudyngfold' in 1382.[6] The two John Schurterres, father and son, who were 'glasiers' were also 'parkers' of 'Shullyngleghe' and the son held land on the northern slope below Shillinglee Park called Shorterhurst, now known as Surreylands (C). There may have been a glass furnace in Brambly Field on this property (*see* p. 158) which remained in the family until *c.*1507 (C). The surviving evidence is unsatisfactory. There is no proof that any of the three local branches of the Schurterre family were connected with the glass industry after Peter's time, *c.*1400, though those at Almeyns and Combe may have been. Almeyns remained in the family until at least 1610, an association of nearly 250 years.

The evidence, mainly from Cooper's 'History of Chiddingfold' and the Sadler deeds, is that both the two indisputable glassmaking families in Chiddingfold, the Schurterres and the much more prosperous family of Peytowe, had been long established in the Weald before they are recorded as making glass and only a few members of those families were so engaged. The amount of information relating to Chiddingfold in the fourteenth century is considerable and if others besides John Alemayne (possibly) and the Schurterres were making glass we should probably know.

Their long association with Chiddingfold[7] has possibly given the wrong impression of the scale of their glassmaking activities, and of the length of time a given furnace was used. It is very probable that the life of a furnace was measured in years and not in decades.

[4] In the 1380 deed the word is *domus*.

[5] GMR., 105/1/121.

[6] Loseley MSS. 204. Brewing and glassmaking, neither always whole-time occupations, possibly were combined.

[7] The Schurterres were in Chiddingfold from early in the fourteenth to the early seventeenth century.

The Peytowes[8]

After Alemayne and the Schurterres in the fourteenth century there is a gap in our knowledge of glassmakers and glassmaking in the Weald until the sixteenth century. The Peytowes had been established in Chiddingfold c.1440 but there is no record of them as glassmakers until 1536. There were two main branches of the family, at Pickhurst and Combe, both of which had members making glass in the sixteenth century, when the family were substantial yeomen and owned about 1500 acres in the parish. One of the Sadler deeds gives evidence of marriage between the Peytowes and Schurterres. This is a 1475 grant of land called Toggeleys and Bokers to Nicholas Paytowe of Chiddingfold, with remainder to Richard Shorter and his wife Elizabeth, daughter of John Paytowe.[9]

In his will (proved 4 April 1536) John Petowe 'at le Bridge'[10] bequeathed to his son John '10s. of suche things as shall come and be made of the glasshowse and all my toyles [tools] and moulds as belongeth to the glasshowse.' The use of moulds is interesting and suggests that some ornamental vessels were produced. Stray glass fragments (see Chapter V) confirm this but they are too small to make any convincing reconstruction possible. John Petowe the testator was the son of William, whose father Nicholas (mentioned above in 1475), and grandfather Thomas (c.1440), had all owned Pickhurst. There are two separate furnace sites on Pickhurst, one at Hazelbridge Hanger (No. 7) and one, 190 yards to the south on the edge of Glasshouse Field (No. 9). Both are less than a mile from the bridge and it is possible that John 'at the bridge' and his son John used these furnaces c.1536. It is improbable that there was a glass furnace in the centre of the village (though as Cooper says they may have had a depot there), not only because of the fire risk but because it would more suitably be sited in the woods from which it drew its fuel. There was a Henry Peytowe of le Combe in 1455, probably the ancestor of the branch which was settled there for at least another 150 years.

Thomas Peytowe, head of the Combe branch, in his will[11] left to his only son William, 'his tools, woodstuff and other things belonging to his glasshouse.' William, who was eleven at his father's death, died in 1576. There may have been three

---

[8] For all the information on the Peytowes, except Stephen of Witley, I am much indebted to the late Rev. T. S. Cooper's 'History of Chiddingfold.' He suggests that John Peytowe, jun., may have been the owner of one of the 'three or four glasshouses' mentioned by John Norden in his *Surveyor's Dialogue* as being in Sussex and Surrey in 1544. Three possibly, but more probably one or two.

[9] GMR., 105/2/9.

[10] His property adjoined the present road bridge in the village.

[11] V.C.H., *Surrey*, vol. 2, p. 297, gives the date as about April 1563 and the reference as Chan. Proc. ser. ii, bdle. 10, No. 101. This document contains the interesting detail that Thomas's wife Agnes mentions his inventory total was £57 9s. 8d.; the sum probably represents some modest domestic comfort. I know of no other reference to a glassmaker's inventory. There is a Thomas Peytoe, the younger, glassmaker, who occurs as a witness in 1547; he may be this man. I am indebted to Miss G. M. A. Beck for this reference (GMR. 105/10/1).

generations of Peytowes working at Combe, because William's son John appears to have carried on the trade and is described in the Parish Registers as a glassmaker in 1613; he died three years later. The furnace site at Combe is not known but Cooper suggests it was in or near Furnace Copse to the SW of Combe House Farm. The Peytowe family's known glassmaking activities extend from 1536 until shortly before the industry closed down in 1618. Other Peytowes described as glassmakers were William, buried 1614, and John, buried 1610. There was a Stephen Peyto of Witley, glassmaker in 1580.[12] Witley parish is only a few hundred yards from Combe so he may have worked at the undiscovered Combe furnace. There were still Peytowes in Chiddingfold after 1650.

One Schurterre and a number of Peytowes owned land on which glass furnaces have been found but they are not described as glassmakers. There are two furnace sites on what is now Gostrode Farm: in Broomfield Hanger (No. 2) and one 600 yards SW. (No. 6), on the edge of Glasshouse Field. The latter site was probably on the 70 acres west of Whites Hill, held by Thomas Schurterre in the fourteenth century and added to Gostrode after 1650 by Thomas Peytowe. The main Gostrode Farm was owned by William Peytowe of Pickhurst at his death, c.1546, and was probably bought by the family between 1503 and 1524 (C). Site No. 6 could have been worked by the Schurterres in the fourteenth century and No. 2 by the Peytowes in the sixteenth.

Chaleshurst, where there were two furnace sites (Nos. 3 and 4) 40 yards apart, was purchased by John Peytowe of Combe soon after 1503; it remained in the family until at least 1614. In his will proved March 1517–8, John left it to his second son Harry. John's eldest son, Thomas, inherited Combe and may be the father of the glassmaker, Thomas, who in 1562 left his son William his glasshouse, tools, etc. Harry died in 1544 leaving three sons John, Steven and Davy (C). None of the Chaleshurst family are described as glassmakers; it is possible, though unlikely, that Stephen Peytowe, glassmaker, of Witley 1580[13] was Harry's second son. The date and the glass suggest that the family may have worked at Chaleshurst (No. 4).

Prestwick was owned by Thomas Petowe, c.1619, but there is no record connecting any glassmaker with the furnace there. The Peytowes owned upwards of a quarter of Chiddingfold so one tends to associate them with the industry. Cooper suggests that this furnace was worked by the Le Frenche family in the fourteenth century, but he had no convincing evidence of this.

The Strudwicks

The Strudwicks, another family of yeoman landowners in the adjoining parish of Kirdford, appear to have settled there as early as the fifteenth century,[14] but are not known to have become considerable landowners until the early seventeenth century when they owned about 1500 acres in Kirdford. They first occur as glass-

---

[12] Shillinglee MSS. in West Sussex Record Office.　　　　　　[13] See note 12.
[14] V.C.H. refs. I am indebted to Dr L. F. Salzman for his permission to see these.

makers in 1557. During the next forty years, six of the family were glassmakers, and two others were glasscarriers, in 1575 and 1614.

The Strudwicks and the Peytowes were primarily yeoman; their date limits in the industry are roughly similar and fit the increased domestic building activity and the general rise in living standards in southern England in the latter half of the sixteenth century. Both families survived the great change in the middle of the sixteenth century and continued to make glass for at least another thirty years.

In 1557 Henry Strudwycke of Kirdford, yeoman,'[15] left to his eldest son Robert 'my mansyon howse of Idehurst'; to Robert and his brother William 'the profyt of my Glasse Howse with all the beches that I have bought, and halfe the beches in and uppon Idehurst and Croftes aforesaid,' until Robert is 22, then the brothers are directed to divide between them 'all and every suche implementes, as is ther occupied, as ovyns, irons and other thinges necessarye to ye said Glasse Howse be-longinge.' This suggests that Henry and later his two sons worked the glasshouse themselves and did not lease it out. The extract is given in full because glassmakers' wills are rare, and because in this case the site of the glasshouse (Nos. 16 and 17) is known. He mentions only one glasshouse, so the sons may have been responsible for the second one. The wording 'ovyns' suggests there was more than one oven in the glasshouse, possibly the fritting and annealing ovens were separate.

Three other Strudwicks appear as witnesses in the deposition books of the Chichester Consistory Court.[16]

1575. George Strudewick of Kirdford, glasse carryer 'where he has lived from his birth, born there aged 30 years or thereabouts.'
1575. Gilbert Strudewyck of Kirdford, glasse maker, where he has lived from his birth, born there, aged 40 or thereabouts.
c.1586. Robert Strudwyk of Kyrdford, glassmaker, born at Greene,[17] aged 27 years or thereabouts.

In 1595 and 1597 two children of William Strudwick, 'glassman' were baptized;[18] in 1614 we have Henry Strudwick *alias* Deane, glasscarryer.[19] None of these five can be identified with a farm, but the Robert of c.1586 may be the Robert of Idehurst buried in 1614 (P.R.). He could not be Henry's son mentioned in the will because of his age.

The Strudwicks were an enterprising and fertile family who, between 1550 and

[15] S.R.S., vol. 43, p. 72. The Idehurst Strudwick's glassmaking is discussed in *S.N.Q.*, vol. 7, p. 171; I have since corrected the charcoal fuel error.
[16] I am indebted to Dr L. F. Salzman for these references, from Dunkin's extracts (B.M. Add. MS. 39437) from the Chichester Diocesan records.
[17] *i.e.*, Wisborough Green.
[18] Kirdford P.R. He cannot be identified with Idehurst. 'Glassman' appears to be a normal variant of glassmaker.
[19] *See* also Chapter VII, p. 112, where his inventory, which has survived in the Chichester Diocesan Record Office is discussed.

1650, farmed and frequently owned, twenty-two Kirdford farms, about one-third the total number in this large parish. They also appear frequently in the Wisborough Green P.R. How long the family continued to make glass at Idehurst after Henry's death in 1557 is not known. The glass carrier Henry Strudwick *alias* Deane who died in 1614 owed his 'master' William Strudwick £6 10s. so the family may have carried on until that date.[20] We know that the Idehurst Strudwicks owned an iron forge on their land from *c.*1584 until *c.*1614.[21] The two industries overlapped here for at least forty years,[22] reaching their peak in Kirdford and Wisborough Green, as did the Strudwicks, at broadly the same time. The parish register shows that the family had declined rapidly by the middle of the seventeenth century.

The Mose Family

The Mose family are the only other local family of substantial yeomen known to have been glassmakers. There is a single reference to a Richard Mose of Kyrdeforde, glassmaker, who in 1547 bought small parcels of land in Kirdford and Plaistow. In 1558 when he made over to his son and heir, Henry, a house in Plaistow and pieces of land including Hardnepp he is described as yeoman.[23] He may have given up glassmaking. The name Hardnepp is interesting because the glasshouse site No. 12, now part of Crouchland, was once part of Hardnips. Unlike the French who suddenly appear in the records in 1567–8 and as suddenly disappear with the end of the industry fifty years later, the Schurterres, Peytowes, Strudwicks and Moses had their roots in the Weald long before and after they are recorded as glassmakers.

Jean Carré

There are numerous references to Carré in this paper but the evidence of his personal contact with the Weald relates only to his glasshouse at Fernfold. Some of Carré's applications for licences to make glass have survived, and in one, in the summer of 1567,[24] Carré states 'I have erected two glasshouses at Fernefol, Sussex, for Normandy and Lorraine glass, by H. M. licence, and one in London for crystal glass, also brought over workmen at my own great cost, and to the benefit of the Kingdom.' His burial at Alfold on 25 May 1572 is entered in the Wisborough Green P.R. (*see* p. 137) so presumably he died in that parish. Fernefol is in Wisborough Green old parish, and he may have had a house nearby. Glassmaking in the Weald seems to have been at a low ebb in the mid-sixteenth century and W. A. Thorpe[25] says

[20] Their possible connections with two other late sixteenth-century sites (Nos. 13 and 14) are mentioned in Chapter IX.

[21] *See* note on Wealden iron in *S.N.Q.*, vol. 13, p. 238.

[22] The first iron furnace in the parish was working by 1574, *ibid.*, p. 237.

[23] I am indebted to the late Rev. W. Budgen for sending me the extracts relating to Kirdford in his calendar of deeds now at Barbican House, Lewes. The two Mose deeds are B.541 and B.542.

[24] 'English Glassmaking in the sixteenth & seventeenth centuries,' by E. Wyndham Hulme, in *The Antiquary*, vol. 30, p. 210.

[25] W. A. Thorpe, *English Glass*, 2nd edn. (London, 1949), p. 86.

'several promoters from the Netherlands saw an opportunity of introducing their own men and making a corner in the English industry. The most successful and important of them was Jean Carré (John Carry) of Arras, and later of Antwerp, London and Alfold. He had the duel intention of making clear-glass vessels in London and window glass in the Weald. After prolonged negotiations with the Government, with his own partners, and with the established Wealden industry, he obtained in 1567 a licence to manufacture "glass for glazing such as is made in France, Burgundy and Lorraine." For this purpose he introduced a number of glassmakers from Lorraine; but this enterprise terminated with his death at Alfold in 1572.'

As will be shown, the enterprise in the Weald was carried on by the glassmakers he introduced.

There are a number of interesting details in one of Carré's letters to Lord Burghley in 1567.[26] He asks for a thirty-year monopoly to make glass (from internal evidence probably window glass) in England. He assures Burghley that no English glassmaker will be displaced, because on his enquiry at Chiddingfold 'of one of the masters of the furnaces' at that place he found that this man could make only 'such little works as primitive bottles and other small things.' He offers to pay Her Majesty one halfpenny for 'each glass of three squares' (*trois tables carrées*) which was the same as the custom duty on such imported glass. He offers to build up to twelve furnaces in England and six in Ireland. Carré claims that he will be using 'certain almost useless materials, these are certain plants such as bracken, briars and some marine plants, certain pebbles or small stones, sand and other small things of little worth which are of no value to the country.' While 'wood is the most precious thing which is used in this work' he goes on to say that he will need only branches and not 'actual trunks of good trees.' A translation is not clear but it looks as if he proposed to pollard timber trees and to cut copse 'stams' for fuel (*see* Chapter III). He forecasts a weekly production from each furnace 'by four men [of] about eight Liens of the said glass.' I cannot define a lien or a square (below), but the team of four, possibly three glassmakers and a stoker, is interesting. He says 'at certain times of the year as at the height of summer the furnaces will be out for eight or ten weeks during the great heat.' This gives us some idea of a working year.[27] He estimates that his offer of one halfpenny 'for each of three squares' of glass would bring to the Queen's dominions about £40 or £50 a year from each furnace. He told Burghley that he and his partner 'need a person of quality who will always be a protector or adviser' and offered him a commission of 2*d*. a lien for his life. Hartshorne says this was declined. Carré undertook to keep and submit proper accounts and he points out the rich revenue accruing to Lorraine from the glass industry. Jean Carré and Anthony

---

[26] S.P. 12/43, old No. 43 [new No. 104].

[27] This is also broadly confirmed by Guttery (p. 7) when discussing Paul Tysack, one of the pioneers at Stourbridge in the early seventeenth century, who worked forty weeks in the year.

Becku were in 1567 given the exclusive right to make window glass for a term of 21 years.[28] According to George Longe (*see* p. 143) neither of these men had any practical knowledge of the art, being only merchants, and they were compelled to lease out the benefit of their patent to the Frenchmen. Carré and Becku soon fell out; in July 1568 they quarrelled when two of Carré's employees, Perrot and John Boungard, attacked and injured James Arnold, Becku's son-in-law.[29] Hartshorne comments that it is difficult to get at the truth of the matter owing to the paucity of documents. A special Commission, Richard Onslow, esq and William More, esq, were instructed on 11 August 1569[30] to examine both parties because the quarrel might endanger the production of window glass in Her Majesty's realm. The dispute dragged on and six years later William More and Mr Apsley wrote to Lord Burghley, in reply to the latter's letter of 12 September 1575, that they had tried to deal with Perrot and John 'Bowngar' in their dispute with Anthony Becku, but that a settlement was postponed.[31]

There is no direct evidence that the French glassmakers worked the Fernefold furnace for Carré, but it is very probable (*see* p. 125). Some of them may have been involved in Carré's attempt to make crystal glass in London with men not experienced in its manufacture. He appears to have found that they could not manage this and by 1570[32] he had to import skilled Venetian glassmakers. Mr Thorpe says (p. 97) 'It is to him [Carré] and to the year 1571, that we must attribute the first permanent establishment for making crystal glass in England.' To which might be added that he was almost certainly the man who, by importing Lorraine and Norman glassmakers, brought about the great, progressive and lasting improvement in the Weald product. His Fernfold site is discussed in Chapter IX.

It is possible that the first Henseys and Bungars did not bring their families over until they were well established because, though the earliest 'Frenchman' appears in the Wisborough Green P.R. in 1567, from then until 1581 (apart from Carré's burial) there are only four entries of 'Frenchmen.' But by 1579 the 'French' community had grown enough to warrant Pero Bungar being licensed to hold services in Wisborough Green church. Carré was living in London in 1571 and Mr Thorpe shows that in June 1571[33] he had lived in the parish of St Bennet Fink for four and a half years. Carré's will is in the P.C.C. wills (Daper 39) under the name of Johis

[28] Hartshorne gives the reference, Patent Roll, Eliz. I, p. 11, memb. 4, 33. 8 Sept. 1567.

[29] *See* H.M.C. App. to seventh report, p. 621, for a summary of the affair. It seems that Hartshorne and his copiers read this as Peter and John Boungard, whereas it is, I suggest, a surname, Perott, a well-known French family of glassmakers, *see* p. 138, note 102. It is complicated because there was a Pero Bungar licensed to hold services at Wisborough Green in 1579.

[30] Loseley Correspondence, Vol. 12, No. 34.

[31] Loseley Correspondence, Vol. 12, No. 39. I am much obliged to Miss G. M. A. Beck for searching the Loseley MSS.; *see also* Chapter I, p. 25, note 6.

[32] W. A. Thorpe, *English Glass*, p. 96.

[33] Thorpe, p. 97, quoting from the Huguenot Society's publications, vol. 10 (ii), pp. 39, 41. Carré was 'now living in London' in April 1568 when he made his contract with Thomas and Balthazar de Hennezel &c. (Lansdowne MS. [59] No. 76, enclosure), ex Hartshorne, p. 398.

Carr; it is dated 11 May 1572, two weeks before he was buried at Alfold. It is long and there is not much about his glass interests. He says he was born in Arras. He bequeathed to his wife Jone [later Jane] Campe his goods and appointed her in his place to the 'privilege obtained from the Queen's majesty to make great glasses for glazing in England.' He also bequeathed to her half of the lease of the woods and of the ground of Fernfold in Sussex[34] and also all his movables and immovables for her life, after his debts have first been paid. He requests his son, John Baptist Carré, to assist his mother and desires them to fulfil the contracts 'I have made with the Italians'[35] requiring his brother-in-law, Peter Campe, and his [Carré's] wife to assist them. He commands his wife and son to assist Peter Appele and Hans ten Rade 'our' two sons-in-law[36] to 'set forth the little furnace of the small glass' as we agreed with Jacob Lalemon and the brethren and to account the finishing off the furnace 'from the time of putting in the fire therein.' He directs that his wife shall specially remember 'my daughter Mary [who married Appele] and her children and also my two young children Anne and Gillyan as yet unmarried.' He directs his family to act on the advice of 'my Friend Mr Peter Bougarte, my cousin Anthonie Goddarde,[37] and Mr Anthonye Cocqwell, and Mr Julian Hanty, minister of the word of God, and my brother [in-law] Peter Campe.' He leaves to the discretion of his wife and his said friends 'to admit one other governor or more for the government of the works of glass.' He wishes his son Baptist to be taught the art of making small glass[38] as Jacob Lalemon hath promised me. The will, signed in the presence of 'Mr Tous Saintes Christian minister of the word of God at Fernfold and of Peter Campe elders[39] of the said church,' was proved on the 19 November 1572.

Mrs E. S. Godfrey (*D.E.G.*, p. 39) writes:

'While Carré did not live long enough to see the full fruition of his plans, his is certainly the honor of establishing the manufacture of window glass in England on a permanent basis. He not only conceived the plan for establishing the glass works but had the knowledge and persistence to carry it through ... Nor were his results temporary, for many of the men he brought from the continent and their descendants continued to make glass in the Weald for generations,[40] while the London works had a long unbroken history.'

[34] The lease of woods and ground of Fernfold suggest that the glasshouse was still working.

[35] Almost certainly his London glassworks. There is no mention of his contracts with any Frenchmen.

[36] Carré seems to have had five children, two married and two unmarried daughters and a son.

[37] His friend Peter Bougarte may be Pero Bungar (*see* p. 128); his cousin Anthonie Goddarde may be some connection with John Goddarde, the last 'owlde' Frenchman to be buried at Wisborough Green in 1624.

[38] There is no reference to his London house nor any clue as to where the little furnace of the small glass was.

[39] Elders suggest that they were all Protestants.

[40] The crucial evidence is that their names are known and they can be identified and traced as leaders of the industry; *see* also Introduction, p. 16. [G.H.K.]

Mr E. B. Haynes says that Carré 'has the honour of having established modern glass-making in England.'[41] Within about twenty years of this renaissance, Late glass-making had expanded to at least five other counties, Kent, Hampshire, Gloucester-shire, Staffordshire and Herefordshire, and the forest glass production by 1600 may have been about ten times that of fifty years earlier.

The Norman and Lorraine Glassmakers

Gerspach[42] says that since the beginning of the fourteenth century there have been seventy glassworks in Normandy, the most ancient being that of de la Haye in the forêt de Lyons about fifteen miles east of Rouen, and that originally the industry was in the hands of four families, de Cacqueray, Le Vaillant, de Brossard and de Bungars. Representatives of three of these families made glass in England in the sixteenth century; the Cakerys and Bungars at Wisborough Green and Pierre Vaillant at Buckholt (in 1576). The earliest reference to the Cakerys in the Wisborough Green P.R. is 1600, and to the Bungars in 1594, though Pero Bungar was licensed to minister and serve (i.e., hold services in the church) at Wisborough Green in 1579. A John Boungard an employee of Carré was involved in a glass house quarrel in 1568 (see p. 122). Of the principal Lorraine families, the Hennezels, Tytterys, Tysacks and du Houx who made glass in England, the first three are found in the Weald and Mons. du Houx at Buckholt in 1579. The earliest reference in the Wisborough Green P.R. to the Hennezels and the Tytterys is 1599; the Tysacks first appear in 1588 in Kirdford P.R. Though the three Lorraine families had members over here in 1568, before the massacre of St. Bartholomew in 1572, the bulk of our references is after that date. One cannot be sure, but the massacre may have increased the numbers of French glassmakers coming to England; the demand for English glass may also be due to the troubled state of France.

It will be seen later that, in the case of Balthazar de Hennezel, religious persecu-tion played no part; he came and went from Lorraine as he wished, before and after 1572. The Lorraine families spread to other districts and some survived for another 250 years in the glass trade, but the Normans can be traced as glassmakers no further than London, and disappear in the seventeenth century (see p. 135). Thus in the St Saviour P.R. Anne Cawkerye, daughter of Hector, a glassmaker, was baptized in July 1615. Hector appears along with Benjamin Henzey as 'glassemen,' in a Clink Liberty token book of St Saviour Southwark in 1615.[43] Hector probably moved from Wisborough Green where two children of his were baptized in 1600 and in 1613. His appearance in Southwark may be connected with the Proclamation forbidding the use of wood fuel.

The later history of the Henseys, Tyzacks and Titterys at Stourbridge is discussed by Mr D. R. Guttery in his *From Broad Glass to Cut Crystal*, which contains much

[41] E. B. Haynes, *Glass Through The Ages* (Pelican Books, 1948), p. 110.
[42] *L'Art de la Verrerie*, 1885.
[43] Ref. London C.R.O. P 92/SAV/263. I am much indebted to Miss A. Reeve for these references.

interesting social and economic material, drawn where possible from original sources. Thus he makes it clear that the Lorrainers were soon absorbed into, and took an active part in, local affairs. They had come to stay. Mr Guttery devotes his opening chapter to Paul Tyzack, the first Stourbridge glassmaker, who 'occupies a most important place in the history of English glassmaking ... He may have been the first glassmaker ever to have brought the use of pit-coal as the glassmakers' fuel to complete success ... his success at Colemans [Stourbridge] put an end to the Lorrainer nomad tradition and fixed for ever the site of a world famous industry'. Mr Guttery says that Paul Tyzack moved in the early years of the seventeenth century from a glasshouse in Bishop's Wood, Eccleshall (see p. 217), to the Stour valley about twenty-five miles south and he appears in the P.R. of Kingswinford, four miles north of Stourbridge, in April 1612 when his son was baptized.[44] 'Once here he discovered that in addition to an abundance of pit-coal there was also mined a very useful clay for making pots, in fact, the best clay he had ever used and enough of both to satisfy any demand.' Paul Tyzack died in 1665. 'He had little estate to leave. Pioneering costs, doweries for his four daughters, ten years of retirement and an inate generosity had eaten deeply into his substance.' Mr Guttery gives two chapters to the Henzeys.

The Henseys alias Hennezels

It is proposed to discuss only two French families who made glass in the Weald – the Henseys from Lorraine and the Bungars from Normandy. The best known (except possibly in Stourbridge) and longest surviving family were the Henseys (de Hennezels) who started their trade in England under Jean Carré in 1568, probably at Fernfold and much less likely also in London, and were making glass until the mid-nineteenth century in England. We have Carré's statement in 1567 that he had set up two furnaces at Fernfold[45] for making Normandy and Lorraine glass (i.e., window). The following year he contracted with three cousins, Thomas and Balthazar Hennezel and Jean Chevalier, to transport themselves to England to build two ovens to make 'grande verre' (window) and to bring four 'gentilhommes verriers' i.e., two tercieurs (? fire tenders) and two gatherers and with their help to make, every day, in each of the ovens, thirty bundles of glass.[46] Carré was making crystal glass vessel in London and window glass in the Weald, and it seems very probable that some Henseys came to Fernfold in 1568 for the new window glass production, but we have no solid evidence. They were primarily forest window glassmakers, used to forest conditions. The first references to the Henseys in the Weald are in the Petworth

[44] By 1614–5 Paul Tyzack appears in the P.R. of Oldswinford, in which parish Stourbridge lies, when a daughter was baptized; and where in 1663 he made his will; ex Grazebrook, pp. 107 and 138.

[45] S.P. Dom., Eliz., XLIII, No. 42.

[46] Lansdowne MS. No. 76, 17 April 1568 (enclosure). M. Varlot, see p. 126, states that Thomas Henzey's glasshouse was at Grammont near Viomenil, six miles east of Darney, Balthazar's was at Lichecourt, two miles N.W. of Darney, Jean Chevalier was Castelain and receiver of Fontenay le Castle, ten miles S.E. of Darney. Varlot says they constructed their first oven at Fernfold, where Jehan Carré was living, but he does not give his reference.

P.R. in 1592 and in the Wisborough Green P.R. in 1599. Some of the early un-named 'French' entries in the P.R. may have been Henseys, possibly the early Henseys were migrants not settlers, and left their families in Lorraine, returning at intervals as we shall see that Balthazar did in 1570 and finally in 1576. Thomas and Balthazar Hennezel brought over other relatives, de Tysacs from Lichecourt and the de Thietrys makers of 'grande verre.' They also brought the de Bigots and du Houx families, makers of 'petit verre' (vessel). The du Houx also came from the Darney district and were relatives of the Hennezels.[47] The Bigots are found at Purbeck in 1618 and the du Houx at Buckholt in 1579. The Hennezels seem to have gone from Bohemia in the fifteenth century to the forêt de Darney in the Vosges about forty-five miles south of Nancy; here we have forest glassmakers moving to another region. There appear to have been thirty or forty known glasshouses between about 1420 and 1731 in the Darney region, an area very similar in extent (about 100 square miles) to the Weald district. Darney is in the foothills of the Vosges mountains, a spacious rolling country with very large blocks of some thousands of acres of fine beech forests, a magnificent sight in autumn. In 1953, two descendants of glassmaking families called to see me. A Strudwick from Australia, whose ancestors derived from Idehurst, and who still had the family bible of that branch, and Monsieur Georges Varlot of Gerardmer in the Vosges,[48] whose mother was a Hennezel and on whose property La Pille, near Darney, the Hennezels made glass. La Pille has been in the Hennezel family for nearly 400 years and M. Varlot uses the eighteenth-century house for holidays. The visitors provided a sense of intimacy with the Wealden glassmakers and their art and I, in turn, visited the lovely, remote woodland at the headwaters of the Saône in October 1955 when, unhappily, the family were not in residence. Madame Varlot wrote and told me that there are no traces of the fifteenth- and sixteenth-century glass furnaces but only pieces of crucible and furnace stones in the stream. I could see no exhibit of the forest glass industry in the Musée Lorraine at Nancy. M. Varlot has no glass material; that sent to Winbolt over thirty years ago is discussed on p. 205 (the Sidney Wood site, Chapter IX) and probably came from the Comte. M. Varlot agrees that it was not religious persecution which persuaded some of the Lorraine glassmakers to migrate, but over-production and oppressive taxation. He suggests that the earliest glass furnace in the Darney region was built by Jehan Hennezel about 1420 behind the church of Hennezel village. Of the thirty or forty glasshouses in the Darney region and of thirty-one named, eight were worked by Hennezels, seven by Thysacs, four by Thietrys and three by du Houx; they were the principal families of the region and all are found making glass in England. The first

[47] Correspondence with M. G. Varlot, see note below. A fourth related family, de Bisval were also in the secret of making 'grande verre.' I have not traced them in England. Grande verre is probably window glass, but see also p. 129, note 59.

[48] I am very much indebted to M. G. Varlot for sending me the result of the researches which he and his distant kinsman, the Comte de Hennezel d'Ormois made into the history of their family and of glassmaking in Lorraine. The Comte in 1955 was very old and frail and had abandoned all correspondence.

three were closely related, intermarriage being much encouraged to preserve their 'trade secrets.' M. Varlot lists seventeen furnaces as working between 1475 and 1524 and fourteen between 1553 and 1565 in the Darney region. He gives the total numbers known to have been working at given dates in Lorraine as twenty-three in 1594, which is probably about double the number working in the Weald at that time, nineteen in 1614, and long after ours had closed down in 1759 there were nineteen working in Lorraine. Possibly some were still burning wood. Glass, mainly wine glasses, was still being made in 1955 at La Rochère, 7 miles south of Darney. It is the only surviving name on M. Varlot's list, which shows that Simon de Thysac was making glass there in 1496. It is unlikely to have been continuous, if indeed it remained on the same site. Some of the Darney furnaces seem to have had long lives, and M. Varlot gives dates for the La Pille furnace as 1524–1730. I suggest various sites on the La Pille property were worked when demand warranted it and when the timber was ripe for fuel.

In the late sixteenth century some of the Henseys, Tysacks and Tytterys expanded from the Weald and some went direct from Lorraine to other glassmaking districts in England. The three families became managers under Mansell at Newcastle upon Tyne and later, at the Restoration, became owners.[49] The Henseys continued to make glass at Stourbridge until 1737[50] and with the Tysacks were associated with glassmaking in England until the middle of the nineteenth century.[51] The movements of the Lorraine, Norman, Venetian and Flemish glassmaking families are discussed by Mr W. A. Thorpe in *English Glass*, pp. 87–113. He says (p. 90) of the Lorraine families at Stourbridge that they 'founded the glass industry which has flourished there until the present time. Here as elsewhere they were mainly occupied with window glass, but they also made bottles and *Waldglas* vessels, and some of their descendants adopted lead crystal and eventually cutting. The Tyneside coalfield was the third area[52] to attract them.' Mr E. G. Clark's valuable paper on 'Glassmaking in Lorraine' contains points of interest about these families. He says,

'The change for the worse in the economic conditions, which was commencing adversely to affect glassmaking in Lorraine, was probably the determining factor which influenced certain craftsmen of an adventurous disposition to seek more remunerative service abroad untrammelled by officialdom and State interference. Another contributory cause may also have been the high rate of increase amongst the glass-making families, which left little scope for the younger sons entering their fathers' works.'

Commenting on the disappointing lack of records he says it is 'scarcely surprising when account is taken of the primitive nature of the glassworks of the period and of the inaccessibility of the district in which they became established.' He notes that they

---

[49] *D.E.G.*, p. 337.   [50] Guttery, p. 61.

[51] E. G. Clark, 'Glassmaking in Lorraine,' in *Soc. of Glass Tech. Journal*, vol. 15, No. 58, June 1931.

[52] Gloucestershire and Stourbridge were the other two.

ranked as gentlemen glassmakers in Lorraine and that they managed to preserve this status in England. This is seen in the Wisborough Green P.R. Of the Henseys he says,

'in the first years of the seventeenth century, Ananias de Hennezel, a younger son of and an ardent Huguenot made his way to England, and was the first to establish broadglass-making at Stourbridge. His son Joshua continued and extended this business, whilst his nephew Edward is believed to have founded the glassworks at Howden Pans near Wallsend-on-Tyne.'

The Lorraine and Norman glassmakers were probably Huguenots; that Balthazar de Hennezel returned to Darney in 1570 and again finally in 1576 does not suggest any persecution. The licence to Pero Bungar in 1579 to minister and serve in French at Wisborough Green suggests that a French Protestant community existed there. Six Henseys, Henry, Toby, Edward, Joseph, David and Peregrine, were making glass in Sussex and were important enough to be named separately in an order of the Privy Council in 1614; Edward continued as a leader in the Wealden glass industry until 1618.[53] He is probably the 'Edward Henzey, parish of Green, Co. Sussex, glassmaker' who married Sara Tetrye of Eccleshall in October 1602.[54] Toby is probably the Tobias who on 6 August 1610 married Susan Bongar; both were of North Chapel.[55] Joseph is probably the man whose children were baptized at Billingshurst in 1616 and 1618 and Peregrine the one whose daughter was baptized at Wisborough Green in 1616. I have not traced Henry and David.

In addition to the six Henseys named above, three others, Thomas and Balthazar, the original cousins of 1568,[56] and Albert in 1606,[57] made glass in the Weald in the Late period. There is Jacob Hensey, described as a 'gent' in the Wisborough Green P.R. in 1599; he was almost certainly the glassmaker who in 1615 was working for Mansell at Wollaston (Stourbridge) and in 1619 at Newcastle (see p. 138). Of Ananias Hensey whose wife was buried at Petworth in 1592 we know nothing but he was

---

[53] D.E.G., p. 56, note 1. Two Sussex Tisicks were also summoned by the Council in 1614 and 'although not named in the warrant Isaac Bungar turned up as one of their chief spokesmen, he and Edward Hensey appeared for the hearing (the dispute about the supplies, which continued several years, indicates clearly that wood was the fuel used), they maintained that if the new patent was to be strictly enforced, they ought in all justice to be allowed to use up their materials before shutting down their furnaces, or else the new patentee should be forced to buy their supplies. (A.P.C. XXXIII (1613–14) 690.)' D.E.G., p. 127: Nine glassmakers from Sussex in 1614 suggests there were at least nine furnaces still working; there seems no good reason for summoning more than one representative from each. The Inquiry was concerned with the enforcement of Mansell's patent to make glass. [G.H.K.]

[54] Pape, p. 19. A son of Edward Hensey, gent, was baptized at Wisborough Green in December 1603.

[55] S.R.S., vol. 9, p. 43.

[56] See p. 108 for their agreement with Carré to come and make glass.

[57] See p. 130, Star Chamber Proc., James I, 179/7. There was an Albertyne Hensey, gent, overseer of the estate of Danyel Titterye of Wisborough Green in 1599–1600; see p. 144.

probably in the trade. No other French family in the Weald can compare with them in the number of surviving references. Six Henseys at one time in 1614 making glass in Sussex provide further evidence that the busiest period was at the end and that the full flowering of Carré's pioneering in the Weald came forty years after his death. The industry did not fade away, it went out in 1618 with a bang from the formidable Isaac Bungar and a number of Henseys. Mansell's enforcement of his monopoly and coal-firing had triumphed.

In some lengthy notes which M. Varlot kindly lent me there was a description of Balthazar de Hennezel's movements and his death. He returned to Lorraine to settle his affairs in 1570 and again in 1576 when he appears to have stayed for good at his house, Grandmont, about five miles east of Darney. A translation of M. Varlot's description of Balthazar's death provides a vivid little scene: On St Remy's day (1 October 1579), the annual festival of the village of Senonge,[58] several gentlemen of the neighbourhood were celebrating happily at the house of the parish priest. Among them were Christophe de Thysac and Balthazar de Hennezel, called Grandmont, of the glassworks near Darney. After copious libations, without doubt, a quarrel broke out between the two cousins. Grandmont provoked Thysac with some cutting remarks: he stated that his wife resembled a St Nicolas and that each was going to see her. The priest put the two gentlemen outside. The dispute continued in the street. Grandmont advances towards Christophe, he begins to flourish his hat and throwing it to the ground collects some stones to incite his adversary. 'Thief, cuckold, setter of snares on the high road,' he cries, 'at this hour you shall die.' Grandmont having his naked dagger in his hand, Thysac draws for fear of being attacked. After having exchanged and parried several thrusts, the insulted husband retires towards the church near a little elm tree, where a number of people are grouped. He began to chat with them paying no further heed to Grandmont but the latter, some time after, mounted on a horse, charged at his cousin, dagger in hand still shouting 'Where is he this cuckold, this thief, and setter of snares on the high road?' Thysac again drew his sword and held its point to Grandmont who, in throwing himself on it, pricked his horse very greatly. Mortally wounded he fell to the ground and expired shortly after.

M. Varlot's notes make it clear that the Lorrainers, from the first, said it was impossible for them to teach foreigners their manufacturing methods. They were not bound by Carré's undertaking.[59] The secret of the art of 'grande verre,' transmitted from father to son from time immemorial, was imparted only to the descendants of the four ancient houses: de Hennezel, de Tysac, de Thietry and de Bisval. This secret formed the subject of a solemn oath taken by all the gentlemen of these families on reaching manhood; Balthazar and Thomas de Hennezel could not

[58] About five miles north of Darney.

[59] The secret is always related to the making of 'grande verre,' which Mrs Godfrey equates with window glass. I suggest it may have been the technique of making uniformly fine quality large 'muffs.' There is no evidence of any heavy plate or mirror glass in the Weald.

reveal it without forfeiting their honour. They set up their oven in the midst of forests to conceal their manufactures; they surrounded their works with ditches in order better to prevent access and admitted only people of their own family.[60] M. Varlot quotes 'an English author,' not named, who describes the French gentlemen glassmakers: 'They are silent, haughty, masters of themselves. They do not mingle with the nobility of the district and scorn to form ties with the commoners. They carry swords, wear ruffs, and plumed hats and ride where their fancy leads.'

A Hensey Quarrel at Wisborough Green

Mrs Godfey picks her way carefully through the records of petitions, quarrels and broken agreements after 1567,[61] as also does Hartshorne, working from fewer sources. One document escaped their notice, the Star Chamber Proceedings James I, 179/7 and I am very much indebted to Dr L. F. Salzman for copying it for me. It is the only document I know in which the two principal Elizabethan glassmaking families in the Weald are related to a 'glasshouse in Wisborough Green,' and therefore it is given in full.

Albert Hensey of Wisborough Green complains that Thomas Jackson of the same, yeoman, being seized of a messuage and buildings erected and used for the making of glass and commonly called a 'Glasse-house' in Wisborough Green, on 15 December, 4 James I. [1606] leased to him [Albert Hensey] who hath byn allwayes brought upp and used in the Art of makinge of Glasse, the premises with free access, for 3 years at rent of £3. He brought great store of wood and other things there and followed the making of glass to his good profit, whereby he maintained his wife and children. On 7 February last (5 Jas. I) 'being Shrove Sunday,' while Albert Hensey was at church, Thomas Jackson riotously assembled John Jackson, Robert Jackson, John Crockforde, John Boxolde, Harry Walker, Thomas Myghall, Richard Charlewode and others, armed with bows and arrows 'pykes staves, muskettes' &c and so came to John Bennett and Peter Curson, two of Albert Hensey's servants, who refused to give up the glasshouse. They then surrounded the house, to prevent food being brought in. On Monday about midday Anne Bongar, wife of Isaack Bongar, and Margaret wife of the said Peter Curson, and Susan Hensey, compplainant's daughter, fearing that John Bennett and Peter Curson would be starved, took some food to the glasshouse. But Thomas Jackson &c beat them, and then broke down the walls of the glasshouse, beat up John Bennett and Peter Curson and thrust them out and seized and wasted the stock of wood &c. Thomas Jackson gives a general denial of any riot and violence. He says, that he never made any lease to Albert Hensey but only discussed it vaguely; but Albert Hensey 'by procurement of Isaack Bungar, as he is informed, and not of his own disposition,' entered on and

---

[60] How long they managed to preserve their secrets is not known, but thirteen years after the arrival of the Lorrainers a glasshouse at Northiam was being worked by two glass workers, Sondaye Exanta of Lorraine and John Okes of Beckley, who had a good Sussex name (*see* p. 211).

[61] *D.E.G.*, pp. 26–44.

detained the glasshouse and refused to allow anyone to go near it. He adds that Albert Hensey is an alien born in France, and therefore is not able to take any such lease.

Dr L. F. Salzman's comment on the case is: 'It looks as if Hensey, as an alien, not being able to lease property in England, had arranged for Bungar to act on his behalf and that Bungar had tricked him and no doubt pocketed the rent. The 'riot' may, as usual, be largely discounted.' The outcome is not known. I have not been able to trace Jackson's farm in the Chichester wills or the P.Rs., and the owners of two possible sites, Nos. 23 and 26, have no ancient deeds. In this case the glassmaker bought his own fuel and paid a rent of £3 for a dwelling and the glasshouse; the shortness of the lease is interesting. The names mentioned appear to be local men and the three women referred to were of Norman, Lorraine and English origin acting in unison. Hensey's two servants were local men and it is difficult to believe that any trade secrets can have remained or that after forty years much anti-French feeling survived. Hensey referred to the 'art' of glassmaking, and art it remained until the eighteenth or nineteenth century (*see* p. 21, note 77). Albert was not one of the six Henseys mentioned in 1614 as still in business (*see* p. 128). Isaac Bongar is discussed below. There is only one site (No. 26) with a contemporary dwelling still surviving, and still named 'Glasshouse.' The rent at this date for local holdings of about 15 acres would be about £3.

The Bungars

Carré, by his enterprise and by importing new men and techniques, has some claim to be a founder of the modern British glass industry in 1567. He lived only another five years and during the next forty years before the rise of Mansell in 1615, two other men appear as leaders in the industry, Giacomo Verzelini, a Venetian, making fine crystal vessel in London,[62] who does not concern us, and Isaac Bungar, a Norman window glass maker in the Weald, about whom Mrs Godfrey has much of interest to say. It is important therefore to set out all the evidence linking him with glassmaking in the Wisborough Green district. We have seen that Isaac Bungar said his forebears came from Normandy to teach the English to make window glass,[63] so he was probably at least one generation from France. The Bungars were one of the original glassmaking families in Normandy; they were probably introduced to the Weald by Carré by 1568 (*see* p. 122). In 1579 another member of the family, Pero Bungar, was licenced to hold services in Wisborough Green church.[64] In 1594 Ja' Bungar was buried.[65] We do not know who was the father of a son called Isaac. A member of the family may have been working in London in 1589 when Anthony, son of Peter, Bougar was buried at All Hallows, London Wall.[66] There is a badly faded document described by C. H. Ashdown in his *History of the Glaziers*

[62] Mansell and Verzelini are fully discussed by W. A. Thorpe in *English Glass* (1949). Verzelini was probably brought over by Carré, *c*.1571. Hand-blown vessel is still produced in Wealdstone.

[63] S.P. 14/162, No. 231A, Chapter V, p. 84.

[64] *See* p. 111, note 12.   [65] Wisborough Green P.R.

[66] H. J. Powell, *Glassmaking in England* (C.U.P., 1923), p. 25.

Company 1328–1918: 'In 1595 Madalen Bongard of Greenwich, widow and Isaac Bongard of Greenwich, gent, of the one part and Thomas Lawrence, citizen and goldsmith of London, of the other part. A Contract with respect to payment of glass. Five hundred cases of Normandy glass are mentioned.'[67] We do not know if Isaac of Greenwich is the same glassmaker who from 1600 to 1618 was firmly established in the Wisborough Green and Billingshurst district and who opposed the enforcement of Mansell's monopoly with great determination. For the crucial concluding period of the industry, Isaac Bungar can be firmly tied to the Weald but not, so far, to a farm or a known furnace site. The first reference to him in the Weald is in 1600 in the Wisborough Green P.R. when his daughter Ann was baptized. His wife's name was Anne so this may have been his first daughter while he was still a young man. Three other children were baptized there in 1602, 1604 and 1606; in these cases he is described as 'gent' as were the other French glassmakers at this time. In the Billingshurst P.R. two sons of Isaac Bungar are entered as baptized in 1610 and in 1614, another son of Isaac Bungar of West Chiltington[68] is entered as baptized.

There is a reference to Isaac Bongar in 1608 when his wife Anne was involved in a quarrel over the tenancy of a 'glasshouse in Wisborough Green' (*see* p. 130) between Albert Hensey, glassmaker and Thomas Jackson, yeoman, both of Wisborough Green. The various references to Isaac Bungar in the Wisborough Green – Billingshurst district describe him as 'gentleman' and only twice is his trade mentioned, viz in 1614 when Edward Henzey and Isaac Bungard are described as masters and owners of glass furnaces in Surrey and Sussex;[69] and in 1616 when they are described as broad glass makers.[70] In each case Edward Henzey's name comes first, so their importance was probably at least equal. Lorraine and Norman families united to hang on to the end. Discussing the problem of fuel supply and Isaac Bungar's attempts to solve it, Mrs Godfrey says (*D.E.G.*, p. 96),

> 'The London market for window glass was still supplied by those who chose not to move about – the Wealden glassmen, descendants of the original Normans and Lorrainers . . . As they prospered they not only took over from Carré's defunct company the ownership of the glasshouses but they followed Verzelini's precedent by buying up wooded lands as sources of fuel supply. Isaac Bungar alone came to own considerable woodlands.'[71]

[67] Guildhall MS. 5758, No. 5, deposited by the Glaziers' Company. It is one of the very few early MS. of that Company that survives. According to Hartshorne there was a glasshouse at Greenwich c.1619 and in 1641.

[68] This is explained on p. 141, note 120.

[69] Acts of the Privy Council, 2/27. A son of Edward Hensey, gent, was baptized in 1603 (Wisborough Green P.R.).

[70] A.P.C. 2/28.

[71] Mrs Godfrey's reference (*D.E.G.*, p. 97) is Chan. Proc., Bungar *v.* Martin, C.5/593/19. She says the case 'makes clear that after he was forced to quit in 1618 making glass with wood he sold considerable timber for revenue.' The suit took place in 1620 and shows that Isaac Bungar of

Such ownership 'avoided some of the constant increase in price' and gave them some security during the final period of intense competition for accessible woodland. In addition to his more distant woods at Slinfold and Cranleigh, Bungar appears to have bought some more accessible 'wood' at Ifold. This can be seen from the following reference. In the will of Samsonn Coulstocke, yeoman of Kirdford, proved in 1615,[72] are two items: to his wife he left 'my farm called Ifold' and among the debts owing to him is 'Mr Bonngard £25 for wood.' Isaac is the only member of the Bungar family for whom I have found any references in the district between 1600 and 1620, and the Ifold 'wood' is probably his. The 'wood' was probably glass-house fuel, and is a large amount.[73] But Mrs Godfrey says,[74]

> 'Ownership of land was not the final answer to the glassmaker's problem, how-ever. Gradually Isaac Bungar came to see that a diminishing fuel supply inevitably meant curtailed production and in order to prosper in such a situation prices must be kept artificially high. This could only be done through control of both production and the market in window glass'.

This he seems to have succeeded in doing as will be seen from the later complaints of the Glaziers.

Mrs Godfrey[75] shows that Bungar as one of the chief producers, bound by close ties of kinship and pride of craft with the other established Wealden men, could count on their co-operation. Needing a London ally with established connections to aid in the marketing, he enlisted the aid of Lionel Bennett, a dealer in glass and prob-ably a member of the Glazier's Company by the early 1600s. Bungar, while not relinquishing his factories, acted as a dealer as well, until by 1605 the pair had managed to get an effective corner on the market. Their helpless customers, the Glaziers, complained bitterly and have described just how Bungar and Bennett monopolized 'all the glass made in Sussex.' And this 'without any benefit of letters patent or liti-gation.' The Glaziers in a formal petition[76] said that glass was 'so scarce under their domination that they were forced to cast lots for the available supply and many could scarcely obtain enough glass to make a living for their families.' Bungar's domination lasted more than a decade, and during this period the fuel shortage was the reason why he did not produce as much glass as he could sell at his current price. 'He was forced to adopt a regime of scarcity and probably could produce not more

Billingshurst, gent, had bought Winstreed's wood at the north end of Dedisham Park, in Slinfold, in 1612 and that in 1614 he joined with others to buy a wood in 'Cranley.' His purchases were roughly five and eight miles north of Wisborough Green or Billingshurst, which suggests that nearby wood-lands were not available and that his glasshouse was neither in nor close to his fuel supply.

[72] P.C.C., 67, Dixy.

[73] On the basis of the Knole fuel consumption (*see* p. 47), which was nearly two and a half cords of wood a day at 3s. 4d. a cord, £25 would represent 150 cords or about sixty days' supply.

[74] D.E.G., p. 98.

[75] D.E.G., pp. 99 and 100.

[76] S.P. 14/120, No. 89. Glaziers' petition, 13 April 1621 (D.E.G., p. 99).

than his own woods could support for fear of reprisals and restrictions from his neighbours and Parliament.'

Mrs Godfrey also says:

'By 1612, possibly by 1611, the technical changes permitting the use of coal solved the problem of fuel and sent the British industry far in advance of the French for many generations. Bungar's economic empire and Robson's alike were threatened. But the truculent Bungar, who had only [just] made his entrance into the story of English glassmaking, was not prepared to give up the traditional ways of his noble forbears or to surrender his position without a long and bitter battle'.[77]

In the closing few years of the Weald industry there was frequent direct conflict between two forceful men, the truculent Isaac Bungar and the versatile Admiral Sir Robert Mansell who was determined to enforce his monopoly of making glass in the newly designed coal-fired furnaces. This most interesting struggle for power, between the old and the new is a major theme in Mrs Godfrey's thesis, where the surviving evidence is fully discussed. Mansell won and ran the English glass industry for the next twenty-four years. She describes the change from wood to coal as 'the most significant occurrence in the English glass industry during the century under consideration'[78] [1560–1640]. By 1612 glass had been successfully produced from a coal-fired furnace and six years later Bungar's last wood-fired furnace in the Weald was shut down.[79]

'Very probably Bungar and Hensey continued to make glass with wood in the meantime though they seem, without much success, to have experimented with coal during 1615.'[80] 'There is no evidence that Bungar ever made glass outside the Weald before 1618 and very definite evidence that his furnaces near Wisborough Green used wood until he was forced to quit in that year.[81] . . .While fighting Mansell later on, Bungar used other methods such as hiring away workmen . . . etc., or bribing workmen who were his friends and kinsmen to spoil the batches deliberately'[82] . . . 'A Proclamation of May 1615[83] expressly prohibited the use of wood in melting glass in any factory in England . . . this strengthened the legal position of the patent and Mansell continued the prosecution of wood burning glassmakers begun by Zouch'.[84]

[77] D.E.G., p. 102.   [78] D.E.G., p. 102.
[79] D.E.G., p. 169. 'A new agreement, sanctioned by the Council on July 6 1617, permitted Bungar to work two furnaces until August 20 next, and one until April, 1618.' A.P.C. XXXV (1616–17), 290–1.
[80] D.E.G., p. 167. [The necessary change in furnace design is shown in Fig. 20, G.H.K.]
[81] D.E.G., p. 109. Mrs Godfrey's references are: A.P.C. XXXIV (1615–16), 469–70, and A.P.C. XXXV (1616–17), 290–1.
[82] D.E.G., p. 122.   [83] S.P. 14/187, No. 42, ex D.E.G., p. 137.
[84] D.E.G., p. 147.

He finally succeeded in shutting the wood-burning Weald glasshouses three years later. Before Bungar ceased work Mansell offered him £200 a year to oversee and manage his new coal factories.[85] Bungar refused and, according to Mansell, told a gentleman of his acquaintance that 'he had £1000 left to confound him (Sir Robert Mansell) and his patent.' Since he continued to make glass, Mansell prosecuted him in the Court of Exchequer and as a result the fires in Bungar's furnaces were put out sometime during 1618.[86] Wood-burning furnaces 'may have lingered on in remote places, making impossible the fixing of a date after which wood was not used in England in glassmaking; certainly very little was used after 1618, as a result of Mansell's vigorous enforcement of his monopoly'.[87]

After 1618 Bungar remained in the retail glass trade in London and was an active member of the Glaziers Company. His opposition to Mansell did not cease,[88] and in July 1619 Mansell had a warrant issued from the Council for the arrest of Bungar, Clavell and Bigo.[89] In 1620 soon after Sir Robert Mansell's departure (to harry the Barbary pirates) Bungar broke his agreement with Mansell and engaged on a violent quarrel with Lady Mansell 'uttering such disgraceful speeches against Sir Robert' that he was imprisoned in the Marshalsea.[90] Discussing the rise of the merchant glazier Mrs Godfrey says,[91]

'Isaac Bungar exemplifies this new sort of glazier. As a young man his business interests were those of a glassmaker who sold to the middlemen supplying the London market. As his wealth and ambition grew, he turned his attention more and more to becoming a merchant himself. While he did not abandon his interests in producing glass without a long struggle, the Isaac Bungar of 1620, "Freeman and Glazier of the City of London", accused by his fellow glaziers of once having had a corner on the window-glass market and aspiring to another, was a man of different interests from the Isaac Bongar of 1590, the provincial owner of one or two glass factories.'[92]

Isaac Bungard (as he signs himself) died in 1643 and his will[93] suggests that the then large sum of £1000, which he proudly boasted as having about twenty-five years earlier had largely disappeared. He was the only member of the glassmaking families brought over by Carré so far known to have stayed on after the industry moved away in 1618. Some of his large family settled and married in the district. The Bungars

[85] S.P. 14/162, No. 231 B, ex *D.E.G.*, p. 169.　　[86] This quotation is from *D.E.G.*, p. 169.
[87] *D.E.G.*, p. 178. *See* also p. 139 on Vinion.　　[88] *D.E.G.*, p. 170.
[89] A.P.C., XXXVII (1619–21), 220–1; *D.E.G.*, p. 186. The reference to Clavell and Bigo probably concerns the glasshouse which operated for a short time at Church Knowle in Dorset. *See* Chapter IX, p. 221, note 43. [G.H.K.]
[90] *D.E.G.*, p. 206.　　[91] *D.E.G.*, p. 335.
[92] *See* p. 132. There is some doubt that he was the same man. [G.H.K.]
[93] Isaac Bungar, senex, buried 16 September 1643 (Pulborough P.R.). His will, dated 12 November 1642, being unproved, is not in the printed index, but was found at Somerset House in Box 633 in a bundle labelled 1547. The Rev. A. W. C. Hallen refers to the will in *The Scottish Antiquary*, vol. 7 (1893), p. 150. I am indebted to Mr W. S. B. Buck for tracing the wills of Bungar and Carré.

had been in Sussex for about 75 years, and he may have been born there. He left his children and grandchildren nine small sums, only two being over 10s., and three sums of £10 payable after the death of his wife Anne. He directed that his land 'at Chiltington called Hore Land'[94] was to be sold to cover his debts and bequests. There is no reference to glass in the will and he describes himself as of Pulborough, gentleman, but there is no doubt this is the 'truculent Bongar' the forest glassmaker of at least 1600 to 1618, because the names of five of his children mentioned in the will, can be traced in the P.R. of Wisborough Green and Billingshurst. One of his daughters 'An,' baptized at Wisborough Green in 1600, had married John Bristowe, clerk. His son John was baptized at Billingshurst in 1614, when Isaac Bongar is described as of West Chiltington. A John Bongard, innholder of Pulborough, very probably this son, left a will proved in 1670;[95] it contains nothing of interest. The latest reference to a possible descendant of Isaac is the marriage of Mary Bungar of Pulborough to T. Boxall of Warningcamp, in 1695–6.[96] Isaac Bungar may have remained as a glazier in London for some years after his glasshouse in the Weald closed down.

Wisborough Green Glassmakers

Wisborough Green is probably the most interesting of the glassmaking parishes, because of the quality and quantity of the glass made and the number of French families known to have worked there. But while much work has been done on the parish history of Chiddingfold and Kirdford and some work on Alfold and Petworth, little is known of the manors and main estates of Wisborough Green until their records become available.[97]

The family name evidence confirms the site evidence that Wisborough Green[98] was the centre of Wealden glass production for the last fifty years of its life, as half the Late sites and half the glassmaking family names so far traced belong to that parish which may well have been one of the centres of English forest glassmaking at that time. The Late period has a big advantage in the matter of records because parish registers may be available and because more records of all kinds tend to survive after the Reformation.

Cooper notes that no French immigrant family appears in the Chiddingfold P.R. The Peytowes continued to make glass there until the end, but the centre of gravity had shifted south and east to Wisborough Green. At least twenty-six and probably thirty-one entries of 'French' families in the Wisborough Green P.R.[99]

[94] There is no trace of the name in the West Chiltington Tithe Award schedule.
[95] D.R.O., Chichester.
[96] S.R.S., vol. 9, p. 121.
[97] In the Duke of Norfolk's archives at Arundel and the Zouche MSS. at Parham.
[98] The parish then included Loxwood.
[99] I am much indebted to the late Mr J. M. Newman for his most careful transcript of this P.R. and to the Rev. J. E. Penney for most kindly lending it to me, thus making it possible for me to study it at home, the only feasible way for the non-professional. The Carré entry was checked with the original.

start abruptly in 1567 and with one exception[100] end in 1617. This fits broadly the date limits of the Late period and this register provides by far the largest number of entries of any parish in the Weald.

The entries, which all probably relate to the glass industry are:

15 June	1567	Leues the son of Hollond a frenchman. bapt.
25 May	1572	John Tarry. Mr. of the Glashouse was buried at Awfolde.*
18 July	1573	Lawrence a french boy was bur.
31 March	1573	Hero a frenchman. bur.
14 Dec.	1578	Anneluy dr of John a frenchman. bapt.
28 April	1581	a french child. bur.
26 July	1588	Laurenc Ffryer frenchman and Joan Wood married.†
3 Oct.	1592	a frenchwoman buried.
6 March	1594	Ja' Bungar. bur. (earliest ref. to the Bungars in P.R.).
10 Oct.	1596	Maudly dr of Pero bapt.
17 April	1597	Katheren Gelat dr of a frenchman bapt.
1 Dec.	1599	James son of Petor als Pero a Frenchman. bapt.
30 Dec.	1599	Abraham son of Jacob Hensey gent. bapt. [earliest ref. to Henseys in P.R.].
21 March	1599	Danyell Tytery. gent. bur.
19 Oct.	1600	William son of Cuttrey als Russell a frenchman. bapt.
28 Dec.	1600	An dr of Isahac Bungar. bapt.
27 Dec.	1602	Debora dr of Isaac Bungar gent. bapt.
27 Dec.	1602	Sara dr of Hector Cockery gent. bapt.
26 Dec.	1603	Isahac s. Edward Hensey gent. bapt.
15 April	1604	Sara d. Ingram Brasso. gent. bapt.
6 May	1604	Elizabeth dr Isahac Bungar. gent. bapt.
23 May	1605	Sara d. of Ingram Brasso. gent. bur.
1 Dec.	1605	Isahac s. Ingram Brasso. gent. bapt.
6 April	1606	Peter s. Isahac Bungar gent. bapt.
19 July	1607	Abraham s. Ingram Brasso. gent. bapt.
28 Aug.	1608	Jacob s. Ingram Brasso gent. bapt.
25 April	1613	Hector son of Hector Cakery. bapt.
22 July	1615	Nicolas Verrell and Mary Fryer. married [see 1588].
6 Feb.	1615	Joan b.b.d. Venns als Ben Bungar. bapt. (and bur. Feb. 23).
26 May	1616	Sara d. Peregrine Henzey. bapt.
4 May	1617	Owen Humphrey and Joan Bungar‡ married.
20 June	1624	John Goddard an owld Frenchman. bur.

* This is almost certainly Jean Carré and has always been read as such. Possibly the transcriber on to vellum from the original register erred. That Carré was buried at Alfold suggests he may have died at a house near his known furnace site at Fernfold, in the north of Wisborough Green, closer to Alfold church.

† Fryer was probably the glassmaker at Ewhurst, see p. 140. The Frenchmen had started to marry local girls and vice versa (see 1617).

‡ Joan Bungar could be a daughter of Isaac Bungar.

In no case is the trade of these Frenchmen given[101] and the only stated link is the entry for John Tarry, 'Mr. of the Glashouse' in 1572. Eleven persons are described

[100] The exception being 'John Goddard an old Frenchman' who was buried in 1624; possibly he was too old to move with the others six years earlier.

[101] It seems to have been a matter of local custom whether trades were mentioned in parish registers. In the P.R. of Oldswinford, the parish which included Stourbridge town, for the entries of 88 Henzeys

as 'French.' The Pero of 1596 is almost certainly the same as 'Pero a frenchman' of 1599 and probably a mispelling of Perrot.[102] Another fourteen are members of known migratory French glassmaking families such as the Henseys and Bungars. If the four children of Ingram Brasso, gent.[103] are included the entries total thirty and there were probably about fifteen separate families. Allowing five to a family and for the known absence of some of them from the P.R. there could have been upwards of forty French persons in the parish at the peak time, c.1600. We know there were enough by 1579 to hold their own services, so that even without their reputed arrogance it is not surprising there was occasional friction. Half the entries occur between 1597 and 1607 and two-thirds of them in the last twenty years of the industry from 1597 to 1617. There are only nine in the first thirty years after Carré arrived. There are three marriages, nine burials and twenty baptisms up to 1617.[104] The surnames are: Holland (1 entry); Ffryer (2); Carré (1); Bungar, (8, four being children of Isaac Bungar); Gelat (1); Henseys (3, Jacob, gent., Edward gent., and Peregrine three separate families); Tyttery (1, Danyell gent.); Cuttrey *alias* Russell (1); Cakery probably Caquery (Hector, two entries, one as gent.); Pero (2); Brasso (Ingram, gent. five entries; children of). This leaves five with no surnames. A mobility among these glassmaking families is illustrated by three Henseys. A Peregrine Hensie was baptized at Eccleshall in 1586[105] A daughter of Peregrine Henzie was

(1615–1780), 105 Tysacks (1615–1759) and 19 Tytterys (1622–81), their trade is never given, whereas in the 465 entries of the three families in the P.R. of All Saints, Newcastle upon Tyne, their trade of glassmaker (often broad glassmaker) is given in three out of four cases. The entries noted are between 1619 and 1712 and up to 1750 for burials only, three-quarters concern Henseys, with some Tysacks and a few Tytterys. Twenty-four of the forty-four marriages were among the three families, sixteen being between Henseys. Only a single alternative trade is noted in this P.R. in 1732 when Peregrine Henzell, master mariner and glassmaker was buried. In his will, 1725, Edward Henzey of Oldswinsford, broad glassmaker, mentions 'the trade of malster which I now follow' (*see* also Guttery, p. 60). The information in this note is taken from *Collections for a genealogy of the Noble families of Henzey, Tyttery and Tyzack* (*De Hennezel, De Thiétry and Du Thisac*), '*Gentilshommes Verriers*' *from Lorraine* by H. Sydney Grazebrook (Stourbridge, 1877) (here abbreviated Grazebrook). The book deals almost entirely with genealogical material dating from after the closing of our industry. It has some general notes on glassmaking in England but contains nothing new.

[102] *See* also the Carré–Becku quarrel, p. 122. The name Perrot is included in M. J. Barrelet's comprehensive list of French glassmaking families in his *La Verrerie en France* (Larousse, 1953), p. 179. They originated from Bormido, near Altare, and worked at Nevers, Orleans, &c.

[103] The Brassos are not included in this list (above). The nearest name is Brossard, who perhaps originated in High Picardy and settled in Normandy in the fourteenth century. Ingram Brasso shares the locally rare distinction of 'gent' with the Bungars, Henseys, Tytterys and Cakerys, all were probably 'gentilhommes verriers.' The Kings of the 'Greate House at Loxwood,' the Nappers of Dunhurst, Gratwicks of Ifold and the Strudwicks of Amblehurst are not so described.

[104] An entry attributed to Wisborough Green in *W.G.*, p. 20, has been traced to S.R.S., vol. 9, p. 9: 6 August 1610, Tobias Hensey and Susan Bungar of Northchapel; *see* above, p. 128, and also Petworth Park, No. 40 (p. 206). I cannot trace another entry in *W.G.*, p. 20, John Tizacke (*alias* Burrye) married Mary, daughter of Peter Bongar, but it may have been copied from *Glassmaking in England* by H. J. Powell (O.U.P., 1923), p. 25.

[106] Pape, p. 19.

baptized at Wisborough Green in 1616[106] and *c*.1625, Peregrine and Daniel Henzey were making broadglass in Newcastle upon Tyne.[107] The three instances all probably relate to one man. Another Henzey, Edward of Wisborough Green, married Sara Tetrye at Eccleshall (Staffs.) on 24 October 1602,[108] and their son was baptized at Wisborough Green 26 December 1603. In 1599 there was a Jacob Hensey, gent., at Wisborough Green,[109] in 1615 a Jacob Hensey was employed by Mansell at Wollaston[110] and in 1619 a Jacob Hensey is recorded as being employed in Newcastle upon Tyne[110] 'The success of the Newcastle works was probably due to Mansell's employment of the Henseys to be his managers there. Sometime during late 1616 he persuaded Edward Hensey and some of his relatives to come to Newcastle as his employees from the Stourbridge area where they had been working with wood furnaces.'[111]

Of the French families appearing in the Wisborough Green P.R. two are from Lorraine, the Hennezels and Tytterys, and two from Normandy, the Cakerys and the Bungars. The origins of the others are unknown. The register has a large number of Strudwick entries but none are shown as glassmakers. Other local names which occur from the earliest dates are Furlongers and Peytowes but neither are named as glassmakers. There were at least two families of Furlongers in the parish and their first entry is in 1561. Our Furlongers were not migratory glassmakers and they survived in this district until recently. There is no evidence that any of them were connected with Weald glassmaking. They appear in the Kirdford P.R.; the earliest entry noted is 1570 and they occur infrequently for about 100 years.

Mrs E. S. Godfrey's thesis provides much information for the Late period glassmaking families, particularly about Isaac Bungar, and I am greatly indebted to her for permission to quote from it. She says

'Bungar's opposition to the patent (Mansell's of 1615) served as a model for the petitions of two small wood-users in the Weald. Paul Vinion who said he was born at Wisborough Green[112] and Peter Comely had been making green drinking glasses with wood in Sussex before the patent and continued to do so afterwards. In April 1618, Mansell complained to the Council of their defiance and secured a warrant for their appearance before the Council Board. They were imprisoned

---

[106] P.R.   [107] Pape, p. 44.

[108] Pape, p. 17.   [109] P.R.

[110] 'Documents relating to the Lorraine Glassmakers in North Staffordshire,' by the late W. Horridge, in *Glass Notes*, No. 15, 1955 (Arthur Churchill Ltd., London).

[111] *D.E.G.*, p. 155.

[112] *D.E.G.*, pp. 171–173, quoting from S.P.14/105, No. 19, in which Vinion says he was born at Wisborough Green and that he had taught some Englishmen to make glass. I have found no entry in the P.R. of his birth, but they start only in 1560. It is possible some Frenchmen were missed. The nearest entry found is 8 February 1573–4: Joan, daughter of John Vivean, stranger, bapt. Neither Vinion nor Comley appear in Barrelet's list of French glassmaking families. [G.H.K.]

for failure to comply with the Royal Proclamation [of 1615] against the use of wood, but in May Sir Robert asked for their release on condition that they give bond not to repeat their offence . . . Vinion and Comely were the last of the wood-burning glassmakers called in person before the Privy Council.'[113]

Later Mrs Godfrey notes that Vinion said he would gladly work for Mansell at £2 a week.

Of Lawrence Fryer who the P.R. shows as being married in 1588, Mrs E. S. Godfrey says,[114] 'Other scattered works in the Weald were more fortunate.[115] In spite of the resentment of his neighbours, Lawrence Fryer used timber for his glasshouse in Somersbury Wood, Ewhurst, Surrey, until his death in 1613[116] and George Gerrat, his manager, may have continued until 1615.' It seems to have been a matter of chance and possibly of some discrimination, who was shut down in the last 30 years, because Vann is only about eight miles from Ewhurst. The P.R. makes it clear that there was no mass movement of French glassmakers from this district following the discovery of a plot, hatched in Petworth in 1574, to rob them and destroy their houses.[117] Some members of the glassmaking families may have moved to Buckholt in 1576 from the Weald or direct from France and others continued to move westward for the next twenty years; their names start to appear in the Eccleshall (Staffs.) P.R. in the 1580s. It was drift rather than a migration; probably their numbers were increasing and the strain on the available fuel supply was becoming impossible. New districts were also reinforced directly from France which confuses a clear pattern. In spite of this influx of skilled French glassmakers our two local families, the Peytowes and the Strudwicks, continued to make glass: possibly they owned sufficient fuel and the local landowners would be more likely to sell to them.

---

[113] *A.P.C.*, XXXVI (1618–19), 115. This is the only reference I know to Late forest vessel glassmaking. It suggests a specialization which is very rarely confirmed by the site evidence. 'Green' glass was probably the ordinary domestic glass as distinct from the luxury crystal glass and corresponds today to bottle glass. [G.H.K.]

[114] *D.E.G.*, p. 60.

[115] For the case of the Italian Ognybene Luthery, *see* Vann No. 35 (p. 199); he was shut down in 1586 because of complaints by local inhabitants, of the destruction of woods. [G.H.K.]

[116] In the will of Laurence Fryer, 'glasse fownder' of Ewhurst, Surrey, in 1612/3, he left his goods to be equally divided between his wife Agnes (he may have remarried) and his daughter Mary, and desired that his master Mr George Gerrat, glassmaker, should keep Mary's portion until she was 21 (V.C.H., *Surrey*, vol. 2, pp. 298, 299). A Mary Fryer married Nicholas Verrell (Wis. P.R.) in 1615. I think the very rare use of 'Mr,' the term glass founder and the fact that Fryer entrusted his daughter's portion to Gerrat, suggest that he was in fact Fryer's master, not manager. Fryer was 'of Ewhurst' and could have worked Somersbury (No. 37) or Ellens Green (No. 36) which was found after *W.G.* was published. [G.H.K.]

[117] Bishop of Chichester to Burghley: 'Of very late aboute Petworth certayne had conference to rob the Frenchmen that made glasse and to burn their houses, but they be apprehended and punished. S.P. Dom., Eliz., vol. 95, No. 82.

Glassmakers in Other Wealden Parishes

The other important glassmaking parish, Kirdford, has only three certain P.R. entries: David Berry sonne of Mr Berry,[118] glassmaker, stranger, was christened Jan. 1589, and two daughters of William Strudwick, glassman, baptized in 1595 and 1597. Rachel and Mary, the daughters of John Tysack who were baptized in 1588 and 1590, are the only evidence we have of the well-known Lorraine glassmaking family in Kirdford or Wisborough Green though John was probably working at Ewhurst, just over the Surrey border, in 1583–4 (see p. 142). The prefix 'Mr' and the trade of glassmaker, are rare in our P.Rs. and they suggest Mr Berry was possibly a foreign *gentilhomme verrier*. A William Strudwick is referred to on pp. 119 and 177. The Southwark entries (see p. 124) suggest the terms glassmaker and glassman are the same. Other local parish registers have been disappointing, but are worth mentioning. Lurgashall, in which parish the Petworth Park (No. 40) glasshouse was situated, has a single entry: 8 Nov. 1600, John Besse[119] 'out of the glasshouse' was buried. John Blease the 'French boy' who was buried at Petworth on 22 June 1575 may have glassmaking ancestors. The only other possible entries in Petworth P.R. up to 1615 are: burials, 26 Feb. 1573–4 a Frenchman, and on 26 Sept. 1592 the wife of Ananias Hensey. Of him I know nothing.

Some other possible references to the industry in local P.R.s are:

Billingshurst. Isaac and Joseph Bungar sons of Isack Bungar[120] bapt. Sept. 1610; John Bougard son of Isacke Bougard of W. Chiltington[120] bapt. 9 June 1614; Ananias son of Joseph Hensey bapt. 5 Jan. 1616; Ananias Henzey buried, April 1617; Judith daughter of Joseph Henzey bapt. 1618.[121]

There are no references to Frenchmen and no other glass family names. Furlonger, a fairly common local name occurs 44 times between 1593 and 1744.

Rudgwick. Winbolt (*W.G.*, p. 23) says there are two entries: 'a child from the glasshouse in Ewhurst, Surrey,' 23 Dec. 1611; secondly 'a stranger of the glasshouse in Ewhurst,' 19 Oct. 1612; there is also a third entry – 30 Jan. 1612–13, 'a labourer from the glasshouse in Ewhurst' (see also site No. 37) but being nearer Rudgwick this

---

[118] Possibly an anglicized form of Buré which Mr W. A. Thorpe says was Flemish. See *English Glass* (London, 1949), p. 88.

[119] There is will of Thomas Bese the elder of Petworth, 1560, in the Diocesan Record Office at Chichester. It is a very humble will; two sons, Thomas and Henry, are mentioned. It may be a local family name.

[120] Four children of Isaac Bungar were baptized at Wisborough Green, 1600–06. He may have moved on to Billingshurst and possibly later to West Chiltington. There are no field name clues in the T/A schedule of West Chiltington. Isaac Bungar is discussed on p. 132. West Chiltington adjoins Billingshurst on the south. The only glasshouse field in Billingshurst is on Lordings Farm in the south of the parish. There is no clue in West Chiltington. Isaac Bungar may have lived then near Adversane, closer to Billingshurst church than West Chiltington.

[121] Either or both Bungar and Henzey may have worked the Lordings Farm glasshouse (No. 41).

glasshouse may be No. 36 at Ellens Green. The glass fits the date. All three of the main Lorraine glassmaking families appear as 'gunners' in the Ewhurst musters of 1583–4.[122] Thus: John Tysack, possibly the same John who appears in the Kirdford P.R. of 1588 and 1590 (see p. 141), Apperteyne Hensye, possibly the Albertyne Hensey, who was overseer of the will of Danyell Tytterye of Wisborough Green in 1599–1600 (see p. 137), and Inconthe Theatrye. They could have worked either or both glasshouses, Nos. 36 and 37. As all three families disappear from the Weald when glassmaking ceased it is reasonable to suppose these men were glassmakers. There are no obvious French names in the Alfold musters of the same date. Hartshorn says that there are glass carriers mentioned in the Rudgwick P.R. at the end of the sixteenth century. I examined the P.R. from 1590 to 1607 but could find nothing. The 1599 entries are in a particularly villianous hand. The Alfold P.R. starts in 1648.[123] Aubrey[124] says in his time there were inscriptions in Alfold churchyard to Frenchmen who came over at the time of the massacre.

Summary of Families by Parishes, and Name Variants

The following twenty glassmaking families are known from various records to have lived and worked in the parishes named.

I have differentiated the evidence:

(a) Specifically named as glassmakers or 'of the glasshouse.'
(b) Members of known French glassmaking families whose names occur here only between 1567 and 1620.
(c) 'Frenchmen' whose names occur here only between 1567 and 1620. Possibly Brasso may not have been French.

Chiddingfold:[125] Alemayne, Schurterre, Peytowe, all (a).
Kirdford: Schurterre (a), Glazewryth (a), Mose (a), Strudwick (a), Berry (a), Tysack (b).
Wisborough Green: Brasso (c), Bungar (a), (Bongar), Cockery (b) (Caquerey), Carré (a), Fryer (a), Gelat (a), (?Gerrat), Hensey (b) (Hennezel), Hollond (c), Pero (b), (?Perrot), Tytery (b), (Thietry), Vinion (a).
Billingshurst: Bungar (a), Henzey (b).
Ewhurst: Fryer (a), Gerrat (a), Tysack (c), Hensy (c), Theatrye (c).
Lurgashall: Besse (a).
Petworth:[126] Henzey (b).

---

[122] Surrey Record Society, vol. 2, p. 20.
[123] *Alfold*, F. W. Cobb, (1935), p. 57.
[124] Aubrey, *see* p. 7, note 26.
[125] Possibly only the Peytowes continued to make glass in Chiddingfold in the Late period, this could account for the fact that no other glassmakers appear in the P.R.
[126] North Chapel was, until 1693, part of Petworth parish; *see* also site No. 40, p. 207.

This list of all the glassmaking family names so far traced may be useful when records turn up showing them as tenants of a known site or as buying woodland which may give a clue as to which glasshouse they used. Something is known of half these twenty families which greatly increases the interest in any glasshouse to which they can be linked; the record may also provide a close date for the site.

The variants and anglicized forms of the principal French families are tedious and the commonest local form is given first, except when quoting from an original reference. The correct French names, given by Monsieur J. Barrelet,[127] are shown in brackets.

Bungar (Bongar): Bougard, Bongard, Bownyard, Bonngard.
Cakery (Caqueray): Cockery, ?Cuttrey.
Hensey (Hennezel): Henzey, Henzell, Henzie, Hensye, Hennezee, Hennezé.
Gerrat: ?Gelat.
Pero: ?(Perrot).
Peytowe: Peto, Peyto.
Tyttery(e), (Thiétry): Tetrye, Tyttere, Theatrye.
Tysack (Thisac): Tyzac(e), Tisac, Teswicke, Tisick.

George Longe's Petition, 1589

Another possible Weald glassmaker was George Longe,[128] the writer of two well-known petitions to Lord Burghley in 1589.[129] Carré and Becku, he says were merchants only and had to lease out their Patent to Frenchmen. He claimed that:

No custom has been paid to the Queen for twenty-one years. There are now fourteen or fifteen glasshouses in England[130] which he proposes to reduce to four (two in the second petition), moving the rest to Ireland.

This will reduce the waste of woodlands and provide useful garrisons in Ireland.

He will employ redundant men in Ireland.

He is the only English glassmaker wholly in the trade [evidently he regarded the Peytowes and Strudwicks as part-time yeomen].

He offered Lord Burghley one hundred angels and also to see 'Your honour's building from time to time repaired with the best glass.' After the first petition Burghley suggested Longe should contact Becku *alias* Dollyn, Carré being dead. Longe did this and in his second petition he asked Burghley to see them both. We know no more.

---

[127] *La Verrerie en France* (Larousse, 1953), p. 170. M. Varlot suggests that the nearer to the French, the more likely that man was to be an original immigrant or first generation.

[128] There is a Henry Longe in Chiddingfold in 1542 and a John Longe in Wisborough Green in 1568–9 (P.R.), so George may have been a local man.

[129] Lansdowne MS., No. 59, Art. 75 and 72.

[130] In 1567 Carré offered to build 'up to twelve furnaces in England and six in Ireland.' *See* p. 121.

Sources Searched with no Result

None of the other members of the French glassmaking families appears to have surviving wills, except Jean Carré (*see* p. 122), Isaac Bongar (*see* p. 135) and Danyell Tytterye of Wisborough Green who died in March 1599/1600.[131] He describes himself as 'Gent' but there is no reference to glassmaking nor to any son in his will. He was clearly a man of some small substance and left to his daughter Susan £30 on her marriage or full age, and two gold rings. The residue of his estate (no lands are mentioned) went to his wife Sara. Albertyne Hensey, gent. (*see* p. 142) was the overseer of his estate.

There are no wills to be found at Somerset House or the Chichester Diocesan Record Office for the following names or their variants, between 1567 and 1620:[132] Berry of Kirdford: Bess of Lurgashall; the Wisborough Green families of Brasso, Cakery, Fryer, Gelat, Hensey; Mose of Kirdford; Tysack of Kirdford. The only Peytowe of Chiddingfold will at Somerset House from 1530 to 1620 is that of William Peyto, yeoman, in 1596. He was a man of considerable substance but there is no reference to any glassmaking. There are no references in the Huguenot Society's volume by William Page on 'Denization and Naturalization in England, 1509–1603' to the following family names or their variants: Berry, Bungar, Hennezell, Tysac or Thietry. In the four *Surrey Record Society* volumes of Wills there are no references to Carré, Gerrat, Fryer or Theatrye.

Family Links with Glasshouse Sites

We know something of the Henseys and the Bungars but unhappily, with the possible exception of Fernfold, I have found no records as to which furnaces they used. The chances of such records of these passing migrants are slight, *e.g.*, only one record refers, unhelpfully, to the glassmakers as 'divers strangers'[133] but it happens in this case that Carré stated that he had in 1567 set up two glasshouses in 'Fernefol'[134] and that two of his employees in 1568 were Thomas and Balthazar de Hennezel. Carré had a glasshouse in London as well as at Fernfold, but the Hennezels were forest window-glass makers and it is probable they worked his forest glasshouse (*see* p. 125). The linking of families with furnaces is far from easy and I think Winbolt would not pass today, some of the links he made in 1933.

Even with a record two difficulties remain:

A. It has, so far, been possible to date only one Early site (No. 33) closely[135] by means of associated pottery. Magnetic dating appears to offer new possibilities in the future.

---

[131] P.C.C., 29 Wallopp.
[132] Isaac Bungar's will is dated 1642 (*see* p. 135).
[133] In the Court rolls of the manor of Bury. Lease of a wood called Farnfold. Add MS. 5701, fol. 150.
[134] *See* site No. 25, p. 185.
[135] *See* also site No. 7 for an authoritative discussion of the potsherd found.

B. Farm boundaries in the Weald have not remained fixed and what may be a copse on Gostrode Farm today was not necessarily part of that property in 1500.

However there are few native glassmaking families such as the Peytowes and the Strudwicks, and where they own and occupy a farm at a date when glass is known to have been made there the association is fair and has already been discussed.

Three sites almost certainly can be tied to families, Fernfold (No. 25) to Carré and his two Henseys, and the two Idehurst sites (Nos. 16 and 17) to the Strudwicks. Another two or three are very probable, Lower Chaleshurst (No. 4) to the Peytowes, Somersbury and, perhaps, Ellens Green in Ewhurst (Nos. 36 and 37) to Lawrence Fryer, John Tysack, Apperteyne Hensey and Inconthe Theatrye (*see* p. 142). More than half the sites have not the vaguest of family ties but tentative suggestions are made in Chapter IX for another thirteen. Four have rather remote ties with the Peytowes, four with the Strudwicks, two with the Schurterres and one with either the Schurterres or Alemayne. All except, Alemayne, were established native landowning families. Only two migrant foreigners apart from the possible four at Ewhurst above, have even the slightest of surviving associations. No. 35 might possibly have been worked by Luthery and No. 40 by Edward Hensey. The story is incomplete, we have the furnace sites and the families but they can rarely be linked with any certainty to produce the complete picture.

IX

DESCRIPTION AND SCHEDULE
OF GLASSHOUSE SITES

THERE are forty-two proved, probable and possible sites listed and described in this chapter; another few sites of Cooper's for which I can find no evidence are also discussed. It is doubtful if half the glasshouses in this district are known or suspected. Their main expense was not in their structural works, like the iron-masters with their costly furnaces, forges and dams, but rather in their purchase of fuel and very high wages. It must be emphasized that all the sites are on private property[1] and also that there is usually nothing to see. Fernfold is now buried in a twenty-year old jungle of blackthorn and birch, and at least six sites are under crops, or grass. The map references given may help when any of the sites turns up again or when any of the possible sites is confirmed.[2]

It is uncertain how much should be read into the concentration of furnace sites south and east of Chiddingfold. A lot depends on chance finds and the residence of the Cooper family over many years at Chaleshurst in Chiddingfold may have some significance. As in all distributions this chance hunting ground of the local enthusiast plays an unknown and possibly considerable part. The schedule tabulates the descriptions of the sites, and the final summary in 1966 divides the sites into:

26 Proved.

10 Probable. Some are marginal above and below; *e.g.*, Nos. 4 and 15.

6 Possible. (In italics).

The eight rejects are not included, but are discussed on p. 155. Twenty-four of the sites are in Sussex and eighteen in Surrey. Eleven are in Chiddingfold parish, ten in Kirdford and eleven in Wisborough Green, and ten in five other parishes. They are divided into periods:[3]

13 Early (3 being provisional).

3 Transitional.

16 Late (3 being provisional).

4 have no known date, due to insufficient glass evidence (Nos. 20, 28, 39 and 41).

6 are possibles only (Nos. 22 and 24 probably being Late and No. 34 Early).

---

[1] It is impossible to thank all the site owners, and many have changed at least once in the last 30 years.

[2] The centre of the symbol on the distribution map shows the glasshouse site position.

[3] *See* Chapter VI.

Field or Copse Names

More than half the sites have field-name clues, and half the known sites were found as a result of following up such a clue; there is no doubt that a distinctive prefix such as 'Glasshouse' was used only when there was a furnace close by. It is solid evidence, though the area covered may be tantalizingly large, at times perhaps forty acres of copse. A handful of glass fragments alone means almost nothing, and glazed brick or stone is even more unreliable[4] but crucible, almost indestructible, is infallible evidence because there is nothing else like it. But it is not uncommon within quarter of a mile, and can stray half a mile or more to a yard bottom and be carted out with dung, like the ubiquitous iron slag so widespread in Sussex. Thus I have accepted Bowbrooks, No. 1, as a possible site though it has little more than a field-name and I have rejected Cooper's Surreylands, because it has only a few scraps of glass, one small fragment of crucible and no field-name. Furthermore neither Winbolt nor I could find a trace of it. It remains a marginal site and might turn up some day.

I used field-names as a means of deciding the limits of the industry and examined thirty-five parish Tithe Apportionment schedules in Sussex and Surrey.[5] Not all our field-names are included in the Tithe schedules; some had been forgotten by 1840 and occur only in earlier deeds, some have been revived by the Ordnance Survey, but the majority can be found in the Tithe schedules. One has to watch for corruptions such as Glassus or Glasses or even Glassets. A field-name is solid evidence of a site usually within about 100 yards and a few fragments of crucible are evidence that it is within about half a mile. A concentration of crucible and glass fragments suggests the kiln is very close, perhaps within twenty yards. When a glasshouse site in the Weald is cultivated deeply a burnt area may be exposed, as the great heat developed in these small furnaces burned the ground underneath for a depth of about twelve inches; the clay is baked hard and red with a layer of black ash sometimes showing. The stone or brick structure of the furnace has usually been carted away or dug out to prevent breaking tackle, but this hard base may remain about nine inches below the present ground level to be found by spear or plough point (*see* p. 150). These bases are useful because they are often all that survives, they locate the site, and they provide evidence of the shape and a rough idea of the size of the furnace. It is doubt-

---

[4] Many farms in this district had their own lime-kilns in the seventeenth, eighteenth and nineteenth centuries and there are some brickyards, which may produce a great deal of glazed brick and stone. But if there is a thick coating of molten glass, quarter of an inch or more, it very probably originated from a glass furnace. The waste dross from forest glass furnaces is much less useful evidence than crucible because it is not always easy to distinguish from other vitreous slags.

[5] They were: Sussex—North and South Ambersham, Billingshurst, Duncton, Fernhurst, Fittleworth, Graffham, Heyshott, Horsham, Itchingfield, Kirdford, Lodsworth, Lurgashall, North Chapel, Petworth, Pulborough, Rudgwick, Shipley, Slinfold, Stopham, Tillington, Thakeham, Warnham, West Chiltington, Wisborough Green. In Surrey—Alfold, Chiddingfold, Cranleigh, Dunsfold, Ewhurst, Godalming, Hambledon, Hascombe, Haslemere, Thursley, Witley.

ful if any of the Early sites had brick floors and this pan of red hard-baked clay can easily be mistaken for a rough brick floor (*see* site No. 2, note 3). A copse may have been cleared later and become a 'field'; this happened in at least six cases, Nos. 8, 14, 18, 23, 25, 37. Winbolt rightly commented 'Ploughed fields are our good allies, but woods and copses are the best preservers.'[6] It is possible occasionally on copse sites to find bricks and broken crucible and glass lying about on the surface; this is unusual and has occurred only on sites Nos. 13, 29, 33 and 42. Possibly some of the sites which were dug over before we visited them may have had such surface evidence.

A copse site though subject to being heaved up by roots is greatly to be preferred to a field site, because the latter has probably been completely destroyed for its stone and because it interfered with cultivation. Also, and this is important, the field has had dung carted on to it and that means household refuse and modern broken glass, not always easily distinguishable from the local Late product. This difficulty also applies in the rare cases where a site is close to a dwelling, existing or demolished, as for example Nos. 14, 26 and 36.

If there is a field-name and the field is ploughed, it is worth searching the head-lands, ditches or small nearby stream for crucible fragments. The tractor driver may have seen some crucible, hit the floor or ploughed up a burnt patch. The name does not imply more than proximity and the site may be in an adjoining copse; it is then largely luck if it ever turns up, but any stream, however small, is worth examining. There may be a small mound in a copse, as at Nos. 5, 7, 21, 29, 33 and 35, the first four being complete with traces of surrounding ditches, outlining what was probably the glasshouse (*see* p. 79). The higher the mound the more likely the site is untouched and worth complete excavation. Two of the above sites, Nos. 7 and 29, were on the edge of a small steep hanger running down to a small stream. Four sites, Nos. 14, 15, 32 and 40, had a small pond almost adjoining the glasshouse. No. 42 may have had a pond on the site.

Reviewing all the known sites in the Weald, none is on a steep slope, for carting fuel and sand would be too difficult, and with two inexplicable exceptions, Nos. 15 and 25, all are reasonably dry and have a level access. The two exceptions are very badly sited, low and wet, for no apparent reason. The water supply is puzzling and is discussed below.

Field sites are seldom worth uncovering, unless a floor is found by spearing, because nothing of the structure survives. Even if the floor remains, the chances of getting anything more than its measurement are negligible.

By far the most important characteristic of all sites is that they must be in or very close, with access that was dry and level, to their fuel supply. A few sites, such as No. 2 and No. 37, possibly No. 32, and the three Hambledon sites, may have been fortunate in also having sand very close by. A small pond would seem to have been useful but only one third of the sites have a convenient water supply from pond or stream; for another third the water supply was inconvenient; the remaining third were

[6] *S.C.M.*, vol. 9, p. 791.

more than 200 yards away from any supply pond or stream. I cannot explain this, because the Weald has a network of small streams, which most sites appear to ignore. Water was needed to clean sand and flux, and also if crucibles were made on the site.[7] There is no evidence that hilltop sites were chosen to get a draught for the kilns; wind appears to have played no part in the siting. There is only one site (No. 32) which could possibly be said to be on top of high ground; it has a pond within a few yards.[8]

The task of identification is more difficult than Straker had with his iron-works as there is no arguing with a 10-acre pond, a possible mill house and perhaps many hundreds of tons of iron slag, whereas a glasshouse site may have only some pieces of crucible and a few scraps of glass to reinforce the vital field-name. So I must state the standards I have used: of the forty-two sites described and shown on the map and schedule, I have described twenty-six as proved, sixteen of these having some trace or more of the furnace floor or baked clay base,[9] and ten having satisfactory evidence that a furnace existed at or very close to the map reference given.[10] Two of the ten may have been demolished for their stone or brick, two were probably destroyed to make cultivation possible, two more were probably demolished and scattered when gardens were made and at least one was destroyed by earlier digs. That leaves ten probables and six possibles to be accounted for. The probables certainly existed and must be included in the distribution map though their exact site may never be found. Six of these, Nos. 6, 10, 27, 28, 30 and 39, have the vital field-name and both crucible and glass fragments in support but not in the necessary concentration to find the actual site. Two, Nos. 11 and 41, have a field-name and a little glass or crucible only.[11] Two, Nos. 15 and 16, have no field-name, but in the case of Hog Wood, No. 15 (*see* p. 175), enough evidence survived to suggest that the site may have been partly destroyed by its discoverer, Mr L. Constable, many years ago; the whole area was finally rooted up by pigs. It is inconceivable that anyone would dump a piece of iron blowpipe, and a few fragments of crucible and Early glass in such a remote spot. In the case of Idehurst north, No. 16, there is little doubt that the map reference covers the furnace site; it is one of those marginal sites that could belong to the probables or certainties. There is little to be said about the six possible sites. Two, Nos. 1 and 31, have field-names only and the search for further evidence has been negative. The other four, Nos. 19, 22, 24 and 34, with no field-names, have produced some glass and crucible but no trace of burnt area, stone, or brick structure.

[7] They may have had a well, as Mr Harrington found at Jamestown.   [8] *See* p. 192.

[9] *See* definition of a baked clay base, p. 147. The sixteen are: Nos. 2, 5, 7, 8, 12, 14, 18, 20, 21, 23, 25, 29, 33, 35, 40 and 42. Four, Nos. 25, 33, 35 and 42, were or are being excavated, and had some structural remains.

[10] Nos. 3, 4, 9, 13, 17, 26, 32, 36, 37 and 38. The evidence is discussed at each site. Where there is any doubt the map references are shown as approximate only.

[11] In the case of No. 11 I am relying entirely on Cooper's material and lists and he does not always note the crucible.

The disturbance on about two-thirds of the proved sites is such that it may be useful to describe what is likely to be found in future at the forty-two sites in the schedule. The actual sites of sixteen, ten probable[12] and six possible,[13] have not yet been found and some are probably destroyed. Of the remaining twenty-six:

6 were largely destroyed, mainly by cultivation, but sufficient evidence of their existence remained Nos. 8, 9, 17 and 18 and two in gardens, Nos. 26 and 36.

3 were largely destroyed but were carefully examined; two, Nos. 14 and 23, had been ploughed up, but had traces of a baked base, and one, No. 12, had traces of a burnt patch. It is very unlikely that any of these nine would repay further work.

2 were or will be completely excavated by Mr E. S. Wood; No. 33 in 1960 and No. 42 in 1965-7.

7 Nos. 2, 3, 4, 5 and 7 (Cooper family sites), 37 and 38 were turned over by earlier workers and re-examined by us. Some of them were destroyed long ago and it is very unlikely that they would repay further work.

2 Nos. 25 and 35 were uncovered and had ground plans made by Winbolt.

2 Nos. 21[14] and 29, were examined in some detail.

4 were identified only and remain virtually untouched; they are Nos. 13, 20, 32 and 40 and, though they had no obvious structural remains, Nos. 13 and 32 might repay complete excavation.

A new untouched site, with some small trace of structure surviving above ground and covered by a low mound or mounds, is likely to be more productive than any of the above, except possibly Nos. 13 and 32. It may be useful to outline the procedure used when searching for and proving glasshouse sites in copses. There are all sorts of banks and hollows in the local woodlands, left by old saw pits, iron ore or paludina limestone diggings and boundary banks. They are soon recognized. One hopes for, but rarely finds, a small rectangular low mound with some crucible fragments lying round it, at a dry and level site above a small stream or large ditch. No elaborate equipment is usually needed to find and prove a site, only a worn-down small grafter (spades soon break in this root-filled heavy clay) and a light spear, like a large meat skewer. When a likely spot is found it can be speared; in stoneless country any solid substances such as stone, brick, crucible or glass are easily detected, as they are usually within a few inches of the surface. The grafter can then decide if there is any evidence. More prodding and a minimum of digging may find traces of a stone or brick floor or the burnt clay layer, and more prodding may locate some glass fragments. A useful exercise which leaves the site virtually untouched. It is not excavation and makes no pretence to be. Having established a site it must be recorded precisely,

[12] Nos. 6, 10, 11, 15, 16, 27, 28, 30, 39 and 41. The first three were Cooper family sites.
[13] Nos. 1, 19, 22, 24, 31 and 34. They are shown in italic in the schedule.
[14] These two sites, on which I did much of the work, showed some promise and would have yielded more information if modern methods had been available.

preferably on a 6 in. O.S. map, and reported to the local Archaeological Society who now have members well qualified to decide whether the site, if a new one, is worth excavating.

Of thirty-six proved and probable sites only three, Nos. 15, 30 and 40, have now no known glass or crucible evidence surviving; only four (Nos. 25, 33, 34 and 42) of the remainder are not represented at Haslemere Museum.

The Wealden industry was confined to a few parishes in the thickly wooded part of the north-west Weald on each side of the Sussex-Surrey border, about sixty per cent being in Sussex. It probably started in Chiddingfold and the two adjoining parishes of Hambledon and Kirdford, spreading later to Wisborough Green, Alfold, Ewhurst, Billingshurst, and Lurgashall. Over ninety per cent of the sites are within five miles of Plaistow, the northern half of the old Kirdford parish. Chiddingfold and Kirdford were the centres of the Early period, and Wisborough Green[15] was the centre in Elizabethan times. These parishes have three-quarters of the sites. Wisborough Green has three times the number of known Late sites of any other parish. Its parish registers have at least twenty-six references to Frenchmen, (see p. 137), who appear only from 1567 to 1624.

There is a much tedious and perhaps trivial detail in this chapter but it is necessary to provide some of the evidence for preceding chapters and to collect and clarify earlier work. I have used Winbolt's description in *Wealden Glass* of the sites and their finds, to supplement my own inadequate notes. The Chiddingfold site descriptions are largely taken from Cooper's material, though in the case of Nos. 2, 5 and 7 and to a small extent No. 3, both Winbolt and I did some further work on them which I have used. The Chiddingfold sites presented the most difficult problem because for half of them I had to rely on Cooper's map, his loose notes and glass. I have revisited all the doubtful sites in the last few years except Malham, No. 28, which after the adjoining field was ploughed in 1965 was confirmed by Mr W. S. Taylor. I have selected what I consider valid from 'Glasshouse sites,' *W.G.*, pp. 29–47, and shown it as a quotation. My debt to Winbolt is great, particularly for Fernfold, Vann, Somersbury and Sidney Wood sites. I have used Winbolt's notes in *The Times* and the two *S.C.M.* articles which he wrote after *Wealden Glass* was published, to supplement my own experience and notes. Where Winbolt did most of the work on a site, I have used *W.G.* and shown such quotations clearly; *e.g.*, in No. 38, Sidney Wood. Of the remaining sites outside Chiddingfold and Kirdford, nine were unknown to Winbolt and I know all the other twelve sites, and on two of them, Nos. 23 and 29, did much of the work and kept notes on them.

I have found Cooper's record work very valuable and reliable, but his glass material less so. I know his problem. One is reluctant to discard many hundreds of apparently insignificant fragments and it is pointless to label large numbers of small trifling bits, so one falls back on separate boxes and open trays, because glass, even

---

[15] I use the old parishes, thus Wisborough Green included Loxwood and Kirdford included Plaistow.

Number on Map.	Name of Site.	Parish. P: Plaistow new parish. L: Loxwood new parish.	E: Early. (P): Provisional. T: Transitional. L: Late.	Clue. F: field-name. Ch.: chance find.	Date found.	Museum evidence. G: Guildford. L: Littlehampton. Le.: Lewes. H: Haslemere. V. & A.: Victoria and Albert. K: Kenyon. Later to Haslemere.	A: approx. site only. F: furnace floor or trace of. D: demolished for stone &c. P: ground plan survives, excavated. T: turned over by earlier workers. O.S.: marked on Ordnance Survey map.
1.	*Bowbrooks*	Chiddingfold	—	F.	—	—	—
2.	Broomfield Hanger (Gostrode I)	,,	E.	Ch.	1911	G., H., V. & A.	F., .T
3.	Chaleshurst, Upper	,,	E.	Ch.	1916	G., H., V. & A.	D., T.
4.	Chaleshurst, Lower	,,	L.	Ch.	1916	G., H., V. & A.	D., T.
5.	Fromes Copse	,,	E.	Ch.	1921	H., L., V. & A.	F., T.
6.	Gostrode II	,,	E. (P.)	F.	c.1916	H., G.	A.
7.	Hazelbridge Hanger	,,	E. (P.)	Ch.	1912	G., H. V. & A.	F., P., T.
8.	Imbhams	,,	L. (P.)	F.	1961	H., K.	? D.
9.	Pickhurst	,,	L. (P.)	F.	1951	H.	D.
10.	Prestwick Manor	,,	E.	F.	c.1916	H.	A.
11.	Redwood	,,	E. (P.)	F.	c.1916	H.	A.
12.	Crouchland	Kirdford. P.	E.	F.	1931	G., H., L., Le.	? D.
13.	Frithfold Copse	,,	T.	F.	1937	K.	*See p. 172*
14.	Glasshouse Lane	,,	L.	F.	1939	K., Le.	F.
15.	Hog Wood	,, P.	E.	Ch.	1931	—	D.
16.	Idehurst Copse N.	,,	T.	Ch.	1961	K.	? D.
17.	Idehurst Copse S.	,,	T.	Ch.	1938	K.	F., slight
18.	Little Slifehurst	,,	E.	F.	1934	K.	F., slight
19.	*Lyons Farm*	,, P.	—	Ch.	—	—	—
20.	Shortlands Copse	,, P.	?	Ch.	1935	K.	F., slight ? D.

if it is not flaking, is extremely difficult to label quickly and permanently. Fragments can be taken out for examination and put back in the wrong box or tray and the evidence is ruined. I suspect that this happened in some cases. I have used the term 'provisional' in the dating of sites Nos. 6, 7 and 11 because the odd fragment of Late glass appears among the Cooper material. I think the box system allows this to happen, and in the case of No. 7, I know the site and the glass Winbolt and I found, and I consider it was Early. The material from two sites, Nos. 8 and 9, is insufficient to

Number on Map.	Name of Site.	Parish. P: Plaistow new parish. L: Loxwood new parish.	E: Early. (P): Provisional. T: Transitional. L: Late.	Clue. F: field-name. Ch.: chance find.	Date found.	Museum evidence. G: Guildford. L: Littlehampton. Le.: Lewes. H: Haslemere. V. & A.: Victoria and Albert. K: Kenyon. Later to Haslemere.	A: approx. site only. F: furnace floor or trace of. D: demolished for stone &c. P: ground plan survives, excavated. T: turned over by earlier workers. O.S.: marked on Ordnance Survey map.
21.	Wephurst Copse	,, P.	E.	F.	1931	H., K.	F.
22.	*Barnfold Farm*	Wisborough Green. L.	L.	Ch.	—	K.	—
23.	Brookland I and II	,, ,,	L.	F.	1938	H., K.	F., O.S.
24.	*Burchetts*	,, ,, L.	L.	Ch.	—	K.	—
25.	Fernfold	,, ,, L.	L.	Ch.	1934	Le.	F., P.
26.	Horsebridge	,, ,,	L.	F.	1930	K.	A.
27.	Gunshot	,, ,,	L.	F.	1963	K.	A.
28.	Malham Farm	,, ,, L.	?	F.	1939	K.	A.
29.	Malham Ashfold	,, ,, L.	E.	Ch.	1930	H., Le., L.	F., P.
30.	Songhurst	,, ,, L.	L.	F.	1932	—	A.
31.	*Sparr Farm*	,, ,,	—	F.	19c.	—	O.S.
32.	Woodhouse Farm	,, ,, L.	L.	Ch.	1935	K.	*See p. 192*
33.	Blunden's Wood	Hambledon	E.	Ch.	1960	G., H.	F., P., D.
34.	*Gunter's Wood*	,,	E.	Ch.	1959	G.	A.
35.	Vann Copse, Burgate	,,	L. (P.)	F.	1931	H.	F., P.
36.	Ellen's Green	Ewhurst	L.	Ch.	1937	H., K.	A.
37.	Somersbury	,,	L.	F.	19c.	G., H., K., L.	T., O.S.
38.	Sidney Wood	Alfold	L.	F.	1923	G., H., K., L., V. & A.	F., T.
39.	Lower Roundhurst	Lurgashall	?	F.	1961	H.	A.
40.	Petworth Park	,,	L.	F.	1931	—	F., slight
41.	Lordings Farm	Billingshurst	?	F.	—	—	—
42.	Knightons	Alfold	L.	Ch.	1965	G.	F.

make a confident classification. And at No. 35 I consider the site is Late, but Winbolt's evidence may leave some doubt that it was re-used. Winbolt in his final article in *S.C.M.*, vol. 40, p. 160, says that No. 42 closes the list to date. I have omitted six of his Wealden sites (his Nos. 1, 3, 8, 12, 13 and 16) about all of which he was doubtful, because there is no evidence surviving for them. He counts Brookland three times, Nos. 33, 40 and 41. I have taken these two furnaces as one, No. 23, because they are close together and the glass is identical. He includes the Graffham and Northiam sites and I have dealt with these separately as they are outside the Weald proper. So that we are back to comparable figures arrived at differently, his 42 less 10 equals 32 (3 being possibles only). Since 1945 ten sites, Nos. 8, 9, 16, 22, 24, 27, 33, 34, 41 and 42, have been added to the 32 making my total of 42; of these three, Nos. 22, 24 and 34, are only possibles by my rating. At the end of his list of sites (*W.G.*, p. 51) Winbolt says 'This list is frankly tentative, as dating by the character of glass found is very difficult.'[16] The lists differ because thirty years have passed and new sites have been found and because I had the advantage of seeing all Cooper's glass material, his 'History' and loose notes. This enabled me to assess the merits of six sites about which Winbolt was doubtful. My list is arranged by parishes; his partly by the order in which they were found. I have discussed the sites in detail[17] and the evidence is summarized and analysed, so that anyone can make their own assessment. The sites are examined alphabetically by parishes. But the list remains tentative, particularly on the fringes. Some of my possible sites may be ruled out and some of my rejects may turn up.

Cooper's Sketch Map of Chiddingfold Parish Showing 'Antiquities'[18]

The original is with his papers in Haslemere Museum. It is neat and, like all his work, careful but is too small to be much more than a distribution map. It is printed (Plate XX) because it covers all the known Chiddingfold furnace sites, either as 'kilns' or as field-names, plus some known only to him. It is orientated to the north, and his scale (not shown) is approximately $1\frac{1}{2}$ in. to the mile. It also forms a basis for attempting to relate Cooper's evidence, recorded or glass, with glasshouse sites known today. Cooper was such a meticulous worker that it is unfortunate that no undoubted glass furnace site came to light until he was a semi-invalid (*c.*1909) so we have no proper plans of the Chiddingfold sites as found. Unhappily neither Winbolt nor I met him. I have not numbered Cooper's map because my distribution map and the accompanying schedule with its map references can easily be related to it. He marks fourteen sites as glass kilns; I have accepted seven of these (Nos. 2, 3/4, 5, 6, 7, 9 and 12) as proved or possible while the other seven are listed with approximate map references and reasons given for their rejection. He marks eight Glasshouse fields, four of these I have accepted as furnace sites (Nos. 1, 8, 10 and 11). Three are near to his kiln sites and could possibly relate to the kilns.

[16] I cannot accept his synopsis of sites according to centuries (*W.G.*, p. 51) for the reasons already discussed (*e.g.* p. 9), and have therefore omitted it. The synopsis includes six sites for which there is little or no evidence, these are discussed earlier in this chapter but not included in my schedule.

[17] No. 42 will be reported in full in a future volume of *Sy.A.C.*

[18] Of the other 'antiquities' shown, the Roman villa west of Whitebeech was carefully excavated from 1888 onwards by Cooper and his plan and notes and pottery are in Guildford Museum. Unhappily he did not publish his findings. He comments on the fine quality of the Roman window glass compared to the Weald product, he also notes that it was produced by the muff process. The Bronze age barrow at Gostrode is marked on the O.S. maps. The iron furnace at Furnace Place is discussed by Straker on p. 420 of *Wealden Iron*. Of the others I know nothing.

At least one 'kiln' site must have been added after Cooper's death in 1918, because No. 5 (Fromes Copse) was not found until 1921. How many more were added it is impossible to say. He was a local patriot, but essentially a careful man. It will be seen that over eighty per cent of the glasshouse sites are in the southern half of the parish. Five of his Glasshouse field-names came from the Tithe Apportionment schedule, one from his work on local deeds, one he assumed (viz. Ovenhouse Field to refer to a glasshouse) and one at Dyers Cross he appears to have associated with Laurence Vitrearius without proof. The small scale of the map makes it difficult to say in two cases whether I am discussing the site he has indicated. The Pickhurst (No. 9) confusion is discussed under that heading and the Gostrode (No. 6) is difficult because I have not succeeded in finding the actual furnace site. In the case of Nos. 1, 10 and 11 neither he nor I have found the actual furnace site. The rejections are due to lack of evidence at present and the furnaces may turn up in the future, except probably at Mesells.[19]

The following are Cooper's glass kiln sites on his map which neither Winbolt nor I could trace, or for which the evidence is unsatisfactory:

Atte Bridge	c.SU/961. 353. *W.G.* No. 1. R. (Picards Atte Bridge).
Combe House Farm	c.SU/943. 359. *W.G.* No. 3. R.
Furnace Place	c.SU/931. 331. Not in *W.G.*
Mesells.	c.SU/986. 347. *see* Salt Hanger. *W.G.*, p. 50.
Ovenhouse Field (Hovel Copse)	c.SU/942. 334. *W.G.* No. 12. R. (also marked as a field-name).
Killinghurst–West End }	c.SU/940. 338. Not in *W.G.*
Killinghurst–Wolhook }	c.SU/936. 336. *W.G.* No. 13 ?P.
Surreylands	c.SU/975. 325. *W.G.* No. 16 ?P.

The map references are of necessity very approximate. With the exception of Mesells, I do not rule out these as possible sites. These other suggestions of remotely possible glass sites in Chiddingfold come from Cooper's collection in Haslemere Museum and his appendix on 'Glass':

Rovehurst ($\frac{1}{2}$ mile W. of Broomfield). A label with a very doubtful small lump of glass.

Tugley (in the SW. of the parish). A fragment of blown glass and 4 other bits. No other clue. A wholly unconvincing lot. Tugley was owned and occupied with Pickhurst by the Peytowe family (*see* Hazelbridge Hanger).

Wyersfield, Dunsfold. Wholly unconvincing.

Duns Farm. SU/990. 368; *see* Chapter I, p. 26, note 7.

There remains of Cooper's and Winbolt's glass sites only one viz: Jewsley (c.SU/972. 342), *W.G.*, No. 8. ?P. There is nothing in Cooper's materials about this site;

[19] *See* p. 156.

Winbolt must have got some hint from Mrs Halahan of it as she lived close by. The crucible and glass found in a pond here could have come from my No. 9 site which is only about 600 yards away.

Atte Bridge

There is some confusion here in *W.G.* Pycards is the early form of Pickhurst and Cooper decided there was a furnace in or near the garden[20] of Old Pickhurst House, and marked on his map c.SU/970.342, where his daughter Mrs B. Halahan lived. The evidence from his collection is not convincing and it probably came from my No. 7.

From his notes (it is marked as Glasshouse Field on his map) he seems to have known there was a furnace in Glasshouse Field, 500 yards west of the house where a furnace was found (my No. 9) in 1951 and completely destroyed when a tree was bulldozed over. He suggests that it was worked by the Peytowes (the date of the glass and their ownership coincide) and that their depot was in Chiddingfold 'at the Bridge' where lived John Peytowe, glassmaker.[21] There is no evidence of a furnace in the village and Winbolt's idea seems to have arisen from Cooper's suggestion of a depot plus John's place of residence. It is unlikely that fuel would be carted into the village where there would be some fire risk.

Combe House Farm

There is no evidence in Cooper's material, record or glass, but of all the rejected Cooper map kiln sites I think this may turn up some day when a tree falls over or part of the copse is cleared. It is the one most worth pursuing. It will almost certainly be Late and was very probably worked by the Peytowes, who owned and occupied this land.[22] Cooper suggested that the kiln may be in or near Furnace Copse. Mrs Halahan said nothing was found there.

Furnace Place

There is no evidence in Cooper's material, but one of his daughters, the late Mrs P. Baker thought there was a site near here and there is a cryptic note among Cooper's papers of a kiln found at Furnace Place.

Mesells

This site is fully discussed by Winbolt who calls it Salt Hanger (*W.G.*, p. 50) and in spite of Cooper's confidence that this was a glasshouse, I think Winbolt is correct in his conclusions. He says 'after an exhaustive search I found no particle of

---

[20] With no supporting evidence, early glass fragments in a garden signify little. Many anciently inhabited sites in this district could produce them and the odd fragment of crucible and even stone from the furnace.

[21] *See* p. 117.   [22] *See* p. 117.

glass, a result I think impossible on a site where glass was made.' He found the area littered with tiles, mostly broken. Tiles are rarely found on Wealden glass sites. Mrs Halahan also said no glass was found. Cooper found this probable tile kiln of fairly recent date in 1904, made his usual meticulous drawings and left a detailed description. He had not then seen a glasshouse, and my guess is that because the land belonged to a glassmaking family at the end of the fifteenth century, he called it a glass kiln though he says 'nothing much' was found there. I think for once Jove nodded. I showed the drawings to Dr L. F. Salzman who agreed it was not a glass kiln. There is no field-name or other record to support a glass kiln. It is very unlikely that the Cooper family knew of a site for twenty years and never found a scrap of glass there. Among Cooper's papers are lists of numbered fragments which do not appear to relate to anything recognizable surviving in his collection. In one list there are eight references to fragments of glass from Mesells, but this is crossed out and Redwood written in. Redwood is the nearest probable site, being only 500 yards away. Under crucibles, there is a reference to fragments of whitish ware from Mesells. It is impossible to trace this and it is possible he forgot to alter this label to Redwood from which it could easily be a stray. This is the solitary and almost valueless evidence of glassmaking at Mesells. I have gone very thoroughly into the Mesells evidence, because it was the only place apart from his major task on the Roman villa that Cooper himself examined and of which he has left careful drawings. This may save future workers a deal of labour. I suspect the family scramble for glass did not fulfil his careful ideas; it is unfortunate that Hazelbridge Hanger glasshouse was not found in 1904 because of all the Chiddingfold sites this might have produced some valuable plans in addition to his description (p. 163).

Ovenhouse Field (Hovel Copse)

This site is marked on Cooper's map as a kiln and a field-name; he seems to have been confident that glass was made here. From a letter he wrote to Mr W. Hulme in May 1915, I think he related this name to a glass 'oven.' That name is lost but is mentioned in a deed of c.1282, and Cooper identified it with Hovel Copse on Killinghurst Farm. He says in his loose notes that lumps of crucible, coarsely made and not calculated to withstand fierce heat, and imperfectly fused glass were found here. He gives the dimensions of the pot which are not unlike a Jamestown size. Winbolt added, possibly on Mrs Halahan's evidence, that this site was excavated and demolished in the nineteenth century. There is no material to support this as a glasshouse in Cooper's collection or anywhere else. If it did exist it is very strange that nothing has survived because it was almost on the family doorstep at Chaleshurst.

Killinghurst–West End

Cooper's notes on crucibles record a fragment found at Kiln Copse, Killinghurst, and this may be the kiln site he marks on his map. Neither Miss A. Cooper of Killinghurst nor I know of any other evidence for this site.

Killinghurst–Wolhook

Cooper says there is no furnace here, but he marks it on his map. No other details known.

Schurterreshurst. Part of Surreylands. Chiddingfold. Early(?) c.SU/975.325.

W.G. No. 16. ?P. in Brambley Meadow. Clue: Unknown. Possibly found c.1910; Cooper gives no date; it is marked on his map as a glass kiln. In spite of the Schurterre association, I have considerable doubts about this site. Neither Winbolt in 1931 nor I twenty years later could find a trace of it. Cooper was sure of it and says it was worked by John Schurterre, glazier and parker of Shillinglee who owned this holding in the late fourteenth century (see p. 116). The evidence in his collection at Haslemere is very small, enough to be mentioned but not I think enough to include as a possible. Unhappily it was apparently one of the very rare Early sites (Blunden's Wood was the only other) to provide any convincing pottery. With the pottery is a fragment of crucible, almost the only and very slender evidence. Cooper says the pottery belongs to the fourteenth and fifteenth centuries. He gives details of a fragment of crucible which he links with this site, though it was found between it and Shillinglee near the Kennels. In his collection are seven small fragments of Early vessel glass (they could belong to the inhabited site) and a few unconvincing small lumps of glass from this site. Cooper says that tiles have been thrown up by the plough here as at Salthanger (see Mesells, p. 156). On his list of finds from various sites, which cannot be tied to the surviving collection except in a few odd cases, he says there was a scrap of deep blue, shaped glass found, and part of a vessel. There is an old lime kiln in the field. Commenting on pottery, Cooper, who had done a fine excavation of the Roman Villa, and was well aware of its value, says: 'very little pottery, besides crucibles, has been found on the glass sites and what there is of it is of the domestic kind. It was not needed for the production of glass, and therefore must have been in use by those engaged at the kilns.' We found exactly the same absence of pottery on the Early sites.

CATALOGUE OF NUMBERED SITES

No. 1, Bowbrooks, Chiddingfold. c.SU/9375.3257.

(c. = only approximate). W.G., No. 14R.[23] A possible site; no material evidence but a field-name, Glasse Field (not in Tithe/App), occurs as part of a small holding called Bowbrooks in a conveyance of 1803.[24] Cooper knew of this name and marked it as a Glasshouse field on his small map[25] and on his traced map No. IV in Haslemere

---

[23] W.G. No. 14. Furnaces mentioned in Winbolt's *Wealden Glass* will be shown thus. His P.: proved by excavation, finds &c.; his R.: reputed by documentary evidence, place names &c. Winbolt described sites found after 1931 and up to 1939 in the *Sussex County Magazine* (here abbreviated S.C.M.), December 1935 and May 1940 (i.e., vols. 9 and 14).

[24] Petworth House MSS., OG., 12/AP.

[25] In future shown as C.F. C.K. means the site of glass kiln on Cooper's map.

Museum. It may be the furnace he describes as Rodgate. The late Miss J. Cooper and I searched for it *c*.1951 and ten years later I searched all the headlands and ditches with no result. Cooper (p. 521) notes it came into Peytowe ownership, but not until 1633.

He calls it Bowbrooks and Glassefield, a house (demolished) and 30 acres of land. Glassefield comprised a copse of 5 acres abutting on Brookland Copse (6 acres) abutting on Rodgate land and a close of 3 acres abutting on lands called Cophall, known as Glassfield.

No. 2, Broomfield Hanger (Gostrode I), Chiddingfold. Early. SU/9610.3350.

W.G. No. 15P. Clues: unknown. It is marked as a glass kiln site on Cooper's sketch map. This was probably the first glasshouse site found by the Cooper family, in 1911. Mrs B. Halahan noted that they found no trace of a surrounding ditch as there was at Fromes (No. 5) or Hazelbridge (No. 7). We[26] examined this glasshouse in 1931 and found 'part of the red-brick floor of the furnace.'[27] 'Worked flints were found (H).'[28] They may have been used for cutting window glass to make the packing and transport easier to town workshops.

Found: 'Both window and vessel. Two good examples of disc (or spun) glass with selvedge edge and striation as the result of spinning. One piece shows that the disc had a diameter of 14 in. One flat piece of glass consists of two layers of the same green window.'

This being the first site for which I have used *W.G.*, I will give an example of my selection from it, to save tedious comments on other sites. I have italicized the selections in this one instance and commented on others. After describing how to find the site Winbolt says, 'This glasshouse appears to have been made in the fifteenth and early sixteenth centuries. Found: Glass, etc., and *worked flints* (H). Much of the glass is of the characteristic Chiddingfold type, *i.e.*, milky-green in colour, and of rough surface. *Hemmed bases of ale glasses suggest early sixteenth century date.*

In May *1931* I dug Broomfield Hanger with the help of Mr G. H. Kenyon. We found *part of the red-brick floor of the furnace*, quite close to (east of) the track, and six paces (west of) the fork in the tracks. The advantage of this site was that *sand is all around*, the supply was dug out just north of the track, opposite the furnace. The character of much of the glass, both *window and vessel*, is the light milky green of the thirteenth and fourteenth century, and a piece of crucible with inturned rim seems to corroborate this dating.

---

[26] Winbolt and I.

[27] Quotations from *W.G.* are shown in inverted commas. Winbolt in his own copy of *W.G.* amended 'red brick floor' to 'red clay floor' for site No. 5. I have no doubt this is correct and I think three other site floors, Nos. 2 (above), 20 and 21, might also be changed from brick to clay. *See also* p. 147.

[28] (H) = reported by Mrs B. Halahan. There is a Bronze Age barrow in the adjoining field, 200 yards away. A rare occurence in the Weald.

Window glass: *two good examples of disc (or spun) glass with selvedge edge and striation as the result of spinning. One piece shows that the disc had a diameter of 14in. One flat piece of glass consists of two layers of the same green colour; etc., etc'.* He goes on to discuss the use of pointed flints for marking glass.

There is no evidence for dating this glasshouse except broadly as Early.[29] There is no specific Chiddingfold type of glass, other than Early or Late. Hemmed or folded rim bases cannot be tightly dated in the Weald. I do not know if the adjoining sand was used, but judging by the quality, I think it is doubtful. It was ample fuel which brought and kept the glassmakers here. The light milky-green glass is here characteristic of Early glass and cannot be dated more closely. Inturned and outurned crucible rims may be found on sites of any date, and some of the most heavily inturned rims belong quite certainly (*see* site No. 32) to the late sixteenth or early seventeenth century. I have included the reference to disc or Crown window glass, because it is not common on the Early sites, and is usually rare on the more prolific Late sites. The two layers of flat glass of the same colour are probably due to successive 'gatherings' on to the blow pipe until sufficient glass had been collected.[30]

This site has probably always been a part of Gostrode Farm, unlike Gostrode II, (No. 6), which was only added to Gostrode after 1650 by Thomas Peytowe.[31] The main Gostrode Farm was owned by William Peytowe of Pickhurst at his death *c.*1546 and was probably bought by the family between 1503 and 1524.[31] Until this site (No. 2) can be closely dated we can only suggest that it could be a Peytowe furnace. It is one of the few that has reasonable claims. Cooper spent much time tracing the owners of Gostrode and says: 'It was held and occupied by a family called Gostrode *c.*1300–1423. They were followed by the family of Novell or Novelt; and they in the sixteenth century by the Peytowes ... of Pycards (Pickhurst) in the hands of whose descendants Gostrode remained until 1648.'

No. 3, Chaleshurst, Upper. Chiddingfold. Early. SU/9480.3323.

*W.*G. No. 10P. Found in 1916. Clues: unknown. C.K. I have separated the two furnaces, Upper and Lower (Cooper's terms) because though only about 40 yards apart they belong to two different periods. The ample glass evidence in the Cooper collection at Haslemere from the Upper site is all Early glass and might be any date before the mid-sixteenth century whereas glass from the Lower site is Late. Both the Chaleshurst furnaces were very close to the Cooper family mansion (now demolished) and no doubt thoroughly dug by them; they found a good many pieces both plain and coloured (with painting) at Upper, and many pieces with grozed

---

[29] There is a quantity of glass fragments of little significance from this site in the Cooper collection at Haslemere. One or two of these scraps might be Transitional, and must be mentioned. They may or may not belong. All our material was Early, and I have dated the site accordingly. Early does not exclude early sixteenth century.

[30] D. B. Harden, 'Domestic Window Glass, &c.', p. 46.

[31] *See* p. 118.

edges. Winbolt (*W.G.*, p. 36) quotes from a letter from Cooper to Mr Hulme that there was found here 'besides bits of vessels, bottles, crucibles, blow-pipes etc. an immense quantity of window glass,[32] both white and coloured. Add to this, over two dozen pieces with design on; of as I think, the thirteenth, fourteenth and fifteenth centuries.'

This painted glass would all be cullet brought in and if Cooper was correct in his dating of design it suggests that the furnace may have been working as late as the early sixteenth century. His collection at Haslemere is useful and contains crown, muff, and vessel, some of the crown having heavy 'bull's eye' centres, all pre-mid-sixteenth century. The window in Chiddingfold Church was put in by Cooper in 1916 and he said that 'it was made up of 427 fragments (224 being coloured) dug up by his family near what remains of three glass furnaces in the copses of two local farms.'[33]

The Lower furnace was probably worked by the Peytowe family, who owned Chaleshurst from *c.*1503 (*see* p. 118) and so they could have also worked the Upper furnace. There is no evidence of the Ropleys having any connection.

No. 4, Chaleshurst, Lower. Chiddingfold. Late. SU/9485.3328.

W.G. No. 11P. C.K. found in 1916. This site is 40 yards NW. of No. 3.

There are two separate furnace sites and I have retained Cooper's names of Upper and Lower as his specimens at Guildford and Haslemere are so labelled. The most interesting find here was almost half a small shallow crucible with some ruby glass still in the bottom (*see* Plate No. III). There is no doubt ruby glass was made here, after the mid-sixteenth century; whether it was more than experimental is not known.[34] Apart from a few bits in Guildford the only glass fragments surviving, and labelled by Cooper (now in Haslemere Museum) as from this site are good quality Late thin vessel glass, two or three having ruby glass applied on as opaque decoration. I might have dismissed these as probably cullet but for the fact of the crucible above. In view of the cullet difficulties, and as the bits Cooper found may represent only the latest batch, it is impossible to say whether only vessel was produced at this furnace. It is surmise, but it might have been the furnace which Jean Carré visited in 1567 where the glassmaker (probably Peytowe) told him he could make only vessel. There are two or three small fragments of Early glass among some hundreds of pieces from this site but they are probably cullet from the Early furnace (Upper) close by.

---

[32] Miss A. Cooper confirmed that this was their most prolific site.

[33] Mrs Halahan's notes (Haslemere Museum) state that the glass came from Chaleshurst, Gostrode (Broomfield Hanger No. 2) and two Pickhurst sites, one of which would be No. 7. Miss A. Cooper in 1964 said the bulk of the window came from Upper Chaleshurst (No. 3) and our Hazelbridge Hanger (No. 7), with a little from No. 2.

[34] Mr R. J. Charleston kindly arranged for this ruby glass to be analysed by the Corning Museum of Glass, U.S.A., and he says that 'Copper was evidently the colorant for the ruby,' as it was at the only other Weald site, No. 29, where ruby glass is known to have been made.

The glass is not the finest quality of Late. Winbolt notes that this site 'has now been destroyed by drainage works.' He notes that the fragment of a large crucible having a diameter of about 15 in. as having come from here; it is now in Guildford Museum.

Apart from No. 8, Imbhams (found 1961), and No. 9, Pickhurst (found 1951), which I have provisionally dated as Late, Winbolt was correct in saying that 'this is the only Chiddingfold furnace proved by the character of its glass to have been in operation after 1550.' There is a high concentration of eight known glass furnaces and four iron furnaces within a radius of two miles of this site, the latter being due to ample fuel supplies, some iron ore and suitable streams coming from the Haslemere Greensand ridge, providing water power. It is unlikely that any of the eight glass furnaces overlapped with the later iron industry, though it is just possible that Nos. 4 and 8 might have done for a short time.

No. 5, Fromes Copse, Childddingfold. Early SU/9721.3489.

W.G., No. 7P. Found in 1921 by the late Mrs B. Halahan. C.K. Clues: probably a small mound, see below. I know of no reliable evidence for dating this furnace or its glass except that the local product is unmistakably Early. The main characteristic in my recollection was the quantity of very small segments of window glass of a variety of colours, almost certainly the 'trimmings' from some glazier's workshop and bought as cullet. There is no evidence of colour being made here. Winbolt notes[35] that he 'dug out, barely a spit down the red Clay[36] floor of the furnace (18 ft. east-west by 15 ft. north-south) in the centre of a mound surrounded by slight ditches.[37] There may have been another furnace a few yards away to the northwest. The northeast corner was littered with window glass. The shape of the site was much obscured by earlier digging, our predecessors having no doubt skimmed the cream of it.' We found 'both vessel and window fragments. The vessel glass was ribbed and fluted, bases, necks and handles of bottles. There were rough lumps and pieces of crucible.' The palm glasses referred to by Winbolt (he later amended to their correct description) are undoubtedly the bases of glass hanging-lamps. Mrs Halahan found threads for decoration. It is just possible, no more, that this furnace could have been worked by either Alemayne or a Schurterre; the difficulty is to know the limits of these small properties at any date. It appears to have been purchased by the Peytowes in 1585.

Mrs Halahan discusses the site in Sy. A.C., vol. 34, pp. 24–31[38] and some of her notes are included in the Cooper MSS. Her dating has no supporting evidence; she found a shallow earthenware pan in fragments, which has not survived. She des-

[35] The information from W.G. is selected and compressed, see p. 159.

[36] In his own copy of W.G. brick is altered to clay. See p. 159, note 27.

[37] Small mounds of roughly such proportions occurred at three other sites, Nos. 7, 21 and 29. All Early and naturally still copses.

[38] She includes a small plan with no scale which tells us little and appears to ignore the possibility of cullet. The composite coloured window glass she describes is almost certainly cullet as we found no evidence of colour production. This is not a very useful paper.

cribes the vessel: bottles with wide flat lips, and straight sides, some with flute necks, swelling out of a pear-shaped body, some 'splendid examples of fluted glass,' both bottles and tumblers and a few pieces of very fine glass with laid-on veining. Very little painted glass. The remains of an iron axe (Haslemere Museum) were found here by Mrs Halahan.

No. 6, Gostrode II, Chiddingfold. Early (Provisional). c.SU/9645.3310.

W.G. No. 5?P. found 1916 or earlier. C.K. The clues are: Glasshouse Copse and two Glasshouse Fields (originally one), adjoining the County boundary and totalling 21 acres.[39] The approximate map reference relates to surface finds of a few bits of glass (Early) and crucible by Mr R. S. Porter of Chiddingfold and myself, after the east Glasshouse Field had been ploughed in 1961. They were a few yards north of the copse and 10–20 yards west of the gate from Glasshouse Field to Glasshouse Copse and Griggs Bottom. There was no burnt patch in the field and the kiln may be in Glasshouse Copse adjoining it to the north.[40] The glass evidence is not good. It is labelled Gostrode in Guildford Museum and is a few scraps of Early glass. In Haslemere in one box and two drawers, it is labelled, Glasshouse Field, Gostrode (my No. 6) to distinguish it from Gostrode, Broomfield Hanger (my No. 2).[41] The great bulk is Early, but there are a few bits of Late or Transitional, which must be noted, though in one case the drawer is a magpie hoard and I do not rate its witness very high, as I am not satisfied this is genuine Cooper sorting; the bits may have been dropped in by the family later. Mrs Halahan (W.G., p. 32) says part of a goblet of fine glass was found here, this does not seem to have survived. I am not satisfied that kiln sites were re-used (see p. 106) and have therefore described the site as Early (Provisional). It is an unsatisfactory site, because there is an element of doubt in the dating of the glass and because Cooper's site has not yet been located. However, I have no doubt of its existence because of the field- and copse-names plus the crucible and glass found by Mr R. S. Porter and myself. This site could have been worked by the Schurterre family who owned it in the fourteenth century, when it was not part of Gostrode Farm (see p. 118).

No. 7, Hazelbridge Hanger, Chiddingfold. Early (Provisional). SU/9660.3450.

W.G., No. 6.P., C.K. Clues: none, except a small mound surrounded by a ditch, found by the Cooper family in 1912. They refer to it as being in Roaring Pond Copse. It is, and probably always has been, part of Pickhurst Farm, the stream to the north,

[39] Tithe apportionment schedule and map; hereafter abbreviated to (T).

[40] Mr R. S. Porter has spent much time searching for glass sites in Chiddingfold and knows this copse well, but neither he nor Winbolt thirty years ago succeeded in finding any traces. He kindly drew my attention to this provisional site.

[41] Cooper marked both sites on his small sketch map; both correspond to my map refs. Miss A. Cooper told me they never found the furnace site, but like us only glass material in the field. In Sy.A.C., vol. 37, p. 245, Mrs Halahan describes and gives a drawing of a poor fragment of a vessel base found on Glasshouse Fields, probably this site.

below the hanger, being a natural boundary. Here the glasshouse was surrounded by a surviving ditch; only three others (Nos. 5, 21 and 29) had such ditches. This is the largest of the four, having a western extension shown on the plan; without this, its

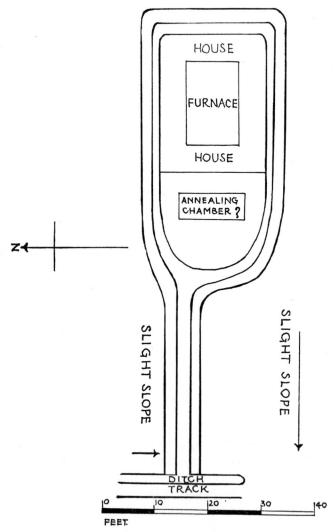

Fig. 15. Plan of Hazelbridge Hanger glasshouse (No. 7).

dimensions were normal. It was about 42 ft. by 20 ft. inside the well-defined ditch (*see* Fig. 15). The west end is shown by Winbolt as [?] annealing chamber, separate from the 'furnace floor of brick, still dark with wood ash, [which] proved to be about

15 ft. by 10 ft. (cf. Malham [Ashfold])[42] and the house floor about 25 ft. by 20 ft.'[43] Cooper has left a good description in his loose notes on Hazelbridge furnace site (No. 7), as they found it in 1912:

'Indications of the site of a glass kiln observed in the portion of Roaring pond copse (926) lying to the left of anyone passing along the footpath from the village to Pickhurst. Part of the footpath borders on two enclosures each called Glasshouse Field (964 and 954). There were one or two blocks of stone apparently still in their original position which formed one of the sides of the kiln. Clay burnt to the consistancy of brick in good sized lumps was found on what had evidently formed the hearth, and the soil below to the depth of at least a foot was of a brick red colour. Judging from such burnt earth the original kiln would have been oblong of from 12 to 15 feet by 5 or 6 feet [Mrs Halahan added correctly that the long axis was roughly east and west] this being the size of kiln found at Salthanger, Measles. [The Measles site had no sign of glass but many tiles, and Winbolt decided it was not a glass kiln, see p. 156]. The kiln had been practically demolished[44] at some period and most of the stone removed. There were no signs of tiles as at Salthanger suggesting they were not used here.[45]

Small fragments of crucibles were found within the area of the kiln but no glass to speak of. Outside the kiln what may be described as a refuse heap was found, containing innumerable fragments of glass and pieces of crucible.'

It is a familiar pattern we were to find on the few good sites, but I think he was more fortunate than usual in his 'innumerable' fragments of glass on a (provisional) Early site. I should not be surprised if much of the unlabelled glass in the Cooper collections at Haslemere and Guildford came from this site. It had been well worked and disturbed, before we refound it in 1931. Mrs Halahan notes that glass clear and coloured from this site and Broomfield Hanger is included in the window in Chiddingfold church.

This is a difficult site to deal with as one naturally prefers one's own evidence and not that of two other writers. I think Winbolt would have revised much of what he wrote in 1931 regarding the sites found or refound in that year. This was one of the first and he was full of enthusiasm and surmise. To be fair to his idea that glasshouse sites were reused, I think the best plan is to reprint those ideas for this site because, if any glasshouse was reused, this is the most likely.[46] He says: 'As this site affords an exceptional opportunity of defining the difference between thirteenth and fifteenth century (i.e., Lawrence and Peytowe) glass, we may go into detail.

[42] In the case of Malham Ashfold (No. 29) the area inside the ditches is the size of a part of the glasshouse with a furnace in its centre. [G.H.K.]

[43] Miss A. Cooper told me there was nothing left for her father to have made a plan. See also p. 80.

[44] I think Winbolt's 'some remains of the kiln' came from this note, because I recollect nothing surviving above the floor when we re-examined the site, after the Coopers had dug it over. [G.H.K.]

[45] I suggest no tiles, because it was a glasshouse and not a tile kiln. [G.H.K.]

[46] See also Chapter VI, p. 107.

The thirteenth century material is found at the bottom of the ditch. The glass is milky-green, opaque, and rough-surfaced, and has taken on a rusty-brown patina. The window glass is thinner than one would expect. There was one fragment of "bull's eye," broken right through the swollen centre. I found several small rounded bottoms of vessels, about the size of, or smaller than, the bottom quarter of a hen's egg: these are the remains of "palm glasses,"[47] of Saxon character. Also pieces of necks and lips of small bottles, one of $1\frac{1}{2}$ in. diameter at the mouth.

The fifteenth century is very distinct from the thirteenth century product. It is always near the surface of the ditch, clinging to the roots of the grass. Its characteristics are: a blue-green glass with a glossy surface, and a silver-grey irridescence with small brown spots: its appearance suggests a piece of metal. Of precisely the same character are fragments from Lichecourt, Vosges (sent by M. Varlot d'Hennezel) of the same century.[48] The blue-green glass is not so blue as at Sidney Wood (sixteenth century) [my No. 38].

Both window and vessel were made here at this period. The former is clearer and more burnished than the thirteenth century examples. Of vessel glass I found the wide out-turned rim of a jug ($2\frac{3}{4}$ in. diameter), broad necks, a base ($2\frac{1}{2}$ in. diameter) with a slight kick-up, two bases of biggish bottles, and other fragments. Mouldings on vessels are: (i) slightly raised ridges, e.g., on a neck, 3 ridges to $\frac{5}{8}$ in., the glass being $\frac{3}{32}$ in. thick; (ii) slight grooves, on the side of a small square bottle, 4 grooves to $\frac{1}{2}$ in., glass $\frac{1}{32}$ in. thick. This thickness appears to have been not uncommon.'

I know of no surviving evidence of all this except for a fragment of a 'welting-off ring' in Guildford Museum. The Cooper family called this site Roaring Pond Copse and there is a considerable amount of glass including some coloured window (?cullet) in their collection at Haslemere. It is all unmistakably Early except two fragments which might be Transitional. These odd scraps are puzzling among some hundreds of undoubted fragments of Early glass. They could be part of a chance batch which turned out better than usual, but more probably due to being unmarked they have got into the wrong drawer. But taken with Winbolt's 'blue-green' glass, I decided to call the site Early (provisional). The Coopers seem to have dug this site thoroughly; it was close to Mrs Halahan's house. It is this digging which makes me very doubtful whether any stratification could survive twenty years later and whether there were two periods here. It is not satisfactory and the doubt remains. I do not accept the dating; we have as yet no glasshouse evidence for thirteenth-century production and even if Laurence Vitrearius produced glass in Chiddingfold, there is nothing to associate him with this site. The poor opaque glass found by Winbolt could be a bad batch. Winbolt's blue-green glass is puzzling, and I have no recollection of it, but it does suggest that this site may have been reused. The fact that it was found on the surface probably means it was thrown out by the Coopers. Cooper notes that crucible from this site was glazed. Winbolt remarked on the

[47] Probably the bases of hanging lamps; they are only found on Early sites. [G.H.K.]
[48] Dated 1487 – c.1560; *W.G.*, p. 40. [G.H.K.]

scarcity of crucible here, and also that 'fragments of leading suggest that broken window glass was brought to the glasshouse as cullet.' They certainly do, as does the painted window glass found here by the Coopers. They found pieces of blow-pipe here. We found very corroded bits of iron on one or two other sites which could have been parts of blow-pipes or puntee rods. In Haselmere Museum there is a primitive form of spout of a glass jug from this site, found by Mr R. S. Porter (*see* Plate XIII). In 1958 he also found what may be another furnace site 22 yards due south of Hazelbridge glasshouse. The few fragments I have seen from it are Early.

Family associations here are uncertain. John Alemayne who supplied glass from Chiddingfold in 1351 was a local man having a small holding at Hazelbridge Hill afterwards known as Almeyns (*see* p. 29). In 1367 he granted to John Schurterre 'glazier' a 20-year lease of his tenement at Heyzulbrigg, not long after the property passed into Schurterre's possession and remained in the family for 200 years. (C). This small holding seems to be south-east of the road at Hazelbridge and cannot refer to our site. I have little doubt that the link with any family working this site must come with the ownership or tenancy of Pickhurst, and the only glassmaking family we know of owning or occupying Pickhurst are the Peytowes who were there from at least *c*.1440. Cooper suggests that Thomas Peytowe (1440) was perhaps the first of that family to settle in the parish. We do not have a close date when the furnace was working, but I think the Peytowes have a good claim and almost certainly worked No. 9, Pickhurst, which on the slight evidence surviving was working in the sixteenth century. There is a fragment of pottery found by Mr R. S. Porter, in the part marked by Winbolt as [?] annealing chamber, and Mr G. C. Dunning very kindly reported on it.[49] After a page of most carefully weighed evidence, he sums up: 'The evidence, which admittedly is not decisive, suggests that the sherd is later than the thirteenth century, and that it may be dated fourteenth century with some confidence, though it could be as late as the fifteenth century.' If the latter it could be a Peytowe furnace.

No. 8, Imbhams, Chiddingfold. Late. (Provisional). SU/9275.3362.

Not in *W.G. C.F.* Found in 1961. Clue: field-name Glasshouse Field (T). The site was known to Cooper as a meadow and could only be revealed when it was ploughed up. The glass waste was found by Mr A. Stemp of Imbhams Farm, who showed it to me.[50] The site is 250 yards slightly southeast from Imbhams farmhouse and 90 yards from the gate down the bridle road leading to Furnace Place, then 75 yards into the field. It is a fairly usual position on high ground above a useful stream which is only 100 yards away. There is a hard red pan of burnt clay about 9 in. down found when ploughing in Glasshouse Field at the map reference given. Scattered round this site are lumps of glass and fragments of crucible. It is curious that with

[49] Mr Dunning kindly reviewed the dating in 1964 but said that neither Mr J. G. Hurst nor he feels that it can, as yet, be dated more closely.

[50] I am indebted to Miss Stemp for informing the Haslemere Museum.

the exception of a tiny scrap of ruby window cullet, and a fragment of thick Early 'crown' window (?cullet) I could not find a trace of *certain* blown or finished glass fragments.[51] The lumps are large and there is one of almost certain 'frit.' With no finished glass, dating is uncertain so I have only provisionally dated it. The quality of the product is fair but the appearance is Late. Being now an arable field, it is probable that the furnace is completely demolished. I would however welcome some finished glass and some closely datable pottery from this site. The field is well sprinkled with iron slag but the glass furnace had probably shut down before the iron furnace 800 yards southwest was in production.

The variation in surviving glass material at different sites is puzzling. At Imbhams, for example, there were almost no vessel or window fragments lying about but there were considerable quantities of glass 'blobs,' and rough lumps of clear glass. I do not know what stage in the process they represent: they are not from a broken crucible. At Glasshouse Lane, Kirdford, the field around the two furnaces was littered with finished window glass fragments; it had very little of this lump glass.

No. 9, Pickhurst, Chiddingfold. Late (Provisional). SU/9660.3434.

Clue: Glasshouse Field (T). Not in *W*.G. C.F. Possibly found by the Cooper family *c.*1912,[52] Mrs Halahan refers to the two furnaces on Pickhurst but this site is marked only as a field-name (which it has) on the small Cooper sketch map; the second Pickhurst site is marked at Old Pickhurst House. I have seen no convincing evidence of the latter, though it may be there, and I have not accepted it. Almost any garden of a long-established dwelling in the four parishes which contain the majority of the glasshouses, may produce varying quantities of ancient glass fragments. I found four good Early hemmed-rim drinking-glass bases in my own garden. Garden surface material, even if combined with fragments of crucible, is suspect without other supporting evidence as for example, No. 26. The site at the map reference given above was discovered and destroyed when a hedge and tree adjoining Glasshouse Field were bulldozed in 1951. I have to thank Mr J. Clegg for telling me of it. It is 190 yards south of my No. 7 and from the few fragments of glass found it appears to be Late. I would have liked more evidence. The tree roots pulled out and destroyed any remains of the furnace floor. The site is puzzling because the tree above the furnace was possibly over 100 years old; it is difficult to see how Cooper can have known of it. Another baffling site with confused evidence, but one which certainly existed.

There are three boxes of Cooper material simply labelled 'Pickhurst'; they are useless because we do not know to which site they belong. I suspect they are garden finds. There is also a box of crucible fragments labelled 'Pickhurst' and some pottery from Pickhurst garden in the Cooper collection at Haslemere. There are many fragments of coloured glass labelled 'Pickhurst' in the smaller (and I think unreliable)

[51] No. 32 Woodhouse Farm also provided almost only lumps, very similar but bluer. Woodhouse site provided late sixteenth-century speckled ware.

[52] *See* also p. 156.

of the two lots of drawers of the Cooper collection. It is now impossible to determine where this came from, but from another labelled lot of glass which appears to be Transitional and is labelled 'Pickhurst, G. H. Field' (in the large cabinet of drawers) seems to have remained as found, so possibly Cooper knew of the 1951 site. The Coopers appear to have had three Pickhurst sites. Pickhurst Roaring Pond Copse (my No. 7), Pickhurst G.H. Field (my No. 9) and Old Pickhurst, which I consider are only garden finds.

The Rev. T. S. Cooper lived at Chaleshurst and his daughter Mrs Halahan at Old Pickhurst, under two miles away; Gostrode lay in between and Fromes close by. It is not surprising that seven of the ten probable Chiddingfold sites so far found are within this small area, the greatest concentration of furnaces in the district. So great was the competition between the six daughters to find a new site, that they kept their finds a secret. All this detailed attempt to identify the sites may seem trifling but if the material available is to mean anything now or to future discoverers of the same glasshouses it must be linked with an identifiable site.

No. 10, Prestwick Manor, Chiddingfold. Early. c.SU/9730.3530.

W.G., No. 4.R. Clue: The field-name is Glasshouse Close (T). C.F. Cooper on p. 73 of his 'Glass' appendix dates the furnace as fourteenth century and worked by the family of Le Frenche; there is no convincing evidence for either of these statements, but his record work is such that I would not dismiss the latter, though, with no known associated pottery, dating is unacceptable. Cooper notes that he found a bit of crucible here. There are the remains of a lime-kiln here and Cooper says that Glasshouse Close is 'close by' the lime kiln. I have not found the site of the glasshouse nor any material, but we have the required combination of field-name, crucible and some fragments of glass in the Cooper collection. The main evidence at Haslemere (a fair amount of glass) is in a grey boot-box, and has two labels, but the contents are un-happily mixed; the two labels are: Glasshouse Close, High Prestwick (this site) and Glasses Field, Redwood. Some of this may be the material listed by Cooper (see Redwood furnace).

The present farmer's wife, Mrs Cherryman, was very keen to find the furnace site (1961) and she followed the plough when the small Glasshouse Close was ploughed in 1957 and 1961, but found no trace of crucible or glass although she has found both in her garden at the house.

No. 11, Redwood, Chiddingfold. Early (Provisional). c.SU/9825.3495.

W.G., No. 9?P., C.F. Clue: The field-name is Glasses Field (T) – a very usual phonetic spelling. Miss A. Cooper says it was found before the 1914–18 war. Cooper says of 'Glasses Field,' Redwood: 'it is the only holding in the parish with such a name, that the fragments of crucible are superior to any found elsewhere, and can hardly be earlier than the sixteenth century but some of the glass is quite as ancient as any found at Surreylands (see Schurterreshurst). The glassmakers were therefore busy here, in all probability from the fourteenth century to the close of the sixteenth century and perhaps into the early years of the seventeenth century.' This is given in full as an example of the pioneers' ideas of dating[53] and continuity. Cooper found no satisfactory evidence as to which family worked this furnace. Being down to grass I could find no trace of glass or crucible here, but I have no doubt that there was a furnace here. We have a field-name, crucible and some glass too far from any known site to be casual scattered finds. Winbolt was doubtful about this site, but he had not seen all the Cooper notes nor his material.

Cooper lists the glass found here with detailed care as:
Lumps of deep green.
Fragment of pale blue (devitrified).
Pale green: 3 fragments of rims of bowls, tubular edges.
             2 fragments of rims of bowls, welted edges.
             1 portion of oval bowl.
             2 fragments of bottle necks.
             1 kick of bottle.
             1 fragment much decayed.
Deeper green:? fragment of kick of bottle.
Yellow green: fragment of neck of bottle.
             fragment roughly shaped.
Dull yellow, much irridesced: part of small handle.
                              part of small object.
White glass: fragment of base of wine glass. Only this can now be identified and
             looks like 'crystal' glass and is quite unlike anything found on the
             Weald sites. It is probably a stray surface find.

Some of the above may be part of the grey boot-box contents noted under Prestwick (p. 169), and some could be in the unlabelled Cooper material. There is also at Haslemere a small round box with a fragment of a glass base from Redwood. In the Cooper collection five-drawer cabinet are (5th and bottom drawer) about two dozen fragments of different vessels labelled Redwood, Glasshouse Field. They are mainly Early but some may be later, so I have dated the site Early (Provisional). Cooper meticulously described the shade and thickness of many fragments of colour; at one stage he seems to have ignored the possibility of cullet, but later mentions it. Like his records it is easy to get bogged down in the great weight of unselective and often trivial detail. Cooper took immense but unselective care; I have tried to note any fragments of the slightest interest but of this lot would probably have mentioned only the wine glass base.

No. 12, Crouchland, Kirdford. Early. TQ/0102.2967.

W.G., No. 25.P. Found in 1931. Clues: Glasshouse Mead and Glasshouse Fields together totalling 25 acres (T).

[53] *See* Chapter VI.

The site is in a narrow rew running south from Hardnip's Copse; it is possible that the furnace was on a former separate small holding called Hardnips (*see* p. 120). The glass is Early and the ownership of Crouchland, even if it then included Hardnips, is not known until 1618, when it belonged to Robert Strudwick. Some Strudwicks were glassmakers, but whether before the mid-sixteenth century at Crouchland is not known. There were no ground indications. The glass is Early, though I agree with Winbolt that it might be in the latter part of the Early period. The site was much disturbed and I have no note of finding more than a trace of the furnace floor – the usual deep layer of red, burnt clay running under the edge of the rew to the ditch, the digging of which probably destroyed further traces of the floor. In 1931 everything was new and wonderful and Winbolt's 'great variety of glass, both window and vessel' was somewhat enthusiastic. He lists some of the more distinctive pieces: 'hemmed feet, both over and under-turned; rigaree base; feet with very fine rilled moulding underneath; rods and tubes of many shapes and thicknesses, some with remarkably fine rilling; one tube is $\frac{1}{16}$ in. diameter (external); vessels with fluting, both perpendicular and oblique; applied ornament of thin wavy lines; spherical stoppers; bead rims, two pieces of flashed vessel glass with ornament, between the layers, of parallel lines in which a light brown colour merges into light blue; one piece of spun window glass $\frac{1}{32}$ in. thick, with "grozed" (pincered) edge, and another piece of the same thickness showing the outer curve with selvedge. By far the commonest thing found was shearings. The older specimens have brown metallic irridescence and are much corroded. Two pieces of crucibles with inturned rims suggest an earlier use of the site. Locally made medieval glass is found in the garden of Crouchland.'

This is given in full because much of it is useful although there are details which Winbolt would have amended today. The grozed edge glass is probably cullet from a glazier's shop or from a broken window, as windows (except small quarries) are unlikely to have been shaped at the furnace. The idea that the older glass was the more corroded is very doubtful. The remains of bad batches can occur at any Early site but are, so far, unknown on the Late sites, except Nos. 37 and 42 (*see* p. 102). In the Weald, crucibles cannot be dated by the shape of their rims. Some of the most heavily inturned rims came from an undoubted Late site, Woodhouse Farm (No. 33). The reuse of sites, one of Winbolt's favourite ideas, is discussed on p. 106. Garden glass can occur on any formerly inhabited site; unless from a bad batch, it can last for centuries, and people threw out their breakages then as now. By themselves, the bits may be interesting, but their origin is uncertain. This site was fairly prolific in glass fragments, more so than any other Early site, outside Chiddingfold, except possibly Malham Ashfold (No. 29). No other site produced anything like the number of shearings[54] from vessel glass. It is pure chance what happened to miss the cullet collection. There seems no significance in the fact that here were about a hundred bits of vessel for every bit of window. The question of surviving fragments is

[54] Some of these twisted shearings can be seen in Guildford Museum.

discussed on p. 18, but the cullet practice ruins the material evidence; it may hint but does not convince.

No. 13, Frithfold Copse, Kirdford. Transitional. SU/9793.2850.

W.G., No. 37. Found 1937. Clues: Glasshouse Field adjoining (T). *S.C.M.*, vol. 14, p. 156. Winbolt describes the site as 'typical'. Thirty years ago we tended to regard such a site as typical whereas, today, reviewing all the known sites, possibly only about a third had most of necessary requirements (*see* p. 148): a dry, level site, with easy access to fuel supply, and some water available. Frithfold was perhaps the perfect site by these standards. It had no convincing mounds, but more than any site it had a quantity of bricks[55] and broken crucible still lying about on the surface scattered over an area of 60 ft. square. It lies in a small rew, on the east side above a shallow valley, on level ground 25 yards south of, and above, a small pond (marked on the 6 in. O.S.) made by damming the stream which is little more than a large ditch. Doubtless the pond was used by the glassmaker; it is far too small to be a reserve supply for the iron forge (hammer) pond of Wassel, 250 yards away. The site is 15 yards in from the edge of the rew. It is one of the very few sites (No. 32 is another) which might be worth complete excavation, though with nothing above ground it is unlikely to provide much fresh information.

There are some undoubted Late blue-green fragments, but there are some less good fragments, not typically Early, which may be cullet but perhaps were made there. The glass is therefore difficult to classify and it does not fit neatly into either Early or Late dating, so I have taken refuge in 'Transitional.' There was a great change in the mid-sixteenth century (*see* p. 101) but both here and at Idehurst North and South the change was not clear-cut and came only partially. Curiously enough the three 'Transitional' sites were very close to iron forges[56] with attendant competition for nearby fuel supplies. The dates suggest this, and perhaps all three sites (Nos. 13, 16 and 17) overlapped but gave way to iron demands. Some bright 'gold' surface flaking was found on the glass from this site. Another clear example of this unmistakable flaking was on some of the Woodchester glass now in Stroud Museum. This might suggest a Late date, but this surface breakdown does occur rarely on other

---

[55] Of 32 fragments of bricks found, 62 per cent were 2 in. thick, 26 per cent 2¼ in. and the remainder varied from 1¾ to 2½ in. Only eight had enough to show width, five were 4 in., two were 3¾ and one was 4½ in. Winbolt (*W.G.*, p. 68), discussing the firebricks he had found, says 'Some of those I have found measure *c.*7 in. by 4½ in. by 2 in. thick: the thickness is fairly constant. Sometimes great cavities as much as 1½ in. deep have been eaten by the metal into the brick, so that only ½ in. of the thickness remained. Whole bricks are very rare.' Did he mean bricks found on furnace sites or actual grey crucible-textured bricks?

[56] The operating dates of Wassel forge were at least 1579 to 1640, very probably earlier because it is mentioned in the will of Thomas Smith of 1579. See *S.N.Q.*, vol. XIII, p. 235. The operating dates for the Idehurst forge were at least 1584 to 1634 (and probably 1662). It was owned by the Strudwick family; *see* p. 178. At Frithfold and Idehurst there is little doubt that glassmaking preceded iron working, and whether they overlapped is problematical.

sites, or it may simply be imported cullet, or a combination of special ground conditions and a particular batch. The dating of the Frithfold and Idehurst sites (Nos. 13, 16 and 17) has more than the type of glass to support it. Henry Strudwick left to his two sons, in 1557, his glasshouse etc. (*see* p. 119). Both the furnaces found in the extensive Idehurst copse produced the same type of indeterminate glass, which this recorded date suggests may belong to the period of *c.1550–c.1580*.

Frithfold furnace was found in the copy-book way: a field-name; then a search in the adjoining stream when it was dry in summer for crucible or glass; finding crucible and searching the higher and level ground above for a mound surrounded by a ditch. In this case it was easy, because of brick and crucible scattered on the surface. Both vessel (one bit with diagonal moulding) and window were found, some of the latter very thin and characteristic of the Late product. The thickness test is only a very rough guide. Fragments of pottery from the site were dated as sixteenth century by Mr A. Oswald. In 1963, Mr W. Taylor found some crucible in a newly ploughed field 600 yards NNW. of the furnace. I also found about a dozen pieces of crucible – one with a heavily inturned rim – mainly on the south side of the field, but no evidence of any furnace site. I also found a few indeterminate lumps of glass. The field had had iron slag scattered about and I think the crucible may have come from the furnace site described and been used, like the slag, as a yard bottom and carted out with dung.

The glass from Frithfold and the Idehurst sites is similar, but Frithfold shows more surface corrosion and some is slightly blue-green whereas the Idehurst glass is more yellow-green. It is difficult to make exact comparisons on glass quality and appearance because the shade varies with the thickness and freedom from decomposition and the usual trifling scraps are too few.

There was evidence of Sussex marble being used for parts of the furnace; this is not surprising because the main quarries in the district are close by on both sides of the stream running north from Wassel mill pond. Use was made of whatever material was handy. Some of the crucibles have glazing inside and out; many sites have evidence of this (*see* p. 52). There is a possible connection of Frithfold with the Strudwick family[57] and it may not be a coincidence that the glass is similar to that from Nos. 16 and 17 worked by Strudwicks. It is not up to the standard of the best Late glass and the Strudwicks may have succeeded in getting only part of the Frenchmen's greatly improved technique. On the other hand, it is not as fine a quality as that produced at Glasshouse Lane (No. 14) which may also have been a Strudwick glasshouse of later date.

No. 14, Glasshouse Lane, Kirdford. Late. TQ/0080.2370.

W.G., No. 24?P. and *S.C.M.*, vol. 14, p. 160. Clues: The glasshouse had more field- and place-names than any other. Glasshouse: lane, cottage, two fields and a large copse (T) totalling together 40 acres. We spent much time searching as there

[57] *S.N.Q.*, vol. 7, p. 173.

are no ground indications. There appear to have been two furnaces 50 yards apart. The map reference is for the first site found in 1939[58] and partly destroyed by a ditch and hedge. The second furnace site[59] was found in 1948 after the adjoining small meadow had been ploughed and a burnt area exposed, 50 yards SE. of the first. It is within a few yards of Glasshouse Cottage, demolished about 50 years ago. Both furnaces produced identical Late glass of uniform fine quality, similar to that from No. 23 Brookland, Wisborough Green, but not quite up to that of No. 36 Sidney Wood, Alfold, the finest of all Weald glass. Brookland also had two furnaces, 33 yards apart.[60].

A small stream, little more than a large ditch, was dammed up just behind the furnace and may have supplied the glassmaker with water. A knopped stem of Late vessel glass found in the stream has not survived. More fragments, mainly diamond-shaped window quarries[61] survived here than at any other untouched site I recollect and could be explained by it being among the last furnaces to work in c.1618.[62] When the Weald glassmakers moved away to the coal districts the site may have been abandoned and no one bothered to collect the waste. Much of the window was very thin, from $\frac{3}{32}$ in. to less than $\frac{1}{32}$ in., a characteristic of the late sixteenth and early seventeenth centuries. Being thin it was no doubt cheaper per sq. ft., and let in more light; some appears to be almost colourless. It is all muff, no crown being found. The glass is certainly Late. A base of brown salt-glazed stone ware found here was kindly examined by Mr K. J. Barton in 1963. He said it could well belong to the last quarter of the sixteenth century, but not much earlier and not later; it could easily have been in use up to 1618.

Part of a beautiful glass dish (see Fig. 11, p. 92) was found here, but unhappily it got broken and thrown away. It was the best survival of vessel found in the Weald.[63] Mr A. B. Nicholls, who found it, has approved this sketch. Glass tubes were made

[58] By Mr A. B. Nicholls of Kirdford.

[59] The furnace and its floor were probably dug out for road metal; it is only 25 yards from the road, once a green lane. The quantity of crucible and glass fragments, apparently as left, and the very obvious burnt area, suggest a second furnace.

[60] The question of multiple working furnaces is discussed on p. 81. Chaleshurst (Nos. 3 and 4) had two furnaces, 40 yards apart; No. 29 probably had two 20 yards apart. Five other sites may have had a second furnace.

[61] Subject to the cullet snag, the evidence here, unlike the Early window glass, suggests that the quarries were cut at the glasshouse. This would have the merit of ease of packing, minimum weight for transport and leaving the valuable cullet waste from cutting at the glasshouse. Thickness clearly varied and if it was sold by weight, the very thin might cost only a quarter of the thicker per square foot, a detail to watch if one is trying to assess cost of glazing. The quarry size is impossible to estimate as the fragments are too small, but they were probably within the common limits of 3 to 4 in. sides.

[62] This would fit in with the probability that the finest glass came from the last glasshouses to work. This site and Sidney Wood are the best. Both had much glass surviving, and produced such uniformly fine glass that we can safely accept the great bulk of the glass fragments as of local manufacture.

[63] It was without any doubt a local product. Our glassmakers made some common forms but they no doubt experimented and made some vessels for fun. This and the 'bird's wing' from Fernfold may belong to those classes.

here possibly for experimental equipment. A fragment which may be part of the neck of a retort was also found, it is now in the Barbican House, Lewes, Museum.

A fragment of a posset cup spout was found (Fig. 11). Mr Nicholls who shared with me the work on these sites, built up a very large fireclay vessel, glazed inside and out, from a large number of fragments. He did it by using the patterned glazing running from the base to the rim and noting the varying thickness of the walls. It is $2\frac{1}{2}$ in. thick at the base, $\frac{3}{4}$ in. at the rim, $20\frac{1}{2}$ in. high and roughly ovoid at the mouth being $21\frac{1}{2}$ in. across one way and 17 in. the other.[64] It weighs nearly 1 cwt. empty. He estimates that it is about 75 per cent. of the original pot. It is interesting but does not fit the probable scale and output of our furnaces,[65] though other very thick fragments of crucibles are found. There is no glass in the bottom and while I am not satisfied that it is a crucible, why should it be made of fireclay? Was it a storage jar for finished vessels such as appears on the extreme left-hand side of the Mandeville drawing of a glasshouse (*see* p. 73)?

The glass from this site more nearly approximates to the good quality dark green forest ware type of vessel glass found on the bombed sites in the City of London, than any I know. I have to thank Mr A. Oswald for showing it to me. We have so very little that could be even vaguely reconstructed to a known vessel form that comparison by shape is not possible; furthermore I am not satisfied that the glass is identical. Thanks to Mr N. Cook, I examined the material again in 1962 and have no reason to alter my opinion that this glass was not made in the Weald. A medallion of window glass from the site is in the Pilkington Museum at St Helens.

The question of who worked this site is difficult. The first site found was on the edge of a small field adjoining Marshall's Farm, but it now goes with Buckfold Farm. The Strudwick family, who are known to have been making glass between, at least, 1557 and 1597, owned Marshall's Farm in 1622 and are a strong possibility.[66]

No. 15, Hog Wood, Kirdford. Early. c. TQ/0194.3208.

W.G., No. 22.P. A chance find, no clues. Winbolt calls this Strudwick Wood of which it was possibly once a part; later it was part of Ifold House lands. It would not have been found but for the assistance of the late Mr Hawkins and is about as inaccessible as one can imagine and in a bog of heavy clay. Winbolt was told of it by the late Mr L. Constable who had lived at Ifold House. Judging by the condition of the spot where glass and crucible were found, I think it must have been completely destroyed by pigs running in this copse and woodland. Only enough survived to show there had been a furnace. A short length of much corroded blow-pipe was

---

[64] If crucibles had ovoid mouths, fragments of bases would provide a more reliable guide to their size.

[65] Neither Vann nor the Bishop's Wood furnaces could have accommodated it.

[66] *S.N.Q.*, vol. 7, p. 173. There is always the difficulty of establishing the Farm to which outlying fields belonged at any given time.

found with a hole roughly $\frac{1}{8}$ in. in diameter. From the few scraps of glass found and the possibility that this is the glasshouse referred to in a deed of 1385 (*see* Chapter 1, p. 31) this site appears to be Early. More evidence is desirable; I spent much time there with little result. More than half the Early sites produced almost nothing in the way of floors, glass or crucible. A fragment of ruby glass, probably cullet, found here is now in the centre of the lancet window in Kirdford church (*see* p. 5).

When discussing his Surreylands site, Cooper says the land belonged to the Schurterres in the fourteenth century and they had an interest in the glasshouse in Kirdford 'where glass similar to the earlier types at Shortershurst has been found.' It is likely that the Constable family of Ifold House may have examined the Hog Wood site and showed their finds to Cooper. If so it might account for the confused destruction completed by pigs. Cooper makes no other reference to this 'Kirdford' site and there is no labelled material in his collection. Cooper identified Stroudwickeswoude and Souzwoode as part of the Ifold House estate (not the recent housing estate of that name).

No. 16. Idehurst Copse, North. Kirdford. Transitional. TQ/0315.2596.

Not found until 1961. No clues except slight ground disturbance and scattered crucible. Water from the main Kirdford river is only 50 yards away. Mr W. Taylor of Horsham kindly told me of this site and we examined it in February 1962. It is 650 yards north of the furnace found on Idehurst in 1938. Both are on the edge of a large copse once belonging to Idehurst. I think the glasshouse site was probably just inside the copse at the point given by the map reference but though the ground had clearly had some structure and signs of burning, we could not find the actual furnace floor in the time available and it may not survive. The field on the edge of the copse here, Hammer Field, had scattered glass and crucible fragments: enough to show the close proximity of a glasshouse. A fragment of pottery was kindly dated by Mr N. E. S. Norris as early sixteenth century. The glass is identical to that found at Idehurst Copse south (No. 17) in 1938, and can safely be attributed to the Strudwicks.

The type of glass is discussed under Frithfold, No. 13 (p. 172). The glass from the two Idehurst furnaces may be of slightly inferior quality to that from Frithfold, but unless one had hundreds of fragments from which to judge I do not place any importance on this. What survives may have little precise significance (*see* p. 18). A dozen lumps of glass, five pieces of window, and ten fragments of different crucible, were mostly found just inside the field from the edge of the copse. A broken piece of Purbeck marble[67] slab about 10 in. × 4 in. and 2 in. thick, smoothed and flattened was found on what I believe is the furnace site just inside the copse. It might well be the remains of the mavering slab and is confirmed as Purbeck by the Geological

---

[67] Purbeck 'marble' is found on Roman villa sites and in many churches in the county.

Museum. On the fifteenth-century drawing the glassblower is shown shaping and smoothing a vessel on a mavering slab.[68]

The furnace could be under the oak tree close to the SW. corner of this small extension of the copse into Hammer Field where there is pronounced mound. At Brookland and Pickhurst the kiln sites were directly under oak trees. The site almost adjoins the Idehurst iron forge 175 yards away.[69]

There are six known Strudwick glassmakers (see p. 119); William appears in the Kirdford baptismal register in 1595 and 1597 as "glassman"; unhappily his wife's name is not given so we cannot trace him to Idehurst. This site is one of the few which can be closely dated by record (see p. 178). The Idehurst Strudwicks were probably primarily farmers who worked the hammers when water was available, and the glass when there was no urgent farm call on their labour.

No. 17, Idehurst Copse, South. Kirdford. Transitional. TQ/0316.2535.

S.C.M. vol. 14, p. 167. No. 39. Found 1938 by chance. Winbolt calls it Clarkes farm[70]. Clue: When the house on a 5 acre holding called Hazelhurst, adjoining Idehurst, was being restored, the builder told Winbolt he had found under the third of five successive floors[71] a quantity of glass crucible used as a rubble foundation. This shows one use to which crucible fragments were put. There were no field-name clues nearby and no known glasshouse within about $\frac{1}{2}$ mile, but looking at the 6 in. O.S. map for the nearest combination of small stream, copse and arable field, I went almost straight to the site. There was glass waste just outside Redfield Copse, an outlier of the large Idehurst Copse, and just inside the remains, much dug about, of the glasshouse. It was one of those lucky days; some sites with better clues still elude me after many hours of search.

Hazelhurst was probably rebuilt c.1600–40 (like the majority of the local dwellings); someone remembered the abandoned glasshouse and took a cartload of its remains to the house about 500 yards away. It was a particularly lucky find because we know the date and who worked this glasshouse. A prominent local yeoman family, the Strudwicks, who later were also small ironmasters, provide an interesting and possibly unusual example of diverse activities which may have helped them to become a leading family of their class in the district in the first half of the seventeenth century. The idea that industrial enterprise belonged only to the larger landowners

[68] Prof. W. E. S. Turner, quoting from Merret, says 'the Marble whereon 'tis wrought must be of the hardest stone, and must be wetted else the marble will break and scale.' *Glass Technology*, vol. 3, No. 6, pp. 201–213.

[69] *See also* p. 172.

[70] The field in which the crucible and glass were found was part of Clarkes Farm in 1938, but earlier was part of Idehurst. This ever-changing pattern, the transference of fields, and the absorption of small holdings into larger units, makes correct identification difficult at any date.

[71] An interesting comment on the eternal question 'what date is my house.' In this district, at least it suggests a half-way mark for most inhabited sites, primitive hovels from c.1250 and less primitive houses after c.1600.

is not correct here. The Idehurst iron forge was[72] on their land and they somehow raised the cash to build it; the glass kilns would need very little capital except in the purchase of woodlands for fuel.

Finds: The glass is difficult, but the record, thanks to Henry Strudwick's will of 1557, is clear enough.[73] The glass is identical with No. 16 and classified as Transitional. The site had been thoroughly dug about but I got a fair amount of glass. A stream, little more than a ditch, yielded furnace bricks and crucible and above, on a knoll, were the usual tattered remains of the furnace.

The glass was remarkable for its thinness. Some fragments of coloured window glass were found and there is a possibility that there had been experiments in producing ruby glass; some of the waste scum suggested this. I have a note of odd fragments of ruby, amber, pale blue, white, dark green, pale green and blue-green; they have not survived. There was little demand for coloured window in the mid-sixteenth century and these few scraps and the odd scrap of white were almost certainly simply imported cullet. Sufficient glass fragments were found to have some significance; here, most of it was window. Winbolt notes that the crucibles were distinctive, with 'big heavy rounded rims like those of some Roman pots.' I do not remember the 'copper clinker' which he mentions in connection with the making of ruby glass here. That is strange because I had been much involved with this ruby glass idea at Malham Ashfold. I have a note made at the time, but no other evidence, that there were fragments of devitrified opalescent blue-green glass which suggest they were made into vessels; Pape possibly found the same type at Bishop's Wood.[74] It is produced by maintaining the glass for a long period at a temperature just insufficient to cause fusion.

I noted that the vessel glass was frequently very thin and showed considerable skill in working; that both disc and muff window glass were found (but not necessarily made here) mostly on the east side of the furnace. Crucible fragments showed three or four patterns of simple decoration round the rim. One fragment gave a diameter of 10 in. All the material from this site found in 1938 has disappeared and what I now have was found when I revisited the site after the war; it confirms the suggested date as Transitional.

No. 18, Little Slifehurst, Kirdford. Early. TQ/0020.2831.

S.C.M., vol. 9, p. 787. No. 29. Found by chance draining in 1934. A deed of 1598[75] shows that an adjoining field to the east, once woodland, was then named Glasshouse Wood. The name has since been lost. The site may have been cleared woodland; it is called Rails Field in the Tithe schedule. It is an apple orchard and the

[72] E. Straker, *Wealden Iron* (London, 1931), p. 425. Straker calls the Idehurst forge, Barkfold.
[73] *See* Chapter VIII, p. 119. Only three sites, Carré's Fernfold (No. 25) and the two Idehurst sites (Nos. 16 and 17) can be tied to known persons.
[74] Pape, p. 39.
[75] Shillinglee MS., B.4, No. 4, now in the West Sussex Record Office.

furnace floor is underneath an apple tree. The site is good, well drained, and near the top of a slope with a small spring close by. For three years before the site was found, a furnace was suspected in the vicinity, because crucible and glass fragments were found in nearby fields and a garden. I suspect that a large lump of glazed 'siege' found in the base of a demolished cottage[76] 820 yards away came from the site (see also No. 17). It is likely that relics of demolished furnaces may stray for upwards of $\frac{1}{2}$ mile. The furnace site was found when a lump of glass was found during draining operations; the ground when ploughed showed red, and the furnace floor was at the usual depth of about nine inches, well below normal horse ploughing depth here. It was about nine inches thick of the local stone from the Bedham Greensand ridge, burnt red and covered with a layer of ash and charcoal; the long side was probably intact at 16 ft., there remained only about 2 ft. of width, the rest having been dug out. The usual crucible, lumps of glass and glazed sandstone and a very few fragments of window and vessel were found. There is little doubt that the glass is Early, but I would have liked more finished glass fragments. The product was very similar to that of Crouchland. I am not very happy about Winbolt's 'red plastic clay' nor that red-bodied crucibles at Crouchland and this site were made from it; it is doubtful if this clay would make pots capable of withstanding great heat.[77] The Strudwicks occupied Hills Green, of which Little Slifehurst was once a part, from at least 1578 (P.R.) but as this glass is Early the link is uncertain.

No. 19, Lyons Farm, Kirdford. ?c. TQ/0026.3137.

S.C.M., vol 9, p. 790. No. 31. Winbolt calls this Weald Barkfold, but it is part of Lyons Farm. He says: 'The site [which lower down he says was not found] is $\frac{1}{4}$ m. NW. of Plaistow Church, and NNE. of Nell Ball, on a footpath in a ploughed field leading to Weald Barkfold, opposite (E. of) a duckpond in a gill . . . We found [in 1934] plenty of lump glass, glazed sandstone and much crucible but not the furnace site.' The place is about 150 yards due east of Lyons farmhouse, but a recent search was unrewarding. My recollection is that the glass was Early. I have left the date as undetermined.

I think there was a furnace nearby and mark it as a possibility. It might have been worked by Richard Mose, glassmaker of Kirdford who bought some land in 'Pleystowe' in 1547 and who, in 1558 when he is described as yeoman, made over to his son a house lately built by him with an acre of land between the chapel at Plaistow and the highway to Chiddingfold.[78] This must have been no more than about 400 yards away from the place where the glass and crucible were found.

[76] A large piece of crucible base was dug up on the same site.
[77] This is discussed by Mr E. S. Wood in Sy.A.C., vol. 62, p. 68.
[78] The late Rev. W. Budgen very kindly sent me a copy of these deeds, now in the custody of the Sussex Archaeological Trust; the references are B.541 and B.542.

No. 20. Shortlands Copse, Kirdford. Early (Provisional). SU/9960.3235.

S.C.M., vol. 9, p. 791. No. 32. There are no field-name clues or ground indications. The site was found in 1935, when the copse was cleared, revealing crucible
and glazed siege. It is a good, well-drained, level site and just above a small stream.
Winbolt says: 'The site was found during the driving in of a post. The red-burnt
clay and brick[79] of a floor are about 10 in. down and there is much broken glass and
whitish crucible both on the site and down the slope of the copse to the nearby
stream.' All that remains are two small lumps of glass and six fragments of vessel
and window which appears to be Early and similar to the samples from Hog Wood.
It was not dug out because nothing remained above ground; at the time there were
more profitable sites to be examined. As far as I can find out this woodland, certainly
since 1648, was never inside Shillinglee Park although the boundary is near. The
name has faint suggestions of the Schurterre family but there is nothing more to
associate them with the site. Crucible was seen in the stream in 1964. The site might
turn up again when the copse is next cut *c.*1970.

No. 21. Wephurst, Kirdford. Early. TQ/0242.2938.

W.G., No. 23.P. Clues: Upper and Lower Glasshouse Croft, Glasshouse Copse
(T); the latter is also marked on the 6 in. O.S. The site was discovered as Winbolt
says, by finding crucible and glazed stone in an adjoining field (marked Glasshouse
Copse), close to its northern end. The glasshouse lies within a few feet of the footpath in the middle of this northern boundary which leads to Foxbridge. Instead of
selecting from Winbolt's site description in W.G., I have treated this site differently
because this description probably provides the best example of how ideas have
changed. My comments are in the footnotes and they show how unwieldy is this
method of handling the W.G. descriptions. Winbolt rightly calls it 'a very good
specimen, with a raised central mound surrounded by rectangular ditches and plentiful remains of the red-brick furnace floor[80] and is about six paces along this path
to the right. The glass-house measured about 22 ft. north–south by 16 ft. east–west
and was surrounded by a ditch 5 ft. wide across the top. The characteristic crucible
here is one with a rim slightly inturned and out-turned,[81] as at Malham Ashfold.'
I now give a description based on that by Winbolt (W.G., p. 47):

Found: A lump of glass cooked to opalescent white, strongly resembling a white
flint; a piece of contemporary grey pottery and a piece of buff with yellowish glaze
inside;[82] glass, window and vessel, but mainly the former; big pieces of disc or spun

[79] *See* p. 159, note 27. I think the brick is doubtful. [G.H.K.]

[80] This may have been the baked clay base, *see* p. 147.

[81] Crucible rims are discussed in Chapter III. It is doubtful if the rims show much more than the
range of individual whim.

[82] The only surviving fragment was thought by experts at the British Museum, before the war,
to be not earlier than the sixteenth century, but they were uncertain. After the war, Dr A. E. Wilson
kindly arranged for an expert examination of this sherd which resulted in a long report on it in relation

glass, fourteen inches in diameter; another clear sample of a tessera deliberately cut out of thin crucible;[83] and a piece of puntee rod. All the glass is green and corroded in various degrees through metallic brown to nearly black, and very crumbly; its outstanding characteristic is its thickness. The corrosion is not specially due to damp situation,[84] but either to age or to bad quality; it was perhaps deficient in silica. The technique also is poor.[85] Le Couteur advances the sensible view that corrosion is most noticeable in glass made in the two or three generations following the Black Death of 1349, and that this was due to shortage of competent workmen.[86] It would seem that at Wephurst whole spotted batches were discarded.[87] This bad glass may belong to the late fourteenth or early fifteenth centuries, and Wephurst may have been working contemporaneously with Hog Wood.[88] There is, however, also a light-green glass, and it seems safe to say there are two distinct fabrications, possibly at different dates.[89] The waste seems to have been thrown out mainly into the middle of the east ditch. We recovered a 9 in. length of blowpipe, with a bore of $\frac{5}{16}$ in. at one end, and $\frac{1}{4}$ in. at the other. It is possible that a site may be generally dated by the size of blowpipe bore, the smaller being the later.[90] At Fromes the larger end was $\frac{5}{8}$ in.

There were several instances of a composite glass of two layers, both of the same colour (light green), the two layers together measuring not quite $\frac{1}{4}$ in. thick. The purpose of such composition is not clear.[91] As to who worked this glasshouse, and when, there is no available record.

Apart from exposing part of the baked clay base most of the work was confined to the waste heap in the ditch on the east side; the site might repay complete excavation. Some bases of hanging lamps made of the bad local glass, were found here.

to dated pottery in London. This report said, 'the earliest possible date must be in the region of 1610 with the emphasis towards the middle of the century. The type has been found in an early eighteenth century context at Portsmouth and elsewhere.' This is strange because it is an unlikely place to find an intrusion, and yet of all the sites, Wephurst is unmistakably Early and all the glass found there, both vessel and window, suggests it was one of the earliest sites in the Weald. More window fragments were found than vessel but it is doubtful if this had much significance; *see* also site No. 12.

[83] Tesseræ cut from crucibles were one of Winbolt's pet ideas. I am very doubtful tha tthis was possible from such tough material and I think any shaped fragments are fortuitous.

[84] Wephurst is a dry site. *See* also remarks on corrosion, p. 44.

[85] This comment of Winbolt's probably comes very near the answer. Bad glass, probably due to bad batches and their handling, occurs on most Early sites, but is unusual on Late sites. Wephurst had by far the largest proportion of bad and decayed glass of any site I know.

[86] Le Couteur may have got his idea from J. A. Knowles; *see* p. 44, note 33.

[87] I am very doubtful if bad glass was immediately apparent and refer to this on p. 44.

[88] As so little glass was found at Hog Wood, it is doubtful if any useful comparison can be made.

[89] The reuse of furnace sites was another of Winbolt's ideas; *see* Chapter VI. I think at Wephurst. Winbolt's 'two fabrications' are more probably due to good and bad batches and their handling.

[90] Lengths of blowpipes are rarely found and I doubt if much can be learnt from the few survivals, except the variations in individual fancy. Fragments of blowpipes were found on only four sites, all Early (Nos. 3, 5, 15 and 21).

[91] These layers are explained, *see* Site, p. 160.

This site appeared to have concentrated its waste glass in one place and a fair amount was found though only about a dozen fragments of window and a lamp base (*see* Plate XIII) now survive. It was a paler green than the usual Early glass, and uniformly poor, and some was completely decayed. Dating, except into Early and Late, by quality only, is hazardous, but coupled with the coarseness and thickness of the glass (some window was $\frac{1}{4}$ in. thick), I should be surprised if this site is later than the fourteenth century. There is no documentary information of family connections to provide a possible date.

In an attempt to discover why this glass is so poor, Messrs Pilkingtons kindly carried out an analysis of this and glass from Sidney Wood which is the best of the Late; the results are given in Chapter II, p. 39. Both lots are potash glass but otherwise there is nothing in the analyses to help. It does not appear to be a deficiency of silica because the glass from Blunden's Wood which is of much better quality has an almost identical silica content (*see* p. 39). The reason may lie in bad technique.

No. 22, Barnfold, Wisborough Green. Late. c.TQ/0470.3175.

Not in *W.G.* No field-name. This site is a possibility only. In 1961 Mr W. S. Taylor found glass and crucible in Sandpit Field on Barnfold (probably originally Fernfold). There is a concentration of glass waste at one spot in the field, but though the tenant, Mr Charman, found a hard bottom there when ploughing, I could find no sign of burning on the surface or of a floor by spearing. Where the waste was found is well drained, level and close to a strong spring. Curiously enough it is a far better site than the Fernfold site found in 1934, which is about the worst I know.

The Fernfold furnace site, No. 25, is only 420 yards away, but though one can often find odd bits of crucible and glass waste up to half a mile from a known furnace, the concentration in this field is puzzling and I think there may be another furnace site close to the map reference given; I would not put it higher than that. If there was a site here, it is the only one known that actually adjoins a sandpit. The sand is of poor quality, deep yellow and of doubtful value for the good quality Late glass made here. The material found is perplexing: mostly glass waste, blobs and lumps, with little finished (blown) glass vessel or window, and little crucible. The glass is not of equal quality with Sidney Wood and as only the odd scrap now survives from Fernfold it is difficult to compare the two sites. There is a small fragment of a hemmed rim base with what appears to be ruby paint baked on; it is too thin for a flash.

No. 23, Brookland Farm, I and II, Wisborough Green. Late. TQ/0490.2685.

S.C.M., vol. 9, p. 791. No. 33. *S.C.M.*, vol. 14, pp. 156–8. Nos. 40, 41. Clue: Big and Little Glasshouse Fields (T). Found 1938–9. As the furnaces are only 50 yards apart and their glass is identical they are counted as one. The map reference is given for I., the first site found. It is marked on the 25 in. O.S. and was probably known in the nineteenth century. The other furnace II, 50 yards WNW. was found when an elm tree about 150 years old was blown over in 1938 and a furnace beneath it was revealed. Winbolt, I think, mistook Brook Bridge (his No. 33) for Brookland; it is the same site. As he says, there was a considerable quantity of glasshouse waste around the site, down the field and into the stream, about 100 yards away, and just over the stream on Naldrets Farm.[92] The actual furnace floor of I. was refound when the plough turned up the usual burnt layer in 1939. I dug it out, about 10 in. down and it measured 14 ft. by 10 ft. This would probably be the furnace floor and its surround; the glasshouse would be larger but there was no trace of its extent or the size of the kiln. Both sites are on a gentle slope down to a good stream, fairly dry and being close to the village were probably completely demolished. It is not the usual remote woodland site and is only 500 yards southeast from the other Wisborough Green site marked on the O.S. on Sparr Farm, and also possibly found in the nineteenth century.

The glasshouse site under the elm, was destroyed and one could only pick bits out of the upheaval of roots. Glass waste is still thrown up by the plough as both sites are under cultivation. There was a small floor 9 ft. by 4 ft. with no burnt layer, about half way between the two sites. There was no evidence as to its use.

The glass is of excellent quality and the vessel fragments suggest fine craftsmanship; the fragmentation is, as usual, remarkably complete.[93] Subject always to the cullet qualification, enough glass survived here to suggest that vessel, as at Sidney, was its principal, though not the only, product. Some of the glass though clear, hard, burnished and very similar to Sidney, has not quite the hard blue-green 'modern' appearance, and some shows a trace of surface corrosion or weathering which is absent at Sidney. The fragments included a few scraps of very thin and fine fluted vessel but too broken to suggest a shape, a small bottle lip and base, a vessel handle (Fig. 12), some small thin bowl rims, a rigaree base, a heavy hemmed rim base and pieces that might be fragments of vessel made from devitrified glass. There were some thin scraps characteristic of Late window glass. The most interesting find here was a very small unguent phial, the only complete vessel now known to have been found on any Weald site (see Plate XVI). It is 2 in. high and 1 in. square. There are slight variations in the usual Late dark green, some having a blue shade and some olive. Some tiny freak fragments survive, almost certainly cullet or, being near the village are just later intrusions – bright blue vessel, 'crystal' vessel, and a small fragment of knopped stem of later date. More pottery fragments were found on this site than any other we dug. Winbolt had a note in The Times on Brookland and mentions various finds: 'all the usual debris of a furnace was found – fire-bricks, crucibles, brown

[92] I have to thank Mr W. S. Taylor for this information.

[93] With the possible exception of Glasshouse Lane site, it is a puzzling characteristic of our glass, Early and Late, that the glass seems to have been deliberately smashed and scattered. I can remember only one delicate base with a high kick, from Sidney which was possible to mend; it is now in Haslemere Museum.

mottled Rhenish ware with medallions, vessel and window glass, and an exceptional amount of glass thread, some very fine ... Patterns of vessel mouldings were hexagonal, sharp lozenge and transverse flutings four to an inch. A stem of a candle stick (?) four inches long has six solid knops. A part of a white stone-ware mug $3\frac{1}{4}$ in. diameter has an impressed scroll pattern, in the middle of which is a label with the words, VEIRTAS: 11 ALT WR. Veirtas (representing a natural pronunciation of Veritas) means, no doubt, correct measure; 11 ALT, the measure, and WR the (at present unidentified) maker.'[94]

I have omitted the suggestion that it is 'practically certain' that this site was worked by Jean Carré,[95] because there is no known evidence. The cloudy white transparent glass is probably cullet. The (?) candle stick stem could be the handle of a linen smoother.[96] The 'brown mottled Rhenish ware' and the 'white stone-ware'[97] mentioned by Winbolt were examined by Mr J. G. Hurst in 1966; he dates them to the last quarter of the sixteenth century. Mr Hurst also says that the white stoneware is part of a Siegburg tankard and the Rhenish ware is from a Frechen Bellarmine of early type dating from the last quarter of the sixteenth century, or possibly a trifle earlier. He says the Bellarmines are quite common but Siegburg tankards are very rare and only about six have been found in England and these come from town sites. The glasshouse can therefore be dated between c.1570 and 1600, exactly the dates the glass appearance would suggest as it is not as good as the glass from Sidney Wood (No. 38) which was probably abandoned when the industry closed down in 1618, but it is better than some Late glass. Two scraps of coarse local ware, picked up recently on the site, were dated by Mr N. E. S. Norris as not earlier than the seventeenth century. Being surface finds and close to the village, they may or may not belong to the glasshouse.

There do not appear to be any ancient deeds of Brookland Farm. We know, however, that John Lutman of 'Brookeland' was buried on 6 May 1601.[98] In his will, 21 August 1599,[99] he describes himself as a yeoman and mentions his lease of Brookland. He is described as of the same place in 1599[98] when his son Edward was baptized. There is a John Lutman of Sparre whose son was baptized in May 1583,[98] who may be the same man. But there were so many Frenchmen in the parish between 1567 and 1617 that it is more likely that either at Sparr or Brookland, or both, he let or sublet a glasshouse to one of them. No other glasshouses are known so close to a village; these are only half a mile from the church. It is difficult to believe there could be any secrets or mysteries in such an accessible place.

[94] The fragments are now in Haslemere Museum. [G.H.K.]
[95] Also made in S.C.M., vol. 14, p. 158.
[96] See J. Stuart Daniels, The Woodchester Glass House (Bellows, 1930), plate XV.
[97] Now in Haslemere Museum.
[98] Wisborough Green P.R.
[99] Diocesan Record Office, Chichester. There were other John Lutmans in Wisborough Green in 1544 and 1560.

No. 24, Burchetts, Wisborough Green. Late. c. TQ/0497.2853.

Not in *W.G.* No clues. A chance find of crucible and glass in an arable field by Mr W. S. Taylor of Horsham. This site is a possibility only. The possible Sparr glasshouse as marked on the O.S. is slightly less than a mile distant. The probable site at Gunshot is also just under a mile away and produced very similar glass. The nearest known sites are Brookland which produced very similar Late glass, and Malham Ashfold which is Early and different. Both are over a mile away and it is unlikely that the small concentration of glass waste and crucible could have strayed so far. There is no sign in this arable field of any burnt area nor had the farmer any trouble when ploughing. The field is level and dry with a small pond close by, but these have little significance being very common all over the Weald clay to water stock.

No. 25, Fernfold, Wisborough Green. Late. TQ/0477.3208.

S.C.M., vol. 9, p. 788. No. 30. Clue: Carré's statement of approx. July 1567[1] 'I have erected two glasshouses, at Fernefol Sussex for Normandy and Lorraine glass by H.M. Licence, and one in London for crystal glass.' We also know from an entry (undated, but probably *temp.* Elizabeth I) in the records of the Manor of Bury (B.M., Add. MS. 5701, fol. 150) that Fernfold wood in Wisborough Green was let to 'divers strangers being glassmakers' for a yearly rent of £35, and that they had built there '2 houses to make glass in and one fair dwelling house covered with shingles and windows thereof well glazed.'

There is a large area of scrubland called Great Scrubbs on the O.S. map but Fernfold Scrubs in the Tithe schedule, 1842. In a field adjoining on the west a furnace was found in 1934; it was in a 5-acre clearing surrounded by rough copse. The glass is Late and good, and we can be reasonably certain the site is Carré's Fernefol of 1567. He was buried close by, less than 1½ miles away at Alfold church, having made his will two weeks earlier at Fernfold (*see* Chapter VIII, p. 123). There is very little doubt that Barnfold Farm (only the buildings remain), 500 yards southeast of the furnace site, was once Farn or Fernfold. The site is now, 1964, completely overgrown with a dense thicket of 25 years growth, birch and blackthorn and, short of a costly clearing, cannot even be approached.

This site and the one at Hog Wood, No. 15, are puzzling; both are in very boggy positions with no apparent compensations. Fernfold might have been one of the most important Wealden sites because it was probably here in 1567–8 that Jean Carré's glassmakers laid the foundations for the great, progressive and lasting improvement in English forest glass, after some possibly earlier, transient attempts (*see* p. 17). Unhappily very little glass has survived, and the site being in what became a field, had been almost destroyed above floor level. That was all thirty years ago; today I should have spent more time there instead of on less important

---

[1] *The Antiquary*, vol. 30, p. 211.

sites. There is no photograph of the site and, apart from three scraps at Lewes Museum,[2] no survivals of the exceptional amount of glass that was found. Winbolt who saw all the glass from the field and site had no doubt it belonged to the Carré period (*i.e.*, Late); that is my recollection also. The brick structure of the furnace also points to the site being Late. The other three sites in this group, Nos. 22, 30 and 32, are all Late. The sketch plan in *S.C.M.*, vol. 9, p. 789 (reproduced here as Fig. 16), of this furnace poses queries to which I can only suggest an answer. Thirty years ago we tended to identify all the Late glass we found with Carré but this is the only site, apart possibly from Barnfold (No. 22), which should be attributed to him. The blue knopped stem sketched by Winbolt[3] has been examined by Mr R. J. Charleston who says it is an intrusion and cannot have been locally made. Winbolt wrote 'It is virtually certain, though we have not dug them out, that there were two others [furnaces] aligned with [this furnace][4] just as there was a series of three, as we subsequently found at Malham Ashfold,' but I am not too happy about this (*see* also No. 29). He describes how Miss E. M. O. Farmer of Loxwood found crucible and glass on the surface of this clearing when it had been ploughed, how she informed him and how he tracked down the site by noting the concentration of red-burnt material, and how he dug and found 'Tudor bricks well laid and in good condition.' He says window, vessel and some ornamental glass were manufactured here.

Winbolt describes the furnace: '12 yards from the SW. corner of the field, was the most complete glass structure ever yet found,[5] not excluding that of Vann [No. 35]. There were standing 3–5 courses of bricks in the walls and the floors from end to end were nearly unbroken. It was 20 ft. 10 in. long SE.–NW., so that its length again, as at Slifehurst, faced SW.: and 6 ft. 3 in. wide. The fire chamber was 8 ft. long and 2 ft. 5 in. wide: its walls 1 ft. 11 in. thick were built in alternate courses of shaped sandstones and excellently made fire bricks, each 11 in. long, jointed with an inch of mortar. The fire-chamber floor was of sandstones laid on clay, and 3 in. lower in level than the hearth at either end. The hearths, 3 ft. 8 in. long[6] and 2 ft. 3 in. wide, were of sandstone gradually rising by 4 in. from the brick platforms (used by the stokers) to the step down to the fire-chamber floor. At the extremes the brick platforms, 4 ft. long and 2 ft. 9 in. wide, were of bricks of standard Tudor dimensions. It is thus certain that this furnace was fed, or capable of being fed, from

---

[2] The three scraps are (*a*) a small blob of unblown glass of indeterminate date; (*b*) a fragment which Winbolt describes as a 'moulded wing of a bird' (*see* Fig. 11; *see* also Winbolt's sketch, *S.C.M.*, vol. 9 p. 791) about 2 in. long and perhaps part of an applied decoration. It is pale blue similar to some fragments from No. 32, an undoubted Late furnace. (*c*) A fragment of poor corroded window, probably cullet. Also at the Museum is part of a good quality firebrick, very similar to some from site No. 32, about 1200 yards away.

[3] *S.C.M.*, vol. 9, p. 790.

[4] Winbolt refers to it as No. 30, his numbering.

[5] Winbolt meant in the Weald. No. 33 was not excavated until 1960. [G.H.K.]

[6] In Winbolt's ground plan they appear to be only 3 ft. 3 in. [G.H.K.]

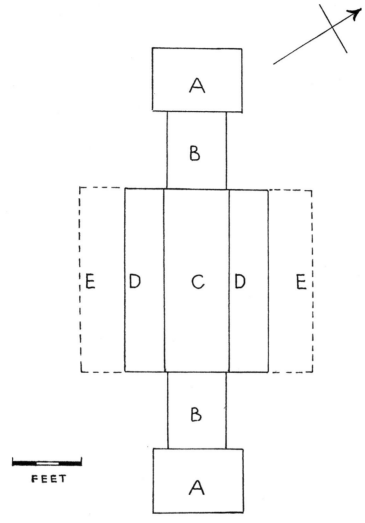

FEET

Fig. 16. From Winbolt's rough sketch plan and suggested key (in *S.C.M.*, vol. 9, p. 789) of Fernfold furnace (No. 25). A. Platform of brick. B. Hearth of sandstone, 3-inch drop to C. C. Fire chamber with sandstone floor. D. Wall of firebricks and sandstones [?siege platforms]. E. Ramp of clay [?base of outer walls].

both ends.[7] The stokers platforms were uncovered. On the covered hearth the fuel was kindled, and the burning billets were pushed up the slope of the hearth to drop on the floor of the fire-chamber.[8] In order to get the fuel to reach the centre, or to pull out the ashes before re-heating, the stoker must have used an iron rod 8 ft. long. In no other instance has it been possible to make an exact ground plan, with complete measurements, of a glass furnace. Outside the walls of the fire-chamber was set a ramp of clay 2 ft. wide at the base, the object of which was to conserve the heat – a feature not observed in any other furnace.' I suggest that the ground-plan only represents the central core and that the outer casing of rough stone walls outside B and D on the plan has been carted away. I am not satisfied with E.E.; if they were clay ramps to conserve the heat, they would seem unnecessary at ground level and they would make access to the glory holes difficult. But if they were the bases of the suggested outer stone covering, the whole structural lay-out becomes comprehensible and a possible explanation of this ground plan is: A, B and C as described by Winbolt; D are siege platforms for more or larger crucibles as some of these late sites with larger teams may well have had twice the capacity of earlier furnaces; E is the base for the outer casing of stone. But it is not satisfactory. Winbolt comments on the very damp site, so damp that after rain he had to dig a drainage trench to expose the floor. It is a bad site and very puzzling. The fact that this field had been ploughed meant that Winbolt's 3–5 courses of bricks must have been at least 6 in. down and so the actual floor was about another one foot below the general ground level, this would be bad anywhere on the Weald clay but here I would have thought it was impossible. The site could have been buried by erosion from the top of the fields in a single summer thunderstorm.[9] His finds were, in addition to the 'bird's wing' and blue knopped stem already mentioned, a double knopped stem (upper knop 1 in. diameter, the lower $\frac{3}{4}$ in), pieces of blue, purple and amber vessel glass, and three more of the usual flint implements for marking.

That is all we know about Carré's furnace. The coloured vessel fragments were almost certainly imported cullet, as I recollect no evidence of any coloured glass being made here. Winbolt had hoped the site might be roofed over and preserved, but there was no support and he filled it in.

No. 26, Horsebridge, Wisborough Green. Late. c.TQ/0325.2288.

W.G., No. 21.P. Clues: A cottage marked 'Glasshouse' on the 6 in. O.S. This and Glasshouse Meadow (T). Found 1930. The furnace site is probably in the cottage garden above a small stream. The glass is unmistakably Late and Winbolt found 'associated Rhenish brown speckled ware' pottery,[10] which may support its late sixteenth-century date. This pottery is found only on sites producing Late glass.[11]

[7] See Vann, No. 35, which also had two hearth tunnels .[G.H.K.]
[8] In Winbolt's ground plan the fire chamber is 2 ft. 9 in. wide. [G.H.K.]
[9] On the heavy clay I have known an 18 in. build-up at the bottom of an arable field on my own farm after a bad storm.   [10] It has not survived.   [11] See also p. 101.

Winbolt found: 'Threading round and flat; threading applied to composite glass (vessel); cut oblong of window, one piece with marked lines, and feathered-cut piece of thicker flash; two thirds of a circular prunt, or applied seal, as at Vann. The glass is mostly window. One piece of red-brown crucible and some pointed black flints.' None of the finds survives. He says this is the only case (No. 36 was not found until 1937) of a glasshouse site now in a garden, the flower beds of which are thickly strewn with scraps of sixteenth-century glass. I confirmed the site in 1962 but the actual furnace floor has not been found and it has probably been destroyed. As he does here, Winbolt often refers to glass slag, but which type he meant is not known.

No family connection is known; the property may have been part of the Barttelot estate. This furnace is almost on the edge of the Weald clay where it joined the Lower Greensand. Winbolt notes that the Arun is 'but a mile down stream' and 'this glass-house like so many others, was in close connection with a waterway for transport.' The evidence for 'so many others' which has turned up since his day suggests pack-horse transport (*see* Chapter VII), some from distant parts. But this and other glass-houses in Wisborough Green may have used water transport for some of their output (*see* Chapter VII, p. 112).

No. 27, Gunshot, Wisborough Green. Late. c. TQ/0360.2909.

Not in *W.G.* Clue: There is a field adjoining 150 yards to the east of the possible site called Glassets, which might be a corruption. Here again I am much indebted to Mr W. S. Taylor for reporting traces of crucible and glass. I confirmed in 1963 a small concentration at the spot given, but no trace of a furnace in the arable field. The glass is Late and the nearest known site on another farm, Wephurst, is of a completely different date. The nearest Late possible site is on Burchetts Farm nearly a mile away, and it is highly improbable that this material could have strayed so far. We have a possible field-name and the necessary material, so I have rated this as a probable, but it could be a possible only. A furnace may be close to the spot given, but so far it has not been found. There is a small pond at the junction of three fields; the site is level and dry. There is no known family connection.

No. 28. Malham Farm, Wisborough Green. Undated. c. TQ/0650.2955.

S.C.M., vol. 14, p. 159. No. 42. Clues: Glasses Field and Glasses Hanger adjoining (T). A common corruption of Glasshouse. Winbolt says that 'some 18–20 ft. inside the wood (hanger) at the top of a steep slope (down to the Arun) is undoubtedly the site of the glasshouse, though here again the deep silting of the soil has obscured the actual spot.' I was with him in 1939 when we visited the place; today I am less confident, but the field-names and the very small amount of material found (all I have is a heavy bit of glass welting-off ring, of indeterminate date) add up to a probable site.

Winbolt says, 'we did not find the furnace floor, but charcoal, burnt sandstone, lumps of glass and pieces of window glass badly corroded, and of crucible are indisputable evidence.'[12] Winbolt suggests that the Arun basin was 'the great begetter of the glass industry, but all the other houses are on its small feeders.' I can find no evidence for this. The water supply is discussed on p. 148.

When Glasses Field was ploughed in 1965, Mr W. S. Taylor found lumps of glass and some crucible at a point adjoining our probable 1939 site. The lumps are difficult to date but may be Late.

No. 29, Malham Ashfold (or, as in some references, Malhamashfold), Wisborough Green. Early. TQ/0560.3007.

W.G., No. 20.P. Clues: none, a chance find when digging for stone in 1930. The glasshouse is on the edge of an arable field just inside a strip of copse which falls steeply to a tiny stream. It has a ditch on three sides and the ground falls away on the fourth (east) side. Nothing had survived above ground but Winbolt records that the 'floor' of red burnt sandstone when dug out about 5–6 in. down was 15 ft. 10 in. by 10 ft. 10 in. This was probably the working furnace only, with a floor surrounding the kiln. It is the only site I know in the Weald which was built on top of a shelf of outcropping sandstone. Writing in the S.C.M., vol. 9, p. 791, Winbolt says: 'it is now certain that there were three furnaces in a line over about 50 yards, with a pond at the N. end. The northern furnace seems to have had wings as at Vann (No. 35). Much ruby glass waste has been found, and a lump of copper $4\frac{1}{2}$ oz. in weight, which had been oxidized for colouring matter . . . Malham [this site] also yielded part of the earliest known safety inkpot. It was 3 in. high, and $3\frac{1}{4}$ in. in diameter with dipping tube $1\frac{7}{8}$ in. long.'

On revisiting this site in 1964 I was not convinced of three furnaces but there were probably a pair, the other one (? a fritting furnace) being destroyed when the stone cutting was made 20 yards to the north of the site described. I have no recollection of a winged kiln. Winbolt, in W.G., notes the finds here as 'pieces of window glass, glass lumps, and all the usual material. There were over 200 fragments of coloured glass . . . of some twenty shades, including cobalt blue, amethyst, olive green, yellowish green, light ruby, with thin flash, and green glass painted with brown oxide of iron lines . . . some muff glass almost white, outcurved bottle mouths, a base with a long pointed kick-up of a phial similar to one found at Upper Chaleshurst by Cooper (in Guildford Museum) but no hemmed feet . . . some flint gravers.' The coloured and the painted pieces were probably cullet as there is not the slightest evidence of any colour except ruby being made on the site.[13] Phial bases with high pointed kicks were found on other Early sites.

Although the arable field is only a few feet away, I could find no crucible or glass close to the furnace. The glasshouse site yielded plenty of fragments of sealing-wax-red glass, a piece of local window experimentally flashed so thickly, as to be completely opaque; presumably when thinly flashed it was transparent. The significance

[12] This material has not survived.
[13] This ruby glass is now in Haslemere Museum.

of the lump of copper is not known.[14] The late Horace Beck, a great authority on glass, examined the lumps of ruby glass and was satisfied that it had been made at this glasshouse. This ruby glass was interesting because, apart from Cooper's find at Chaleshurst (*see* No. 4), it had always been assumed that no colour was made in England until the end of the seventeenth century. Whether its production at either site was more than experimental is not known. As to the ink bottle, it may be the unlabelled fragment in Littlehampton Museum which Winbolt gave to Hulme in 1934. No pottery was found and as there are no family connections the dating is surmise. The glass is better than some of the Early sites, and Winbolt could well be right in suggesting *c.*1500.

No. 30, Songhurst Farm, Wisborough Green, Late. c.TQ/0448.3260.

W.G., No. 19.R. Clue: Glasshouse Field (T), now a fir plantation, called Glasshouse Piece on O.S. In 1932 it was part of Loxwood House estate. This could be the glasshouse marked by Norden and Speed in 1610. The map is on too small a scale to be certain, and Woodhouse Farm furnace (No. 32) has a better claim by its position. In 1610, Speed complains that 'the glasse-houses remove and follow the woods with small charge, which the iron works cannot easily do.' Winbolt searched in and around Glasshouse Piece in 1930 and in 1932 we found, after the field had been ploughed, what he calls Carré's glass waste [what I term Late material] twenty-five yards south from the SE. corner of Glasshouse piece. The material is extended nearly half way over the field south. The material is blue-green glass, precisely similar to that of Sidney Wood [*sic*][15] drops, lumps, thread, hemmed bases, pieces of crucible etc., both window and vessel. The actual site of the furnace was not found. It was probably at the east end of the fir plantation, and when this was made, or prior to that, when it was arable, the site was destroyed, and the debris thrown broadcast over the neighbouring arable.'[16] No doubt there is a furnace close to the map reference given. There is no known family connection.

No. 31, Sparr Farm, Wisborough Green. Date Unknown. c.TQ/0453.2710.

A possible site, mentioned *W.G.*, p. 52. Winbolt saw some seventeenth-century deeds of Sparr Farm relating to Glasshouse Field (11 acres). This was later divided into two and called Great and Little Stennings; it is now again a single field. Being under grass it provided no clue and Winbolt could find nothing in the neighbouring

[14] The late Professor W. E. S. Turner commenting on our finds in March 1934, wrote: 'In making copper ruby, copper oxide or a salt is employed and not metallic copper. The production of the ruby is brought about by the addition of potassium tartrate and heating the glass in a reducing atmosphere. It is the fact that about the end of the eighteenth century when the combustion conditions of glass furnaces had been improved considerably, making ruby glass seemed to be exceedingly difficult, and indeed the art of making it seemed to have disappeared for a time. Metallic copper was treated with sulphur, vitriol or aqua fortis.'

[15] No known Wealden glass is equal to that from Sidney Wood.

[16] None of the material survives.

woodland. He did find glass-furnace waste, glazed bricks and lumps of furnace slag [*sic*] on the site of the old farmyard which, with iron slag, had been used to harden. Possibly a furnace site existed near the spot marked on the 25 in. O.S. and may have been discovered in the nineteenth century, as were other marked sites at Brookland and Somersbury (Ewhurst). The O.S. records were destroyed in the 1939–45 war. When this field was ploughed in April 1965 (about 6 in. deep), I examined the spot marked on the O.S. and its surroundings, but found no evidence of a furnace. It is included as a possible site only because of the field-name and because it is unlikely to have been marked on the O.S. if a furnace site had not been found nearby. A neighbouring field to the east was ploughed in the autumn of 1965, but no evidence of a glasshouse was found. Winbolt's surmise that Sparr was Jean Carré's home has no known evidence to support it. He seems to have lived in London[17] but may have had a house near Fernfold. Except possibly for John Lutman of Sparre in 1582 (*see* No. 23), no family connection is known.

No. 32, Woodhouse Farm, Wisborough Green. Late. (A). TQ/0570.3275.

S.C.M., vol. 9, p. 791. No. 34. It appears to be part of the present Woodhouse Farm, not Brickiln Farm. No field-name clues. Examined in 1935 and again in 1961 after Mr W. Taylor reported finding crucible and glass there. This is the only known site on top of a small hill (trig. point 180 ft.). 300 yards from even a small stream. The furnace (A) may be under a very large oak stam and may come to light when the stam rots away. It is only 5 yards from the west side of a small pond (marked on the 6 in. O.S.). There may be three sites here: (B), 16 yards west of (A), and (C), 70 yards south of (A). As far as I remember it was site (C) which we visited in 1935. The material from these sites has three unusual characteristics: the beautiful blue-green, almost Syrian colour of some of the glass; the heavily inturned rims of some of the crucible fragments (*see* p. 56); and the amount of lumps of unblown glass[18] with very few blown pieces. The glass is certainly Late and the amount lying about the glasshouse suggests its abandonment at the close of the industry *c*.1618. This may be the glasshouse marked on the Norden and the Speed maps of Sussex, 1610 (*see* also No. 30, Songhurst Farm). There was very little finished glass, but as far as it is possible to relate 'lumps' from various sites, the glass is very similar to Barnfold, Burchetts, Brookland, Gunshot and Horsebridge and probably to Fernfold and Songhurst, all in Wisborough Green parish. These six or eight sites were undoubtedly worked by the Frenchmen who appear in the parish register from 1567–1616. The actual floor has not been dug out, and the site might be worth further examination.

Of this site Winbolt says 'There was undoubtedly a glass furnace here. Apart from the heap of crucible which was got out when the pond was cleared, crucible

---

[17] At least until 1571; *see* p. 122.

[18] I cannot suggest how these lumps were produced; at the sites Nos. 8 and 32 there was little else. Both are Late and may not have been cleared up for cullet. Pape (p. 37) says, 'on all the sites [in N. Staffs.] there is a good deal of rough material such as shapeless lumps of crude glass.'

and glass are in plenty under the ground surface. One piece of cobalt blue glass.' Was this last-mentioned a piece of cullet? A single fragment of glass waste here is remarkably blue and this is on the only site which has the smallest evidence of any production of blue as opposed to blue-green glass. It can be noted, but more evidence is needed before accepting that blue or any colour except ruby was made at any Wealden glasshouse.

The brown speckled stone-ware fragment found here was examined in 1963 by Mr K. J. Barton. He said it could well belong to the last quarter of the sixteenth century, not much earlier and not later. Parts of three firebricks of similar composition and hardness to the crucibles were found here, 1 in., 1½ in., and one which tapers from 1¼ in. to 1 in., thus suggesting its use in an arch. There is a sand outcrop in Primrose Copse about 300 yards northeast. No family connection known for this site.

No. 33, Blunden's Wood, Hambledon. Early. SU/974.374.

Not in *W.G.* Found by chance by Mr N. P. Thompson in 1959. No field-name clues. The site was completely excavated in March 1960 by the Surrey Archaeological Society under Mr E. S. Wood, before being bulldozed for brick-clay working. It was on level fairly dry ground above a small stream about 50 yards away. Some part of the furnace survived above ground having been abandoned and left undisturbed. The structural part of Mr Wood's report is given in Chapter IV with his kind permission. The full report is in *Surrey Archaeological Collections*, vol. 62, pp. 54–79, and the material is in Guildford Museum.

No. 34, Gunter's Wood, Hambledon. Early. c.SU/9695.3825.

Not in *W.G.* Found by chance by the owner, Mr Bolton, who told Miss E. Dance, curator of the Guildford Museum in 1959; she asked me to visit the site. No field-name clues. The furnace floor not found, and as so much building has gone on it is very likely buried. The glass and crucible evidence suggests that a possible site, the most productive patch being in the garden, is 50 yards east of a small but permanent stream, and 20 yards north of the bungalow. The evidence is now in the Guildford Museum: one fine piece of 'crown' window, a 'welting-off ring' fragment, glass waste and crucible. The glass is unmistakably Early. The fragments of seven glass hanging lamp bases have turned up and some flint glass-markers. The site is over 1000 yards northwest of No. 33 and too far for so much material to have wandered.

No. 35, Vann Copse (Burgate), Hambledon. Late (Provisional). SU/9842.3772.

W.G., No. 2.P. Clues: Upper and Lower (2 parts) Glasshouse Coppice, Upper Glasshouse Field (T). Upper Glass House Copse (O.S.). In 1840 all these were in Godalming parish and until recently the copses were part of Burgate estate. The site was found in 1931 in Lower Glass House Copse after three years searching by Mr A. D. R. Caroe.

It is a dry, fairly level site on a slight rise above a tiny perennial stream and, like No. 34, it is near the northern limit of the Weald clay where it joins the Lower Greensand. Vann was a rare survival: most sites had far less to show. Perhaps here and at Fernfold (see p. 188) only a fragment of the brick core of the furnace has survived and the outer coating of plaster or clay has disappeared. I can write little at first hand of this site because I spent only the odd afternoon or so there.

It is the only site, prior to 1960, of which any useful photographs survive, Plates XXI (for which I am indebted to Mr Caroe) and XXII. The latter shows the hearth tunnels, central fire chamber and the smallness of these furnaces in a characteristic woodland setting. Of the furnace remains Winbolt says (W.G., p. 30): 'We dug out the floor level of a rectangular building, on foundations [sic] which have on the average a depth of six courses of 2 in. Tudor red bricks. The ground plan of the remains dug out to date[19] is an oblong 12 ft. by 5 ft. 6 in. with projection on the long sides (i.e., north and south) 4 ft. long with 1 ft. projection.[20] At each of the four corners short wings run out diagonally. These chambers were called arcae, translated as "arches" (see for a very similar furnace, Antiquary [vol. 31, p. 105], April 1895, the measurements of which are 12 ft. 9 in. by 9 ft. 6 in. the angular projections being 6 ft. long).'[21]

It has not been easy to interpret Winbolt's provisional sketch plan, the more so as it clearly puzzled him (see p. 195). It would have been impossible without Mr Caroe's remarkable memory and great patience for which I am very grateful. Mr Caroe did most of the excavation for Winbolt, on the understanding that Winbolt would make the detailed recordings. As Mr Caroe is an architect his present recollections and conclusions carry more authority than might usually be expected after the lapse of thirty years.[22] When he found the furnace there was no trace of any ditch – only a slight mound a few inches high – and on uncovering it his recollection is a state of great confusion due to a collapsed structure which he thinks supported a barrel-vaulted roof. He suggests that Winbolt's use of the word 'foundations' was inexact and that he was simply referring to the lowest courses of the wall. Mr Caroe

[19] Winbolt, the expert in charge, clearly regarded his plan as provisional, and may have hoped to complete it later. [G.H.K.]

[20] These dimensions provide a scale for Winbolt's rough ground plan (W.G., p. 30) and with Mr Caroe's notes make possible a revised and comprehensible ground plan, Fig. 17. Winbolt probably measured across the top of the fire chamber, shelves and outer walls, but he may not have known or allowed for the lean outwards of both walls (see definite conclusion No. 4 which follows). This could have increased the apparent overall width by about 4 in. so that the fire chamber and hearth tunnels may have been originally only about 20 in. wide. [G.H.K.]

[21] I have reproduced this ground plan as Fig. 20. Winbolt appears to have used this dimension of 6 ft. for the wing length in his ground plan of Vann. [G.H.K.]

[22] Mr Caroe has kindly read this description of the Vann structure and agreed with it, the plan and conjectural section (Figs. 17 and 18).

points out that most contemporary houses on the Weald Clay had no foundations and he considers that the furnace was built on top of the ground as at other sites where any trace of the floor survived. The glassmakers skimmed off the few inches of top soil and sat the kiln on the clay.

Mr Caroe very kindly made a detailed list of definite conclusions based on a photograph (*see* Plate XXI)[23] taken soon after he found the site and before he excavated the fire chamber. As to the main furnace structure:

1. The brick walls along either side [the outside] of the structure were 9 in. thick.

2. The maximum height left standing was seven courses of bricks at the southeast corner or about 1 ft. 4 in. His impression is that the clay was undisturbed below the bottom course.

3. The bricks outside the north 'shelf' projected far enough above the 'shelf' to prove that this wall originally carried up, whereas the 'shelf' did not.[24]

4. On the south side, the whole wall and 'shelf' leaned southwards, whereas the north wall and 'shelf' leaned northwards [*see* Plates XXI, XXII]. Mr Caroe suggests these leans may have been caused by an arched vault or tunnel forcing its supporting walls outwards as they probably had no foundations.

5. The diagonal wall of the southeast chamber or diagonal wing were not built in any particular brick bond and tapered from little more than $4\frac{1}{2}$ in. thick in the foreground of Plate XXI to 8 in. thick beyond. There was no mortar to distinguish the bricks in position in this wall from those tumbled from the superstructure around them; some of these 'bricks' had distintegrated so far that they were only distinguished from the clay by their red colour.

6. The west end of the kiln [the far end in Plate XXI], was in worse condition than the east because it had been disturbed by the tree which is still there in 1967. This was true not only of the end of the main furnace but even more of the diagonal wing chambers, whose walls were, Mr Caroe believes, only $4\frac{1}{2}$ in. thick and very hard to identify from the general debris.

Thanks to Mr Caroe, the ground plan of the central furnace now becomes comprehensible; it agrees with Plate XXII and it can be interpreted as shown in Fig. 17. I have used Mr Caroe's sketch of the main furnace based on his six conclusions above. I have used Winbolt's overall measurements (*see* p. 194) of the furnace and its projections together with the wings shown in his ground plan (*W.G.*, p. 30) but for which he gives no measurements. To save confusion Winbolt's provisional sketch plan and his interpretations are not reprinted.[25] I doubt if he was satisfied with them because on p. 30 of *W.G.* he says 'so far as I can assign a meaning to this structure

---

[23] Plate XXI shows what may rarely be seen of a glass furnace when the top soil is removed.

[24] There is little doubt that these two shelves were the siege platforms on which the crucibles stood. *See* Plate XXII.

[25] Apart from the uninformative ground plan of Buckholt furnace made in 1865 (*see* p. 216), Winbolt's was, I think, the first ground plan of an English forest glass furnace to be published.

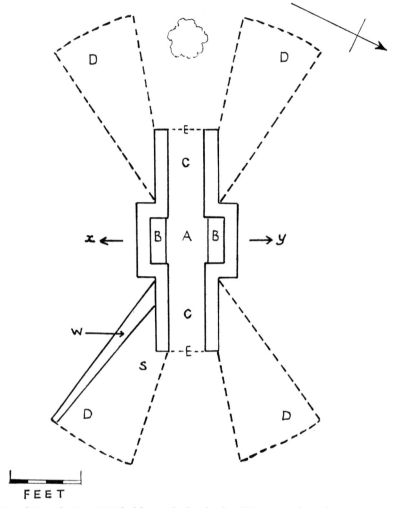

FEET

Fig. 17. Vann (No. 35). From Winbolt's rough sketch plan (*W.G.*, p. 30), with Mr A. D. R. Caroe's modifications. A. Fire chamber. BB. Siege shelves. CC. Hearth tunnels. DD. ?Annealing chambers. E. Hearth lip. W. Taper wing wall (Plate XXI). S. Spade (Plate XXII).

etc.' His ground plan and key are not convincing, mainly because he inexplicably left out the 9 in. brick walls[26] surrounding his 'projections.' The brick walls of the fire chamber and the hearth tunnels are thin, only 9 in., but they may have had an outer coating of clay or plaster, though no evidence of this was found. The shelves

[26] The batter, in addition to its outward lean, on the side walls of the fire chamber below the siege platforms can be seen in Plate XXII and appears to be about $1\frac{1}{2}$ in. These walls are evident in Plates XXI and XXII.

or siege platforms are small, being only 30 in. long and about $10\frac{1}{2}$ in. wide,[27] but they could have accommodated four small crucibles.[28] I suggest that this revised ground plan and its interpretation are substantially correct for the working furnace.

The size and shape of the wings is conjectural and they are shown with single broken lines to make this clear. Enough was found to prove that all these irregular and asymmetrical structures existed, but no accurate dimensions survive. Fig. 17 represents approximately what was found on the site and suggests clear analogies with the eighteenth-century winged French furnaces (*see* Fig. 20 and also p. 215,

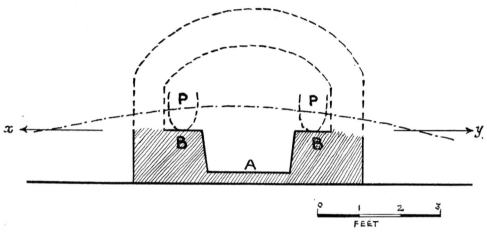

Fig. 18. Vann (No. 35). Suggested reconstructions section *x–y* through fire chamber A. A. Floor of fire chamber and hearth tunnels. BB. Siege Shelves. PP. Crucibles.

— · — · — · Approximate ground level when found.
——————— Approximate original ground level.

note 21). The wings do not appear to have been connected with the hearth tunnels at floor level (*see* Plate XXII) and they remain a problem. Mr Caroe says that none of the wings was fully examined and that it was often difficult to differentiate between bricks in position and those which had fallen at random from the derelict super-structure. Mr Caroe suspects the triangles were wider and not so long and thin as shown in Fig. 17. Both he and Winbolt agree they were not symmetrical and Winbolt suggests the east wings were later additions. They certainly are not but-tresses, being wrongly placed, unnecessary and too fragile. Mr Caroe says they were

[27] The Bishop's Wood (Staffs.) siege platforms were 34 in. by $16\frac{1}{2}$ in. Both furnaces were probably of about the same date.

[28] It is possible that glasshouses producing mainly vessel (and beads) used smaller crucibles than those producing window glass. The indications, which are very far from convincing due to their scarcity and to the cullet problem, are that Vann produced little, if any, window, so that a $10\frac{1}{2}$ in. siege platform might suffice. The surviving part of a crucible from a Late site (No. 4) which appears to have produced only vessel glass had a base diameter of only $5\frac{1}{2}$ in. (*see* Chapter III, p. 52).

unmortared and had no particular constructural design. They might have been annealing chambers or for firing or preheating of crucibles.

Mr Caroe adds some further tentative conclusions, tentative because the photographs offer no evidence. The charcoal layer [no doubt the rakings-out of the furnace] extended over the whole area between the northeast and southeast diagonal chambers [the wings]. His recollection is that this layer was little if at all above the bottom of the seven courses of remaining brickwork of the main kiln.[29] He exposed the whole of this charcoal layer for about 8 ft. back from the lip of the furnace. His recollection is that the lip of the furnace at the east end was about one or two courses above the charcoal layer.[30] The sides and bottom of the furnace had been rendered with mortar which was rounded off at the lip by the process of shovelling. It had the same pink as is characteristically found in buildings which have suffered from a bad fire. He thinks this mortar rendering was continued over the base of the two shelves.[31] The Plates XXI and XXII seem to substantiate this, though not conclusively. He says there were no considerable remains of spilt glass on these shelves.[32] Mr Caroe's recollection is that the western end of the furnace had been identical with the eastern end, but that it had been disturbed by the tree. He thinks he found a trace of the rounded lip (see above) but that the signs of black charcoal were not nearly so extensive.

All these details are necessary to explain the revision of the description and ground plan of Vann furnace. A suggested sectional reconstruction of the fire chamber is shown at Fig. 18.

The dating is difficult because little glass has survived. There is a fragment of a hemmed-rim base of olive-green Late glass, fragments of fine and moulded tubes, and a fragment of a moulded royal-blue handle and a tiny ribbed tube (? cullet), in Haslemere Museum. Mr Caroe has a few fragments[33] but I know of no other Vann glass surviving. There is a firebrick fragment and fragments of crucible from this site also at Haslemere. Fragments of pottery were dated by Mr N. E. S. Norris as early seventeenth century[34] The fact that the few scraps of glass appear to be Late, that the kiln was built of brick, that the potsherd is Late and that Winbolt refers to

[29] It is probably safe to assume from conclusions 2 and 4 above, that the bottom course of bricks was on top of the clay. In copses round here this is usually about 3 in. below ground level. The ash level was therefore probably slightly below the then ground level, and the floor of the hearth tunnel and fire-chamber was approximately at ground level.

[30] This gives us an approximate height of the siege shelves above the furnace floor of about 12 in. This is confirmed in Plate XXII.

[31] It was also my recollection. [G.H.K.]

[32] It is curious that the shelves were not covered with spilt glass. Possibly the inside of the furnace had been rebuilt and soon abandoned. Relining these primitive forest glass furnaces may have been a frequent practice.

[33] There are fragments of bottle seals, and a large sack bottle base, both probably of a later date. Fragment of bright blue vessel and a rilled handle; small unguent bottle rim; a 3 in. long fragment of rilled tube, $\frac{3}{8}$ in. diameter outside; fine quality pale blue neck, and some milky green (?) Early glass, but this could be cullet from another site.

[34] Now with Mr A. D. R. Caroe.

fragments of Rhenish pottery all suggest a Late date. Winbolt also notes that 'Two periods of glassmaking appear to be represented, as at Hazelbridge hanger [No. 7] but here thirteenth and sixteenth century. There is, first, light milky green, rough-exterior glass: mouths of jugs, plain rims, bead rims, lumps, blow-pipe trimmings and very thin fluted glass, almost white. This is probably Laurence product.' There is no known evidence of any Laurence connection with this or any other site. There is the possibility that this is Luthery's Burgate glasshouse (*see* below) but I have added 'provisional' because of Winbolt's finds but these may have been cullet.

Winbolt's second phase is described as 'the later manufacture, a dark, almost black glass with a metallic irridescence. It was originally bluish-green, but with corrosion has become first brown, and then nearly black and opaque. In this technique are: hemmed feet, tubes composed of a series of rods welded together, thin thread, bases with turned-up solid bead rim, necks, flute mouldings, kick-ups of feet, trimmings from blow-pipes, plain rims, drips, lumps, puntee knobs (or buttons) and pieces of disc-shaped prunts or seals. Of this period almost certainly are pieces of cobalt blue vessel glass, and one of ruby, with blue and red irridescence. This is probably Peytowe product.' I cannot comment on this because I have not seen the material. But I do not in general subscribe to the reuse of furnace sites (*see* p. 106). There may well be two types ('techniques') here, and they could be accounted for as cullet or as Transitional, but one cannot offer more than a full quotation from *W.G.* and an unsatisfactory opinion. There was no evidence of any colour being made here, the colour most probably was imported cullet. There is no evidence of a Peytowe family connection. Winbolt notes that charcoal found here was identified by Mr C. Maby as derived from *Quercus Cerris* (Turkey Oak) which has hitherto been supposed to have been introduced into England about A.D. 1735. But the charcoal antedates 1735 by some 150 years. Thus archaeology may help botany. He comments that the furnace was almost entirely for vessel glass. This is based on the finds, which owing to the cullet confusion, may mean little more than that the latest batch was largely vessel.

Until recently this glasshouse was part of Burgate property and could well be the furnace referred to below. In 1951 Miss G. M. A. Beck found a most interesting reference to a glasshouse on Burgate in 1586 worked by an Italian, Ognybene Luthery.[35] Miss Beck says that 'On November 26 1586, the Privy Council wrote to Sir William More of Losely and others (probably Justices of the Peace) about an Italian whose consumption of wood in a glasshouse had drawn complaints from the inhabitants of Guildford, Godalming and Wonersh:[36] he was to be brought before the

[35] *Sy.A.C.*, vol. 52, p. 89. If Vann is Luthery's furnace Miss Beck says it is remarkable that it is a typical French pattern [*i.e.*, rectangular] and not the Venetian round type. A possible answer may be that Luthery followed the Weald forest pattern; all the known Wealden furnaces are rectangular, and the more elaborate tiered round types, shown by Agricola and others, were usually urban.

[36] If his Burgate furnace consumed anything like the amount of fuel used at the possibly larger Knole window glass furnace of the same date (*see* p. 47), it is not surprising that the local people complained.

Council and meanwhile the working of his glasshouse was to be suspended . . . On 8 December 1586 the Justices ruled that Ognybene Luthery who "of late erected a house, furnace, and oven in the wood of Henry Smyth gent. of Burgate above said there to make glass and bugell and hath bought of the said Henry Smyth certain wood to be expended in the making of the said glass and bugell" should be allowed to consume only 100 cords.' This was presumably his stock of fuel or the amount which would enable him to meet his committments, but the order put an end to his glassmaking at Burgate and within 5 miles of Godalming, as 100 cords would not last long (*see* p. 47). Luthery had to give a recognisance for the large sum of a hundred marks that he would abide by the Justices' ruling. The house built as was customary in the wood he had bought, may refer to the complete glasshouse and the 'furnace and oven' may indicate that a fritting oven was separate. The fragments of what I have described as fine and moulded tubes, could be fragments of bugells (cylindrical beads). On the known evidence Luthery has the only possible family connection with this site; the date fits the small amount of surviving glass and with the broadly dated pottery.

Miss Beck tells us that Luthery, or Luteri, was born in Venice, and his wife in Antwerp and they must have come to London about 1569–70. 'Apparently he was the first Venetian whom Carré imported, and lodged in his master's house for a short time before Casseler and the others arrived. We do not know where he was between 1571 and 1586: whether he stayed at the Crutched Friars glasshouse in London, working under Verzelini after Carré's death, or whether he was employed in one of Carré's Wealden furnaces before he set up on his own at Burgate.' Carré's Fernfold glasshouse is $5\frac{1}{2}$ miles away. There was a small fragment of 'crystal' glass vessel found at Vann which in 1952 I then described as being of a technique unmatched in the Weald. A similar fragment turned up at Brookland and Mr R. J. Charleston said it was cullet. The plague of cullet covers all the rare and interesting fragments. I am now satisfied that crystal vessel glass was not produced in the Weald. Miss Beck notes that Luthery left no trace in the Godalming P.R., nor, I can add, in that of Wisborough Green, the centre of Elizabethan glassmaking in the Weald. Miss Beck adds, 'Did Luteri go back to London when he had exhausted his fuel allocation? Mr Thorpe quotes from St Olave's parish register the record of the burial of Angell, daughter of "Omnia Bene glassmaker" in June, 1589.[37] If this is the same man, his Burgate enterprise had been short-lived.'

No. 36, Ellen's Green, Ewhurst. Late. c.TQ/0992.3542.

S.C.M., vol. 14, p. 156. No. 38. No clues: chance find in a garden in 1937. This site is a mile and a half south of that at Somersbury (No. 37) and it is very unlikely that the quantity of glass and crucible could stray so far. The glass is unmistakably Late, but different from, and of finer quality than, the Somersbury glass. This was the only site I did not visit with Winbolt, but when I examined the garden

[37] W. A. Thorpe, *English Glass* (1949), p. 103.

of 'Woodhall' in 1962 I had no doubt there was a furnace somewhere in the garden. The site is dry, level and close to a small stream. Winbolt says, 'a little digging identified the site of at least one furnace.[38] The soil [in the garden] is prolific in glasshouse remains . . . There were many feet of ale glasses and some window glass; vessel had the characteristic broken-rib moulding which was adopted by the early American glassmakers.' The only material surviving that I have is a few scraps including a rigaree base fragment, and some unusual yellow, poor quality, coarse grained [?] crucible. There is no known family connection, but Winbolt suggests the furnace was worked by the Somersbury glassmen, Laurence Fryer and George Gerrat.

No. 37, Somersbury, Ewhurst. Late. TQ/1030.3777.

W.G., No. 18.P. Clue: Glasshouse Field (T). In 1874 the site was known and noted in Sy.A.C., vol. 6, p. 2, but there is no reference in county histories and no remains of buildings were known. The glasshouse is marked on the $2\frac{1}{2}$ in. O.S. and was almost certainly examined in the nineteenth century and may have been the first glasshouse in the Weald to be found because Cooper knew of it about the turn of the century. No records remain as to what was found. It is close to trig. point 298 in a clearing in a large area of woodland and more than 200 yards from any stream; the site is not dry and does not appear to have much to recommend it, except that it probably was surrounded by woodland. The glass, though uniform, has flaked badly; the site is damp and had been much dug about. The pronounced weathering is probably due to some vital detail being missed from the mix or the technique by the Somersbury glassmaker. The outstanding characteristic is that of window glass of exceptional thinness. The few sample fragments I have vary from $\frac{1}{16}$th down to $\frac{1}{32}$nd of an inch. No. 14, Glasshouse Lane, produced some glass of wafer thinness little more than $\frac{1}{64}$ of an inch. It can have been used only for small quarries. The question of cutting quarries at the glasshouse is discussed on p. 87. Possibly another reason for the unusual amount of window glass fragments remaining at No. 14 and at Somersbury, may be that they had a surplus of cullet due to cutting quarries on the site, or they may have been the last furnaces to be abandoned; both were probably working up to c.1618.

Winbolt describes the finds: 'Many pieces of crucibles, on the average stouter than those of Sidney Wood; some $1\frac{3}{4}$ to $2\frac{1}{4}$ in. thick at the angle of wall and base; lumps of crude glass, drippings, fragments of thin vessels,[39] etc. Nearly all the glass is thin spun window glass mostly light green, but some amber (probably owing to decay). Practically all the glass is rather decomposed and irridescent, and of very different quality from Sidney Wood glass. This is probably due to excess of potash or soda and deficiency of silica.'[40] The only surviving evidence of crown glass from Somersbury is a very thick piece which I think is Early cullet; it is now in Guildford

[38] In The Times, 30 March 1937. Winbolt says it was under the vegetable plot.
[39] There are a few fragments of Somersbury vessel in Littlehampton Museum.
[40] See Chapter II.

Museum. Winbolt goes on to describe what he thought were purposely shaped quarries; I am less sure because, apart from the standard quarries, it is far more probable that final cutting was done in the town glaziers' workshops. He found a shaped black flint and suggests that it supports Mrs Halahan's theory that flint was used for cutting glass. On a number of sites there was evidence of 'marking' or scratching the window glass fragments and flints may have been used. Winbolt is probably correct in thinking that it was a fair inference that window glass was the main product here. He says that there were 'coal cinders in plenty' and that he thought some coal was used for fuel, probably before 1615, during the experimental period. Mrs Godfrey says that 'Bungar and Hensey seem, without much success, to have experimented with coal during 1615.'[41] The coal found at this and two other Late sites, Nos. 38 and 40, may be relics of such experiments. They confirm that these three furnaces were among the last to close down. We may safely assume, the 1615 Proclamation notwithstanding, that coal-firing in the Weald was experimental only, because to make effective use of coal would entail completely redesigning the furnace and probably lidding the crucibles. The cost of coal would be prohibitive far from any water transport. Moreover there is evidence that the last glassmakers in the Weald continued to use wood fuel until the end.[42] Winbolt found lumps of lime and a few pieces of white flint. Chalk is found on a number of sites, and the use of lime is discussed on p. 36.

Mr B. C. Worssam of the Geological Survey told me that when he was surveying this place, he found nearby pits of fine-grained sand in the Weald clay. The glassmakers may have used it. The site was probably once part of the Onslow estate, whose ancient deeds are at Guildford Muniment Room. Miss E. Dance says she knows of no references to glassmaking in them.

Cooper, in a letter to Mr E. Wyndham Hulme, May 1915, says 'he never found any glass like Ewhurst (probably Somersbury) which is thinner and superior and of steely quality.' He knew of it and presumably had not then seen any Late glass, because Chaleshurst (No. 4) was not found until 1916. Winbolt quotes Cooper as saying that Somersbury was erected by Frenchmen between 1567 and 1570. The evidence for this may have been in the O.S. records destroyed during the last war.

Among the Wisborough Green P.R. entries is the marriage of Laurence Fryer, frenchman, and Joan Wood, 26 July 1588. He is almost certainly Laurence Fryer, the 'glasse fownder' of Ewhurst, Surrey whose will is dated in Feb. 1612/13. He left his goods to be equally divided between his wife Agnes (he must have remarried) and his daughter Mary Fryer, and desired that his master (i.e., manager of the glasshouse) George Gerrat, glassmaker, should keep Mary's portion until she was twenty-one.[43]

[41] D.E.G., p. 167.
[42] D.E.G., p. 109. A.P.C., XXXV (1616–17), 290–1; see also Chapter VIII, p. 135.
[43] V.C.H. Sy., vol. II, p. 299. For the difference in status between a glass maker and a glass founder see Chapter IV, p. 78.

If Fryer was a French glassmaker, the marriage is interesting because the Woods were a local family and so within twenty years of the arrival of Carré's Frenchmen the 'closed shop' of mating was no longer enforced.[44]

No. 38, Sidney Wood, Alfold. Late. TQ/0220.3372.

W.G., No. 17.P. Clue: Glasshouse Copse. O.S. (part of Sidney Wood). This is probably the glasshouse shown on the Norden maps of 1594 and 1607, and Speed's maps of 1611–2 and 1676.[45] The site is dry and level with a small pond about 50 yards away. The Rev. F. W. Cobb, then vicar of Alfold, found the site and dug there in 1923; the site was much disturbed and the scraps of glass fragmented into insignificance when Winbolt started work on it in 1930–1. I did some work and well remember the material. It was the finest quality glass showing the most skilled craftsmanship which we or Cooper found; no sites found since have quite come up to it. Whoever worked here was a master. But like all the Weald sites the fragments are small and disappointing; though tough they almost appear to have been deliberately crushed. The shiny burnished glass was largely fine quality thin vessel, usually a dark olive or blue-green, completely uncorroded and showing no weathering thirty years later. The glass surpasses the excellent glass from Woodchester, but is far more fragmentary; some Woodchester glass had heavy surface flaking which is absent at Sidney Wood. Because its products are the most interesting so far known in the Weald, I include here a full resumé of the still valid parts from W.G.: 'From the line of foundation bricks found, I should conjecture that the glasshouse was rectangular, thirty to forty feet long and fifteen to twenty feet wide.[46]

Specimens of siege (hearth) bricks with fused glass on the top, and often down the sides when it has penetrated the joints, show that these bricks were well-made for the purpose. They are of yellowish-brown material, liberally grogged with biggish lumps of previously burnt brick. I found a great quantity of fragments of crucibles of many sizes. One small round-bottomed crucible, which had been let into a round hole in the siege, I recovered whole, though slightly chipped round the lip [see Plate IV]; it has a piece of vitrified charcoal adhering to the interior, perhaps pushed down into the molten metal to correct colour. A cutting tool of hard sandstone was shaped with a ridge at the top for hafting. A large amount of glass is all comparatively thin; some of it shows a polished surface on one side, and is probably spun or disc glass. The glass here, both window and vessel, is of many shades of blue-green, all in excellent condition, very clear, and with highly burnished surface[47] ... Some

---

[44] For various persons who may have worked this and/or the Ellen's Green glasshouse, see Chapter VIII, p. 142.

[45] These four maps can be seen in the Guildford Museum. The three earliest could have been drawn while the glasshouses were operating.

[46] Unusually large. [G.H.K.]

[47] Winbolt said the fine quality was probably due to the use of barilla soda, a theory no longer tenable. See also Chapter II.

specimens are remarkably delicate; and there is a variety of moulded patterns, chiefly honeycomb, ribs and flutings.'

Winbolt notes some unusual white or crystal glass fragments which he explained as having been brought in as cullet. He adds, 'We find no waste of crystal glass,' and 'Most of the feet (bases) have a hollow fold-over hem, and a high kick-up; they belonged to funnel-like ale glasses.[48] There are also parts of tumblers with straight sides rising from flat bases with solid beaded rims. Some bases have rigaree ornament, and a diameter of exactly 3 in.: i.e., the tumbler was $4\frac{1}{2}$ to 5 in. high. There are several spouts (nozzles) of posset cups. The base of a small, roughly square moulded bottle, $1\frac{3}{10}$ in. square, has a slight kick-up with puntee mark underneath; a side is moulded with seven slight flutings to the inch, oblique to the base – anything but clumsy work. A specimen worth mentioning is part of the rim of an oblique-fluted vase, the rim being very fine and slightly inturned. The mouth diameter indicated is $3\frac{1}{4}$ in. Others are three-quarters of a blue-green "bullseye" and a complete one. [Winbolt notes some fragments which appear pink and blue when looked through, the former he suggests may be an aberration of green glass; I suspect both were]. Glass tubes are common, about the size of an ordinary lead pencil, or thinner; also solid glass rods or pencils, not quite circular in section. One piece of tubing is very fine work, 4 mm. in diameter, with fine rilling along its length, eighteen rills to the circumference; one end is solid, with a little nipple. There are plenty of lumps of crude glass in many shades of blue,[49] ?turned in cooking from green and devitrified under conditions of low temperature. Drippings of many shapes, and lengths of threading or veining used for ornamenting neck and bulge, were often turned up. Worth mention is a piece of cloudy white glass to which had been applied a thread of blue [almost certainly cullet]. We found a piece of iron puntee 4 in. long [Winbolt returns to his idea that crucibles were deliberately shaped into cubes from broken crucibles for tesserae. An almost impossible task with so hard a pot. He notes two worked flints]. Brown Rhenish speckled stoneware and red pottery with green-brown glaze in the interior associated with the glass, are of late sixteenth century.' In a letter to me Winbolt said he found here a complete puntee rod 21 in. long. Mr J. G. Hurst, kindly dated scraps of two tiger-ware Bellarmines from[50] this site as belonging to the first half of the seventeenth century and possibly before 1618 which neatly fits my suggestion below.

There is no certain evidence known as to who worked this glasshouse.[51] My own surmise, and it is no more, is that this remarkably uniform fine glass is the zenith of

[48] Judging by Mr Francis Buckley's reconstruction of vessel fragments from Sidney Wood (*see W.G.*, pp. 69 and 70), the glass from this site must have been very interesting. We found only Cobb's fragmented leavings. The Buckley drawings have not been traced.
[49] *See* also Woodhouse Farm, No. 32.   [50] In Haslemere Museum.
[51] Largely because Carré was buried at Alfold, Winbolt associated the Sidney Wood glasshouse with him (*W.G.*, pp. 15, 17 and 40). This and Songhurst (No. 31) are only one mile from the church; Fernfold, which we know Carré worked, is only $1\frac{1}{3}$ miles.

the Weald product and of the forest glasshouses in England; it was probably one of
the last forest furnaces to be worked *c.*1600–18, thirty years after Carré's death.
The amount of glass surviving reinforces this idea. A possible owner might be Isaac
Bungar; Winbolt suggested that the Bungars might have taken it over from Carré.
Isaac Bongar fits my suggested dates and in 1605 a Mr Bonngard owed £25 for
wood to Samsonn Coulstocke, yeoman of Ifold.[52] Ifold Farm almost adjoined Sidney
Farm and the furnace is less than a mile from the Ifold boundary. But Bungar was
a window glassmaker and Sidney Wood seems to have produced mainly vessel
glass.

As at No. 37, Winbolt found coal cinders 'enough to prove that coal was used
for fuel as well as wood.' Winbolt notes that fragments of feet and knopped stems
found at Sidney Wood clearly show Venetian influence exerted after 1550 and
probably before that date. The fragmentation is remarkable because the glass, although thin, is tough and strong. The moulded bead rims of vessel, and the folded
rim bases of drinking-glasses, being the strongest, sometimes survive in small pieces,
but the remaining glass is never enough to even guess at a reconstruction. No doubt
Cobb, the first-comer to the site, fared better. The usual appearance is dark burnished
blue-green, different from the olive-green of Woodchester or St Weonards, some
steely-blue vessel was undoubtedly made here, with only the faintest trace of green.
Possibly the sand varied enough to produce this difference. There are the odd bits of
cullet, royal blue, cloudy white and a rolled tube of Early glass. Such little window
glass is very thin indeed. I have a few small fragments of a rigaree base, a bottle lip
showing mouldings, a bead rim of a vessel with applied thread, some devitrified
'blue' lumps,[53] thin bits of small crucibles, and a fragment of tigerware, which was
found only on a number of Late sites. The evidence suggests that some crucibles
here were smaller than usual.

Winbolt, rightly emphasizing that Sidney Wood glass is far better in quality
than any other Surrey–Sussex product, says: 'I am strengthened in the estimate by
the opinions of Mr Francis Buckley and M. Varlot de Hennezel, of Bleurville, Vosges.
The former writes: "I have seen hardly anything comparable in quality with this
Sidney Wood green glass." The latter, "C'est de verre très fin pour l'époque."

M. de Hennezel sent me in exchange fragments of crucible and glass of much
the same texture as those at Sidney Wood from the site of Grandmont, near Visménil,
Vosges, France, which was worked by Thos. and Balthazar de Hennezel till within
a few years of the time they came to England in 1568 ... The glass, vessel and
window, bears a close general resemblance to the Sidney Wood product, but it is
not so well preserved, is of lighter shade of green, and shows nothing so fine; and
there are no mouldings.' Of the crucible Winbolt says they 'are very similar, a fact
which suggests what is generally probable, that glass makers manufactured their

---

[52] S. Coulstocke's will, proved 1605 (P.C.C., Dixy, 67); Coulstocke was a man of substance who
left his son £590.
[53] Winbolt comments on their frequency here.

own pots.' My recollection of the glass from Lorraine is that it was not unlike our poorer Late glass but not comparable to the Sidney Wood product, possibly because it was at least forty years earlier. None of this Lorraine material[54] now survives, or it cannot be traced in the museums to which it was given.

Sidney Wood and Nos. 14 and 23 are all Late sites, where enough glass of uniform appearance and fracture survived to be reasonably sure it was the local product representing a spread of more than the last batch or two. It has some value as evidence. We can say with some accuracy the main product at this site was vessel glass of such fine quality that it is difficult to distinguish some of its fragments from modern glass of the same colour. Alone of all the Wealden glass, some fragments from Sidney Wood appear to the unaided eye to be completely unaffected by age or burial. Sidney Wood glass is in a class by itself in the Weald and it is finer than that from Woodchester or St Weonards glasshouses. It is superior to the Fernfold glass of c.1567 and much better than the Buckholt glass of 1576–9. While the maker may have had a technique unknown to the other Late people, it could be the final flowering of the forest glasshouses in the early seventeenth century. I think both are probable, because the Sidney Wood glassmaker produced finer quality than the next best, and probably very late product, from Glasshouse Lane. Two drinking glass bases found by the Rev. F. W. Cobb at Sidney Wood are shown in Fig. 13 and various other fragments from this site are included in Plates XIV and XVI.

No. 39, Lower Roundhurst, Lurgashall. Early. (Provisional). c.SU/935.303.

W.G., No. 26.R. Clue: Glass Piece (T). The site could not be found thirty years ago and it was only when a field about 200 yards north of Glass Piece was ploughed in 1959 that some glasshouse material was found by Colonel L. F. Messel who owns the farm; the field has now been grassed down again. The field-name and the few scraps of material indicate a glasshouse close by but the actual site is not yet known. The scraps are two pieces of crucible and two of possibly Early glass. The nearest known site is two miles away to the north of Chaleshurst; the material could not stray so far.

There is no known family connection, but North Chapel is about a mile away and it is possible that Edward Henraye [sic] (Henzaye) of Northchapel, glassmaker, 1610–11, may have worked here[55] but he is more likely to have worked the Petworth Park site.

No. 40, Petworth Park, Lurgashall. Late. SU/9540.2587.

W.G., No. 27.P. Clue: Glasshouse Pond Plantation. O.S. The site was found in the southeast corner of the plantation in 1931. The Petworth/Lurgashall parish boundary runs just to the south, the site being in the extreme north of Petworth Park. There is a reference in 1604, in the Petworth House archives, to the pond: 'Paid to John

---

[54] Samples, fifteenth and mid-sixteenth century, from two glasshouses were sent. W.G., p. 40.
[55] See also S.A.C., vol. 99, p. 108.

Mose for making the pond in the Little Parke under the glasshouse Dec. 8th per bill £9 3s. 9d.'[56] From the appearance of the glass, the house was very probably working at this date. The pond is larger than necessary for a glasshouse, but perhaps the glass-maker had moved in in 1604, and asked the estate to dam the small stream close to the site. Winbolt noted in letters that the glasshouse debris was widespread; that he had been told there was a sand pit nearby to the southwest; that the glasshouse was about 27 ft. NE.–SW., and 18ft. SE.–NW. with the furnace towards the southwest end; that the marked blue-green character of the glass, its burnished surface, and the thinness of some of the window glass (made in discs and less than $\frac{1}{16}$ in. thick in some cases) make it practically certain that the house was one of the latest, say, roughly, 1560–1610.

I know of no Petworth Park glass now surviving. My recollection is that the pro-duct of this site was Late, thin and blue-green, and that the glasshouse remains had been largely destroyed when the plantation was made. Winbolt says in *W.G.* (p. 50): 'The burnt floor of the furnace was found a foot down; the fragments of blue-green glass, vessel and window, were of the latest period, say 1550–1610, and the finds were of the usual character ... The glassmaker has not been traced, but it may have been a Hennezel. Some coal cinder[57] was found on the site (cf. Sidney Wood and Somersbury).' Wherever furnace floors or baked clay bases were found, in copses or in arable fields, they seldom seem to vary more than from 10 to 12 in. below the present surface. Winbolt's imaginative guess that a Hennezel may have worked this glasshouse, has some confirmation because of Edward Henraye (*sic.* Henzaye, a corruption of Hennezel) of Northchapel, glassmaker in 1610–11.[58] If the glasshouse was still working in 1610 it is strange that Treswell does not show it on his detailed map of that date.

No. 41, Lordings Farm, Billingshurst. Date (Provisional). c. TQ/076.244.

Not in *W.G.* Clue: Glasshouse Field (T).[59] A probable site which has not been found and may be revealed when the adjoining Great Lordings Wood is next cleared. I searched unsuccessfully in May 1960, when the field was down to grass. When the field was ploughed in 1965, Mr W. S. Taylor found crucible and a blob of glass half way along the east headland. I also found crucible fragments there. Isaac Bungar, after Carré, possibly the most important man in the Wealden Industry, had three children baptized at Billingshurst between 1610 and 1614. This could be one of his furnace sites, or it could be a Hensey glasshouse. The rim of a heavy ribbed and

[56] Sir Ed. Francis's bk 'of disbursements, 1604. I am much indebted to Miss G. M. A. Beck for this reference. The cost represents the work of five or six men's wages for a month. Petworth House MS. 582.

[57] *See* under Somersbury, p. 202.

[58] *See S.A.C.*, vol. 96, p. 73, for the only possible reference in the Petworth and Lurgashall P.R. *See also S.A.C.*, vol. 99, p. 108.

[59] This was the only fresh field-name I found in the examination of 35 Tithe Apportionment schedules.

probably large crucible, 1 in. thick at the top, was found in Glasshouse Field on the east headland. Bungar appears to have been a specialist window glassmaker and if this was his glasshouse I should expect the furnace to be large. There are three references to Joseph Henzey in the Billingshurst P.R., 1616–18; he was one of the six Hensey glassmakers in 1614 (*see* Chapter VIII). Lordings position in the district and the fact that a field-name survives vaguely suggest a Late site. Of all the remaining lost sites, this is the one I would like to examine most.

No. 42. Knightons, Alfold.[60] *Late. TQ/0170.3410.*

Found in 1965 by Mr F. Holling. No field-name. It is 75 yards north of a point where the Alfold–Dunsfold boundary almost meets the old Wey-Arun canal bank. It adjoins a ride through Sidney Wood, 700 yards northwest of the original Sidney Wood glasshouse. The glasshouse appears to have been robbed of its brick and stone and is generally disturbed. There was no obvious sign of surrounding ditches. Plenty of glass fragments and some bits of crucibles were scattered around. The range of glass appearance and quality is considerable and unlike any other known Late site. Some is unmistakably Late and the fragments of pottery confirm this, but there is, for a Late glasshouse, a curious lack of uniformity in the glass, some being of poor quality and semi-opaque; this and some of the crude vessel is more characteristic of the Early period. Some of the glass is brittle and decayed, completely different from any other known Late site. The only other Late site which produced poor glass was Somersbury (No. 37), but its condition is more uniform and confined to heavy superficial flaking. There are at least three possible explanations for the wide range in quality at the Knightons' site (*see* also Chapter VI, p. 102): that the site was used at two periods or, perhaps more likely that for some reason an unusual amount of imported cullet has survived here, or workmen were careless. The problem will no doubt be solved when Mr Wood completes his excavation in 1967. The best glass, though good, does not compare with the excellent glass produced at the original Sidney Wood glasshouse.

[60] This is a provisional note.

X

SUSSEX GLASSHOUSES OUTSIDE THE WEALD DISTRICT

Graffham

THERE was a furnace site at Graffham about 100 yards above and west of the house called 'Glasses.'[1] Judging by the material found, crucible and glass waste, it was very close to, if not in, the present kitchen garden or tennis court. Winbolt says that 'in July 1932 Mr C. Maresco Pearce showed me lumps of different crucibles with glass adhering, found on Glasses Farm, a place ideal for glassmaking, with whitish sand and unstinted supplies of bracken. We searched, but some accident has yet to reveal the furnace site.'

Some of the glass material is of poor quality and pitted. It may be cullet, with very few finished blown fragments, but there is enough of the hard, blue-green type to suggest that it is Late. The reference on a map of 1629 to the glassmakers digging sand rather over a mile away on Graffham common (*see* p. 35) gives support to a Late date. Glass from the actual furnace site would be a more reliable guide.

The crucible is rather coarse and gritty, glazed and unglazed. There is a band of white clay on top of sandstone, running through the garden at Glasses; Mrs Mullins has made excellent pottery with a white 'slip' pattern from this clay, and built her own pottery kiln to fire it. She thinks the crucibles could have been made from this clay. A pottery 'tuyere' (a bellows nozzle) was found among the glass waste.[2] The hole is inadequate for more than a small domestic fire.

It is an interesting area because fragments of Roman hypocaust tiles are found in the stream just across the road and east from the house. Mrs Mullins suggests that ochre pits behind the house were used by the Graffham pottery, about a mile ENE.

The Graffham parish registers have survived only from 1655 and the few earlier Bishops' transcripts contain no references to glassmakers. But we may have a possible reference to local glassmaking in a bond of 25 April 1602 whereby John Felpe and Thomas Baker both of Woolavington, (a small adjoining parish 700 yards from Glasses) brickmakers, were bound to Thomas Bennett of Arundel, draper, in the sum of £12, to deliver to the said Bennett at his house in Arundel, 'one loade of

---

[1] The house is modern and 'Glasses' may have been the name of a cottage near the road. It does not appear in the Tithe Award schedule. Mrs C. Mullins showed me her finds in 1963; the site was probably within a short distance of SU/9965.1818. Glasses Farm was Winbolt's site No. 35 (*S.C.M.,* vol. 9, p. 791).

[2] *See* also Chapter IV; a tuyere was found at Blunden's Wood.

hole broad glasse of the best glasse windowes wth all'; half the load was to be delivered on or before 24 June 1602 and the other half on or before 29 Sept. 1602.[3]

The fact that the glass was to be delivered in two lots suggests it might be produced locally and delivered as it became available.

Great Goteley Wood, Northiam. Late. TQ/842.250.

S.C.M., vol. 9, p. 787, No. 28. Clue: Glasshouse Field (see also W.G., p. 51).

Winbolt says that much glazed sandstone was found in 1882 when some land drains were dug. In 1932 we found 'the usual waste about a spit down. One blue enamelled bead, a "bugle" for sewing on dresses of the kind made by the Venetian Sebastian Orlanden (1578) at Beckley, suggests that the Stoddard Farm [this site] and Beckley sites are identical, for the Stoddard glasshouse is nearer to Beckley than to Northiam, though it is just on the Northiam side of the brook which bounds the parishes [see later]. We found both window and vessel glass of the best type of sixteenth century. Crucibles were dressed outside with an exceptional brown glaze.'

The quality of the glass is interesting because here we have a closely dated glasshouse, whether it is Beckley or Northiam,[4] and I think there is little doubt it is the 1581 Northiam glasshouse, the glass is unmistakably Late, it has the hard burnished fine quality, relatively clear appearance characteristic of Late glass.

This record dating is not tentative with necessarily wide limits. The contemporary brown-speckled stone-ware is useful but who can say how long such tough pottery might last, and its end date is uncertain.

Here, as at Fernfold, we have a close and accurate dating for this unmistakable fine quality Late glass. It is less blue-green and more a pale olive-green than Fernfold.

In 1954 Mr V. F. M. Oliver located and excavated the actual furnace site and reported on it.[5] He says: 'Unfortunately a modern ditch has been dug right through the centre of the furnace floor, but sufficient crucible, glass and brick floor has been found to prove the site; there were also some fragments of pottery. The dimensions of the shed floor on which the furnace stood were found to be about 20 ft. by 11 ft., the long axis running east and west. The foundations were about 2 ft. below the

---

[3] I have to thank Mr F. T. Barrett for kindly sending me this reference in 1955 and Mr F. W. Steer who kindly noted this when the Wilberforce collection was handed to the C.R.O. in 1963. Mr Steer says that the practice was for the bond to be for twice the value of the goods, so that this window glass price was £6 a load. We can only guess the amount of glass because the thickness is not known, but in 1629 an inventory in Petworth valued window glass at 3d. a foot, so on that basis £6 would buy 480 sq. ft., enough for about twenty windows of 6 × 4 ft., large for the period. Mr Steer says that Felpe was a local spelling or variant for Phillip(p)s. The 'hole' suggests that Bennett would not accept broken panes or quarries.

[4] S.N.Q., vol. 14, p. 115. The Beckley and Northiam glasshouses are discussed in V.C.H., Sussex, vol. 2, p. 255. Beckley glasshouse is mentioned in 1579 and after it was pulled down another was set up in Northiam parish in 1580-1. Another glasshouse was set up by Gerard Ansye, with certain other Frenchmen within a mile of Hastings, to the annoyance and injury of the town.

[5] S.N.Q., vol. 14, p. 116. The glasshouse site is in Glasshouse Field.

present ground level...[6] some fragments of small glass rods of about $\frac{1}{8}$ in. and $\frac{1}{16}$ in. in diameter [were found]. No coloured glass was found, nor any glass "bugles".' He gave fragments from this site to the Sussex Archaeological Society's Museum at Lewes, and I have some typical fragments which we found in 1932.

The information collected in V.C.H. *Sussex*, vol. 2, p. 255 by Dr L. F. Salzman in 1907 for the Beckley and Northiam glasshouses is interesting and easily accessible, but perhaps a few points may be extracted here. In March 1579, Sebastian Orlanden, of Venice, was involved in a dispute with John Smith,[7] citizen and glazier of London, concerning a glasshouse at Beckley. Orlanden appears to have had a third share[8] with Godfrey Delahay for the making of 'bugles' at Beckley. Two glassworkers belonging to the works also gave evidence: John Okes (a good Sussex name), of Beckley, said that there were two great baskets of glass, two panniers of 'canvas amell,' and ten cases of 'ameld' canvas. Sondaye Exanta, of Lorraine, the other glassworker, possibly one of Carré's Lorrainers of twelve years earlier, said that one of the partners (Delahay) in the Beckley glasshouse had sold his share to John Smith 'with all the stuff for making amels (?enamels) and glasse in collers, and tools etc.' Smith's right to a share in the glasshouse appears to have been proved, as in 1581 we find a dispute in progress between the well-known Jacomo Verzelini, glassmaker, and John Smith and Sebastian Orlanden concerning a furnace that had been pulled down. This was evidently the Beckley furnace, as in January 1581, the authorities in Rye made a note that a glasshouse which had been 'of late' in Beckley had destroyed much wood, and now another had been set up in the adjoining parish of Northiam. The authorities also noted the harmfulness of glasshouses owing to the ease with which they could be moved as the neighbouring woods were exhausted.

Delahay appears to have sold his share to Smith, so that the new glasshouse was owned by an English glazier[9] and two Venetians, Verzelini and Orlanden, an interesting combination.

Verzelini worked in Crutched Friars, under a patent granted by Queen Elizabeth on 15 December 1575, and he seems to have spread his risks by having a one-third share in a 'forest' glasshouse.

In the Rye Port Books there is an interesting entry of an import to Rye from

[6] As at Fernfold, No. 25, this depth of soil could happen on heavy arable and in one summer cloud burst. [G.H.K.]

[7] Mrs E. S. Godfrey (*D.E.G.*, p. 59) says John Smith operated at Beckley and Ratcliffe, London, and that the ownership of the Knole, Kent, glasshouse is uncertain but he may be the Mr Smyth referred to there also. Winbolt (*W.G.*, p. 11) mentions 'one Henry Smythe, of London [who] was granted [26 April 1552] a 20-years' patent for making "brode glasse" or "Normandy glasse" (Calendar of Patent Rolls of Edward VI); he proposed to bring over workmen from Normandy, but the death of the king prevented the glassmakers, strong Calvinists, from coming.'

[8] From the 1581 reference there is little doubt that the third partner in the Beckley furnace was Verzelini.

[9] Glazier by 1579 was probably coming to mean what it does today. In medieval times when domestic windows were relatively rare, it seems to have covered glassmakers and glaziers.

London in November 1579 of 'broken glass and glassmaking tools' (*see* p. 18, note 65). This was probably destined for either the Beckley or Northiam glasshouses, only five or six miles from Rye. Barrels of 'broken glass' were again imported in September 1580. The supply of cullet was an everlasting problem. The Port Books of Rye show that a considerable export of 'billets' continued, at the same time as the 'authorities', among them possibly the firewood merchants, were complaining of the exhaustion of the neighbouring woods by the glassmakers.[10] The 'bugles' may turn up if the Beckley glasshouse is found. Alas, the one specimen found in 1932 on the Northiam site has not survived. The two great baskets of glass may be the large pedlars' packs shown in contemporary illustrations. The panniers are probably for packhorses (*see* p. 112); ameld canvas and canvas amell are puzzling, and I can offer no explanation. 'Glasse in collers' suggests that coloured glass pot-metal was made here. If, as seems highly probable, this is the new 1580–1 furnace started in Northiam, they could hardly have cut their limit closer as the parish boundary with Beckley is only a few yards away.

———

There is a possible glass site on the large clearing east of Rewell Wood and west of Arundel called Park Farm. Of all the sites in Sussex this would seem the most sensible because being on the chalk, it is, and probably has always been, surrounded by fine beech woods for fuel. I am indebted to Mr F. W. Steer for telling me of a map of Arundel and Lyminster of 1772[11] showing a 'Glass-house-gate' Field on Park Farm, and for sending me a tracing. The approximate map ref. is TQ/9950.0815. In 1959 he found a 'Glastis Gate' roughly in the same place on a map of Arundel Park, 1661. He and I visited the place but could find no trace of glass waste or crucible.

All the outlying glasshouses in southeast England known or recorded – Beckley, Northiam, Graffham (possibly), Knole and Buckholt – are Late and if the Park Farm furnace ever comes to light I think it will belong to the last fifty years of glassmaking in the south-east forest area.

Winbolt gives some references[12] to the industry from the Horsham P.R.; a daughter of Wm Ap Richard, a glassmaker of Luxford [?Loxwood] was buried in 1581. Four glass carriers are mentioned: Robert Goffe in 1590, John Thomas in 1599–1600, Henry Cooper in 1614 and James Mosely in 1621. Writing some years later Winbolt notes that the late Mr Thomas de Honeywood found in a garden on the east side of the Causeway, Horsham, fused glass and glass drops, suggesting a site near the church.[13] Winbolt also mentions that he found unquestionable local glass, associated with Rhenish pottery, on the site of Hill's Place, an Elizabethan house near Horsham, about ten miles from the nearest glasshouse.[14]

[10] *See* V.C.H., *Sussex*, vol. 2, p. 233, for the export of billets and the complaints against the iron-works.

[11] Arundel Castle MS. H.1/3.

[12] *W.G.*, p. 52. 1621 is late, but Mosely may have been a retired glass carrier.

[13] *S.C.M.*, vol. 9, p. 792.   [14] *W.G.*, p. 53.

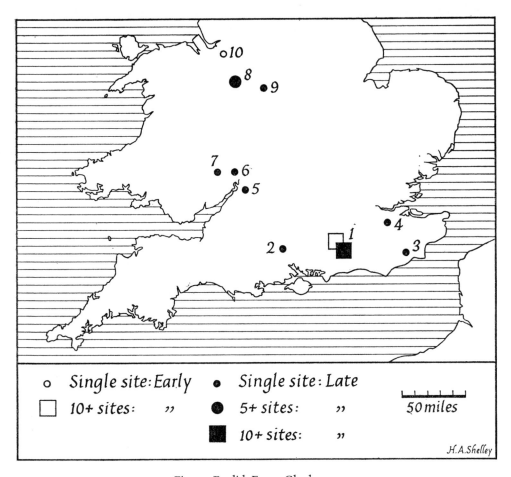

Fig. 19. English Forest Glasshouses.

  1   The Weald, *c.*1330–1618.
  2   Buckholt, Hampshire, 1576–79.
  3   Northiam, Sussex, 1581.
  4   Knole, Kent, 1585.
  5   Woodchester, Gloucestershire.
  6   Newent, Gloucestershire, 1599.
  7   St Weonards, Herefordshire.
  8   Bishop's Wood, Staffordshire, 1584–1604.
  9   Bagot's Park, Staffordshire, 1585.
10   Kingswood, Cheshire.

The dates are from documentary evidence except for the earliest date in the Weald.

It is fair to comment that any anciently inhabited site in this district or further afield may provide fragments of Wealden glass. Fires were frequent and given the right conditions could melt the window glass. The only satisfactory evidence of a glasshouse site remains fragments of unmistakable crucible.

FOREST GLASSHOUSES OUTSIDE SUSSEX

The map (Fig. 19) attempts to show the distribution of Forest glassmaking geographically and historically and emphasizes the expansion achieved by immigrant Frenchmen during the last fifty years of the industry in the Weald and elsewhere. This expansion appears to have reached its peak about 1600. Though it is more than likely that glass was made in other places, no glassmaking site is known in England after the late Saxon glasshouse at Glastonbury until *c.*1330 in the Weald, and until the latter half of the sixteenth century outside that district, except for one possible medieval glasshouse in Cheshire (*see* p. 220).

Even after the mid-sixteenth century more glasshouse sites have been closely examined in the Weald than in the rest of England so the Weald provides the bulk of the evidence for the English forest glass industry (*see* p. 1). Outside the Weald the Late forest glasshouses are mainly in Staffordshire where twenty sites have been noted,[15] two are in Sussex, two in Gloucestershire at Newent and Woodchester and one each in Hampshire (Buckholt), Herefordshire (St Weonards) and Kent (Knole).

Some movements of the French glassmaking families are considered in Chapter VIII (pp. 124 *et seq.*). For the Lorrainers from the Weald there was certainly contact with Staffordshire and it is possible, though there is no evidence for any individual, that some of them may have made glass at Buckholt for two or three years on their way westwards. Both counties were probably reinforced direct from France.

Buckholt, Hampshire

Buckholt[16] is ten miles east of Salisbury and some members of Lorraine and Norman families made glass there between 1576 and 1579. The evidence for this is

15. Mr T. Pape noted six sites (five had been destroyed) in the Bishop's Wood district, (*see* Chapter IV p. 71) and Mr D. W. Crossley of Sheffield University kindly tells me that in Bagot's Park, twenty miles to the east of Bishop's Wood, another fourteen sites came to light during land reclamation in 1965–6. They are only two or three hundred yards apart and most of them were destroyed by deep ploughing. One site was saved and was excavated by him in August 1966. The furnace is rectangular, fed from both ends; there is a separate annealing furnace and the pottery, though sparse, points to a late sixteenth century date. The late W. Horridge in his paper of 1955 (*see* p. 139, note 110) printed an agreement between Richard Bagot, esq. and Ambrose Hensey, gent. to erect a glasshouse in Bagot's Park in 1585 (*see* p. 109, note 4), so at least one site in each district can be dated by documentary evidence. Horridge found glass in the Park closely resembling glass from Bishop's Wood, which was Late. On the available evidence I have provisionally shown both districts as Late.

The remarkable concentration of sites in Bagot's Park presents problems in compiling a distribution map, because one suspects that a family group of glassmakers may have worked a large glasshouse and moved with their fuel supply more frequently and in shorter stages than their fellows in the Weald. The map symbol for No. 9, Bagot's Park should probably be at least as large as that for No. 8.

16 There are two sites marked on the 2½ in. O.S. map about 1,100 yards apart.

in the entries in the register of the Walloon Church of Southampton, where, under the date 7 October 1576 appears: Jan du Tisac, Pierre Vaillant[17] and Claude Potier,[17] 'ouvriers de verre a la verriere de Boucehaut,' who had made their profession of faith and been admitted to the Lord's supper. About a year after, there are further entries of the names of 'Monsieur de Hennezé et son fils, Louis de Hennezee, Arnoul Bisson[17] and Jan Perné[18] tous de bocquehaut.' Finally, on 4 January 1579, a last reference to the Buckholt factory is found, when Monsieur du Hou, 'Verrieren a Bouquehaut,' is admitted to fellowship and communion.[19]

One of the two sites at Buckholt was excavated by the Rev. E. Kell in 1860. He reported on his work in the *Journal of British Archaeology*, vol. 17 (1861), p. 55, and included a whole page plan of the site.[20] The small oblong furnace had a sur- round of brick 4 ft. 9 in. × 6 ft. outside, with a centre floor of mortar 'nearly as hard as stone' and 8 in. thick. The bricks were 11 in. long, 7 in. wide, 2 in. thick and very hard. The curious, irregular, detached walls which Kell called 'rays' and which Hulme later suggested might be annealing passages, were of flint.[21] In the surrounding trench Kell found a layer of wood ashes 10 in. thick. Some crucible fragments had a design on the outside; there were burnt flints in some quantity. Mr H. Syer Cumming followed Kell in the same *Journal* with a report on the glass and pottery found. He mentions large quantities of window glass, and it is very likely that it was the principal product though vessel fragments were also found. He says the glass was of several colours, including a fragment of fourteenth-century window and he suspected the 'whole was mere cullet.' Without knowing the context it is impossible to com- ment. He suggested, with remarkable accuracy, that the furnace dated from the mid-sixteenth century and this was broadly confirmed thirty years later by the Southampton register entries quoted above. Some of the glass from Buckholt was in the Syer Cumming collection in Southwark Public Library.

In a section of his paper on 'English Glassmaking in the sixteenth and seventeenth centuries'[22] Mr E. Wyndham Hulme printed three furnace plans which are here shown as Fig. 20. The "x" plan is Kell's of Buckholt without the surrounding ditch, and Hulme was plainly trying to relate the two eighteenth-century French glass furnace plans given below,[23] to explain the curious detached walls at Buckholt.

[17] M. Varlot says they were Normans. They do not appear in the Weald and may have come straight from France.

[18] Thorpe says Perné was Flemish. See *English Glass* (2nd edn., London, 1949), p. 88, note 2.

[19] V.C.H., *Hants.*, vol. 5, 1912, quoting from Huguenot Soc. Publ., vol. 4, p. 12.

[20] There is a small copy of the complete site plan in Hartshorne, p. 171, who rightly comments that it is rather puzzling. The furnace was partly surrounded by a circular ditch about 22 ft. in diameter, this is not shown on Hulme's plan.

[21] If these detached flint walls were as thick as shown on the plan they would have made access to the 'glory holes' impossible.

[22] The paper is spread over five parts in *The Antiquary*, vols. 30, 31. The plans are on p. 105 of vol. 31.

[23] The two lower plans were taken from the work of Bosc d'Antic, a French savant of the eighteenth century.

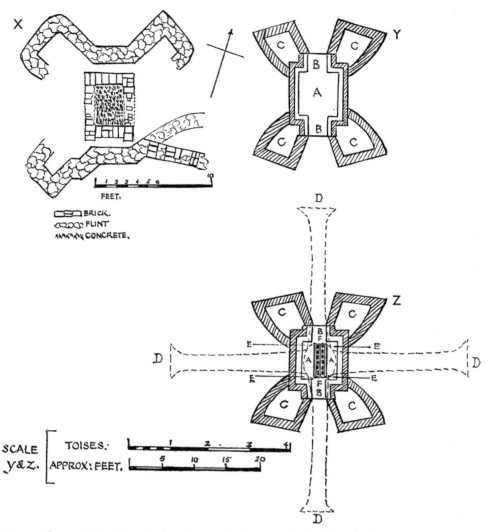

X

FEET.

BRICK.
FLINT
CONCRETE.

D

Y

Z

D

D

D

D

E E

E E

SCALE
y & z.
TOISES.
APPROX: FEET.

Fig. 20. Drawing X, Buckholt Furnace, Hants; drawings Y and Z are of two eighteenth-century French furnaces, the latter showing modifications for coal fuel.

Their attached 'wings' make sense and the plans are shown here to illustrate the two chief modifications needed to change over from a wood to a coal-fired furnace, viz: the latter has underground flues DD, leading up to grate bars FF and EE, the ledges on which the pots were placed.

In 1958 Captain J. A. F. Dalgety took some glass to the London Museum for Dr D. B. Harden to examine. It came from the site 1400 yards east of Buckholt Farm.[24] Dr Harden showed the glass to me. It is Late, similar in appearance but poorer in quality than most of the Late glass from the Weald, or the glass from St Weonard's or Woodchester. It shows more corrosion.[25]

Bishop's Wood, Staffordshire

Two of the Sussex and Buckholt family names Henzey and Tysac occur a few years later in Staffordshire, where the best survival of a forest furnace, so far known in England, was found in Bishop's Wood, Eccleshall, by Mr T. Pape in 1931.[26] The furnace was covered by a mound 6 ft. high and 11 ft. in diameter; a remarkable survival.

It is fully described with plans and photographs in Chapter IV. It was one of six known furnace sites spread over three or four square miles, the other five having been demolished. These glasshouses appear (from the P.Rs.) to have been working between at least 1584 and 1604, and as Mr Pape says 'so for at least twenty years the glass workers were in the old parish of Eccleshall.'[27]

The glassmaking families of the Weald such as the Henseys, the Titterys and the Tysacks appear in these P.Rs. and one of our Wisborough Green Henzeys was married to Sarah Tetrye of Eccleshall.

Twenty miles east of Bishop's Wood, at Bagot's Park, another Hensey, Ambrose, erected a glasshouse in 1585, for which an interesting agreement survives.[28]

The Tyzack family are found in the Newent P.Rs. in 1599 when 'Abraham Tyzack[29] sonne of a frenchman at the glassehouse' was baptized. The Newent glasshouse site is known; it is close to the hamlet of Glasshouse. Mr N. P. Bridgewater hopes to excavate this site which was working between 1599 and 1601.

[24] Map ref. SU/290.323.

[25] This question of quality from a very closely dated site raises an interesting possibility, the more so because we have very little glass from Fernfold, 1567, now surviving. Is the glass from Sidney Wood, Brookland and Glasshouse Lane, as I have suggested, the latest made in the Weald, c.1610? And had the quality greatly improved during these forty years c.1579 to c.1618? I suggest it is likely.

[26] See principally, T. Pape, 'Medieval Glassworkers in North Staffordshire,' in N. Staffs. Field Club Trans., vol. 68 (1934), and also by Mr Pape in the same Transactions (1947–8), 'The Lorraine Glassmakers in North Staffordshire.'

[27] Mr Pape notes that there are references to glassmakers in P.Rs. of the neighbouring parish of Cheswardine from 1601 to 1613.

[28] See p. 109, note 4 and p. 214, note 15.

[29] Pape, p. 18, Newent P.R. entries, Tysack, Voyden and Pilney, glassworkers.

St Weonards, Herefordshire

A full excavation of the glasshouse at St Weonards[30] was done by Mr N. P. Bridgewater in 1961, and his paper on it is published in *The Woolhope Naturalists' Field Club Transactions*, vol. 37, 1963. The glasshouse cannot be dated as no pottery of value for dating was found, nor are there any P.R. entries, but on the glass evidence there is no doubt it is Late and I think about twenty years either side of 1600 would be sound limits. The glass is very similar to much Late glass from the Weald; it is of fine quality, and has a slightly blue tinge.

Mr Bridgewater says: 'A good selection of manufactured glass objects was found – these included parts of drinking vessels, window glass, bottles, and linen smoothers – in addition to wasters ... The vessel forms are very good and comparable to those of Woodchester, and it is this similarity of style which suggests work by the same group of glassmakers.'

Mr Bridgewater did an expert excavation of a large area 50 ft. by 40 ft., but he found only the furnace bed[31] 'the actual furnace which once surrounded it has disappeared.' The general Weald pattern of demolition was repeated in the West. He thinks that the sand was local and that the crucibles probably came from Stourbridge; the fragments were of better quality than those from most if not all of our Wealden pots.

There was a glasshouse at Newnham on the Severn (near the Old Quay) where Mansell may have tried out the new type furnace, fired by coal from the Forest of Dean, in 1616 or soon after.[32]

Woodchester, Gloucestershire

The glasshouse at Woodchester, about 3 miles SSW. of Stroud (Glos.), produced the finest collection of vessel fragments of forest glass so far known in England. Messrs. Powell were encouraged by the late H. J. Powell, *c.*1920, to make some excellent reconstructions of twenty different forms[33] which were on sale until just before the last war. The best collection of forest vessel forms from this site, including one complete bottle, is now in Gloucester Museum which also has fourteen of the Powell reconstructions; six of these are shown in Plate XIX. The Stroud Museum also has a good collection from this glasshouse.

The glasshouse was found by the late B. P. Marmont, *c.*1880, and excavated by him between 1890 and 1920; he lived only half a mile away. His dating of it, on what evidence is not known, 1590–1615, is acceptable on glass type. Unhappily he

---

[30] Both glasshouses were known to the late B. P. Marmont, who excavated the Woodchester site. He read a paper on the St Weonards site in 1922 to the Woolhope Naturalists' Field Club, which is included in *The Woodchester Glass House* by J. S. Daniels (J. Bellows, Gloucester, 1950). The book includes sketch maps showing the position of all three glasshouses. Nos. 5, 6 and 7 on Fig. 20.

[31] Found by means of a proton magnetometer.   [32] *W.G.*, p. 19.

[33] The forms were inevitably to some extent surmise and they have been and will be modified.

PLATE I

THE REVEREND T. S. COOPER. A PHOTO-
GRAPH TAKEN *c.* 1900.

PLATE II

S. E. WINBOLT. A PHOTOGRAPH TAKEN,
c. 1925, AT THE ROMAN ROAD, ELLEN'S
GREEN, SUSSEX.

PLATE III

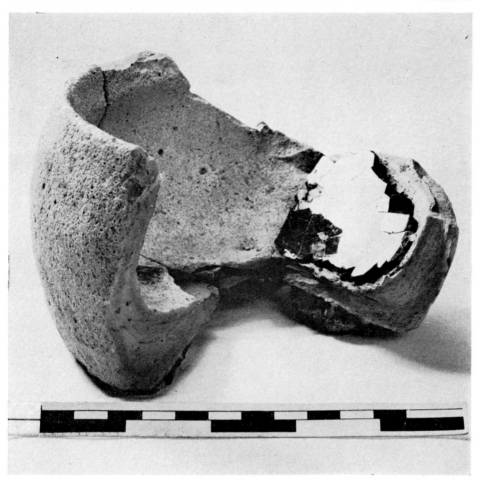

PART OF A CRUCIBLE CONTAINING RUBY
GLASS FROM SITE NO. 4. COOPER COLLEC-
TION, GUILDFORD MUSEUM.

PLATE IV

SMALL COMPLETE CRUCIBLE FROM SITE
NO. 38. WINBOLT COLLECTION, GUILDFORD
MUSEUM.

PLATE V

PART OF A CRUCIBLE CONTAINING GLASS
FROM SITE NO. 29. HASLEMERE MUSEUM.

PLATE VI

1

2

1. BISHOP'S WOOD, STAFFS. INTERIOR OF   2. BISHOP'S WOOD, STAFFS. RESTORED
FURNACE.   GLASS FURNACE.

Reproduced from half-tone illustrations in *North Staffs. Field Club Trans.*, vol. 68.
Original photographs not available.

PLATE VII

I

2

1. BLUNDEN'S WOOD, HAMBLEDON, SUR-
REY. KILN A FROM WEST, SHOWING, FROM
RIGHT TO LEFT, OUTER (S.) WALL, CAVITY,
SIEGE BANK, FLUE (CHOKED WITH WASTE),
N. SIDE COLLAPSED.

2. JAMESTOWN, VIRGINIA, GLASSHOUSE
SHOWING STRUCTURE A IN FOREGROUND.

PLATE VIII

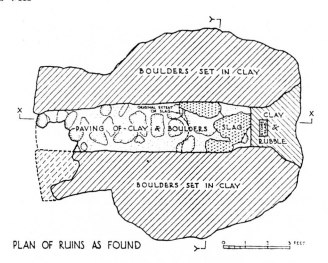

PLAN OF RUINS AS FOUND

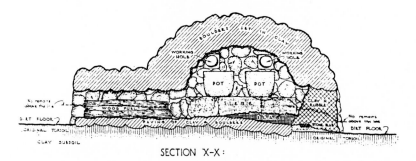

SECTION X-X:

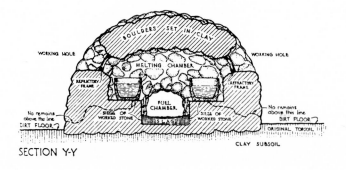

SECTION Y-Y

JAMESTOWN, VIRGINIA. THE MAIN WORK-
ING FURNACE IN WHICH THE GLASS WAS
MELTED. THE SECTIONS ARE CONJECT-
URAL RECONSTRUCTIONS.

PLATE IX

RECONSTRUCTION OF A TWELFTH-CENTURY GLASS FURNACE
BASED ON THEOPHILUS'S DESCRIPTION.

PLATE X

AN EARLY FIFTEENTH-CENTURY DRAWING
OF A FOREST GLASSHOUSE, PROBABLY IN
BOHEMIA. FROM BRITISH MUSEUM ADD.
MS. 24189.

PLATE XI

CRIEUR DES VERRES. FROM ANCIENS CRIS
DE PARIS OF THE FIRST HALF OF THE
SIXTEENTH CENTURY.

PLATE XII

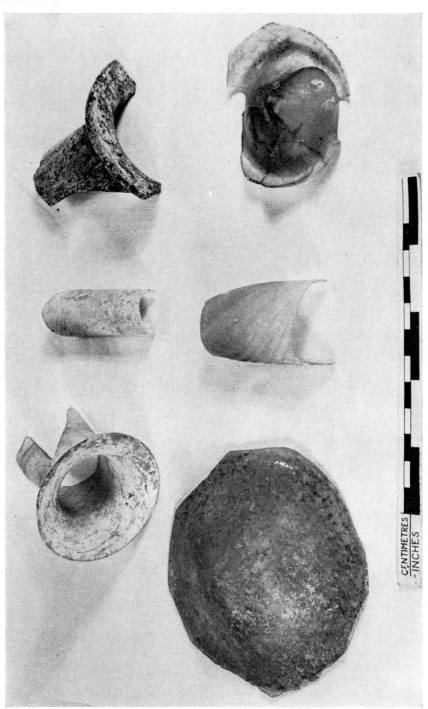

FRAGMENTS OF EARLY GLASS FROM CHIDDINGFOLD, SURREY.
COOPER COLLECTION, GUILDFORD MUSEUM.

PLATE XIII

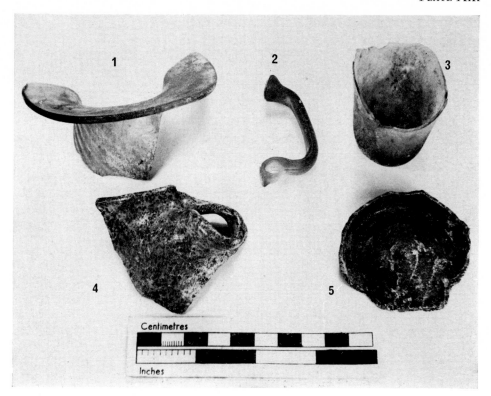

FRAGMENTS OF EARLY GLASS FROM CHIDDINGFOLD, SURREY
AND KIRDFORD, SUSSEX, ALL IN HASLEMERE MUSEUM.

1. Fluted wide rimmed vessel from an unknown Chiddingfold site.
2. Small handle from an unknown Chiddingfold site.
3. Hanging lamp base from site no. 21.
4. Spout of jug from site no.7.
5. Base of a small bottle from an unknown Chiddingfold site.

PLATE XIV

FRAGMENTS OF LATE VESSEL GLASS FROM SITE NO. 38.
WINBOLT COLLECTION, GUILDFORD MUSEUM.

Top row, left to right—
    Knop of stem; base of small square bottle
    fragment showing fluting.

Bottom row, left to right—
    Hemmed-rim base; base of hexagonal bottle.

PLATE XV

THIRTEENTH–CENTURY GLASS HANGING
LAMP IN WINCHESTER CITY MUSEUM.

PLATE XVI

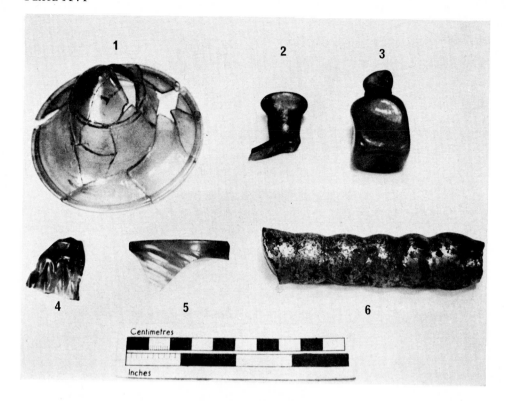

FRAGMENTS OF LATE VESSEL GLASS FROM SITES
NOS. 23 AND 38. HASLEMERE MUSEUM.

1. Base with a high kick from site no. 38.
2. Top of a bottle from site no. 23.
3. A faulty unguent bottle from site no. 23.
4. Fragment from site no. 38 showing honeycomb moulding.
5. Fragment from site no. 38 diagonal fluting.
6. Handle, probably for a linen-smoother, from
   site no. 23.

PLATE XVII

FRAGMENTS OF EARLY GLASS FOUND IN A
KIRDFORD, SUSSEX, GARDEN.

PLATE XVIII

RECONSTRUCTIONS MADE IN 1927 BY MESSRS. JAMES POWELL & SONS FROM FRAGMENTS FROM THE GLASSHOUSE AT WOODCHESTER, GLOS. THE LEFT-HAND GLASS WITH HONEYCOMB MOULDING IS $5\frac{1}{2}$ IN. HIGH; THE GLASS WITH THE WRYTHEN PATTERN IS $6\frac{1}{2}$ IN.

PLATE XIX

RECONSTRUCTIONS MADE IN 1927 BY MESSRS. JAMES POWELL & SONS FROM FRAGMENTS FROM THE GLASSHOUSE AT WOODCHESTER, GLOS. THESE AND OTHER RECONSTRUCTIONS ARE IN GLOUCESTER MUSEUM.

Reproduced from a half-tone illustration in *The Woodchester Glass House* (1960). Original photograph not available.

PLATE XX

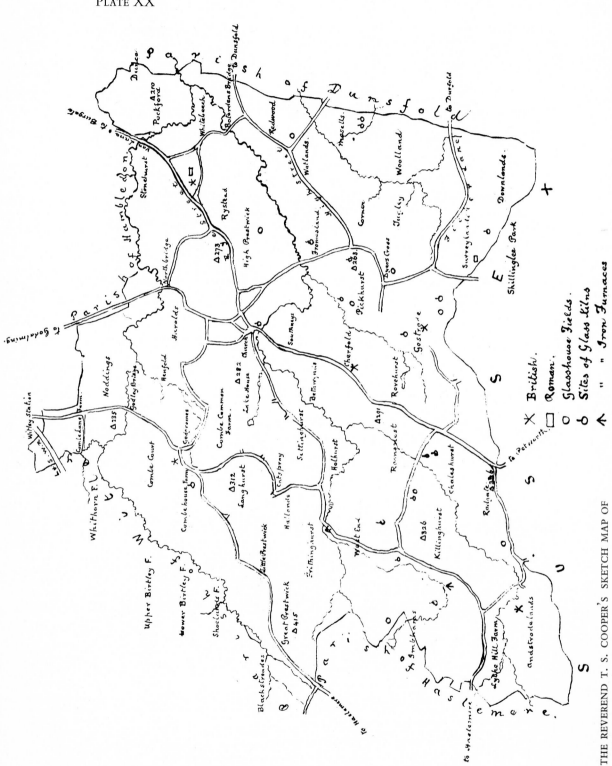

THE REVEREND T. S. COOPER'S SKETCH MAP OF
CHIDDINGFOLD, SURREY.

PLATE XXI

VANN FURNACE, HAMBLEDON, SURREY
(SITE NO 35), FROM THE SOUTH-EAST,
SOON AFTER ITS DISCOVERY IN 1931.

PLATE XXII

VANN FURNACE, FROM THE NORTH-WEST,
SHOWING THE HEARTH TUNNELS AND FIRE
CHAMBER.

xviii of Jany for ye wch he payd me not yn mony but yn thyngs yt he asked (alowayed?) for of me and for 178 bushels of asshes, 28 cords of log wood left at ye of my entry ther, 2 lode pot clay for makyng 12 pots, one lode of bryk clay for makyng of bryks, 4 stones for makyng an oven, 3 syles, 2 payles, 2 shovels, 1 (covlet?), a whele barowe, 4 lb. of safron, 100 of last 4 bushels of fretyng glas and 6 pypes as apareth by hys bylle . . . £18.'[38]

All the materials for a glasshouse are there except sand, it would be good to know just what the ashes were, what part the 'safron' played[39] and where the pot clay came from. Log wood suggests that billets and not copse wood were used. Clay for the making of 12 pots suggests that crucibles were made on the spot. The four stones for making an oven might be large slabs for sieges. The 'fretyng glas' suggests, that they used the intermediate fritting process. The six 'pypes' were probably blow pipes.

Mr T. B. Lennard comments on the letters: 'I have no documents to show whether it [the glass] was merely used for the Mansion House of Knole as the process of manufacturing this glass lasted for at least two or three years, and, for all we know some years longer. The former supposition is perhaps the most probable. Other Kentish landowners appear to have had glass-houses at that period as in the Sydney papers (Letters and Memorials of State, by Collins), a letter from R. Chyte to Sir R. Sydney, dated April 27 1597, refers to "the great glass-house hill towards Penshurst."'

In a letter Pulston reports that 'All the glass he brought home not by horse loade but by carte loade and he handsomely placed in the Chamber where your worship appointed as you shall see at your retorne; there are two locks on the dore to make all fast.'

Kingswood, Cheshire.

A glasshouse site at Kingswood, Delamere, Cheshire, was excavated in 1935 by Prof. R. Newstead, the Rev. Maurice H. Ridgway and Mr George B. Leach. In 1947 the site[40] was again examined by the Rev. M. H. Ridgway, and Mr G. B. Leach,[41] their conclusion is: 'The site explored represents an area on which material from a glasshouse has been dumped. Extensive search in the neighbourhood failed to locate the actual site, although the possibility that it may have been on the spot excavated cannot be completely overuled. The glasshouse from which the debris came made only window glass. The presence of both coloured and painted glass indicates that this was brought to the site as cullet, but eleven fragments of coloured glass with

[38] I have converted Roman to Arabic numerals, but I cannot identify all the terms.

[39] In *W.G.*, p. 14, Winbolt says that Mr Buckley explained saffre in the context of sand and ashes as soda from barilla. On p. 15 he equates saffora with barilla, on p. 22 he suggests saffre as a possible variation of sapphire. Zaffre was probably a colouring agent.

[40] Both excavations were hampered by a growing larch plantation.

[41] 'Glasshouse in Delamere Forest, Cheshire,' by R. Newstead in *Chester and N. Wales Arch. Soc.*, N.S., vol. 33 (1939), p. 36. 'Further Notes on the Glasshouse site at Kingswood, Delamere, Cheshire, by the Rev. M. H. Ridgway and G. B. Leach, in *Chester Arch. Soc. Journal*, vol. 27, Pt. 1, p. 133.

published nothing and it was left to one of his helpers, the late Mr J. S. Daniels, to gather what he could from a few notes and his material, and publish it in 1950 as a small but valuable book, *The Woodchester Glass House*. He had all available material photographed and this gives us the best record of the vessel forms of late sixteenth and early seventeenth century from forest glasshouses in England – forms which are suggested in the much more fragmentary material from Wealden sites.

This might have been the most interesting forest glasshouse in the country. It had the only circular (Venetian) type of furnace known[34] and for some unknown reason, possibly due to more careful annealing, its glass was tougher and the fragments are much larger than those of any other known site. The glass is dark olive-green, without a trace of blue. It is of good quality, but not quite up to that of Sidney Wood. Some window glass was produced. Cooper knew of this furnace because there are some fragments from it in his collection at Haslemere Museum.

Some recently found fragments of glass from this site in the Stroud Museum, and some of Marmont's material at Gloucester, are heavily corroded with golden flaking corrosion which may be due to some very local soil conditions.

Knole, Kent

In 1585 a glasshouse was established at Knole, near Sevenoaks, by John Lennard of Chevening. Some of its records have survived among letters and accounts of his steward Roger Pulston.[35] They provide more light on the quantity of fuel used in a glasshouse than any other records (*see* p. 47), and on the working of a glass furnace in addition to giving the names of glassmakers.

Pulston reports to John Lennard that he visits the glasshouse two or three times a day and that 'the glassmen were never at such unyty and concord amongst themselves . . .' He said that the furnace was consuming wood faster than it was being cut and carried, and faster than two woodmen could cut it. This is not surprising as the consumption was very large.[36] There appear to have been five glassmakers working at the furnace, Valyan and Ferris on one side and Oneby, Brussel and 'the other young man' on the other side.[37] The wording and the three visits a day suggest that unity was not always present.

An account of February 1585/6 includes some interesting details: 'for (108?) cords caryed of them by my owne teme and the rest by hayte betwene yt day and ye forseyd

---

[34] It was large, being 16 ft. in diameter; the whole glasshouse was large by Wealden standards, being 50 ft. square with an annealing furnace in one corner. The crucible was larger than the usual Wealden type. For all these details *see* Plate XIV in Daniels's book above.

[35] T. Barrett Lennard, 'Glassmaking at Knole, Kent,' in *The Antiquary*, vol. 41, p. 127. Of the site Winbolt (*W.G.*, p. 23) quotes: 'Dr Gordon Ward (*Sevenoaks Essays*, pp. 17-19) says that the site of the furnaces was at the junction of Hubbard's Hill and Gracious Lane, at the entrance to Beechmont Farm. It is shown on Lambarde's map of 1630 (the *Perambulation* was first published in 1576).' This is a heavily-wooded area, over 600 ft. above sea-level, and 2,300 yards SSW. of Knole mansion [G.H.K.].

[36] Some of the Late furnaces may have been larger than the Early ones.

[37] Guttery (p. 7), says the Lorrainers [at Stourbridge] worked in teams of three.

xviii of Jany for ye wch he payd me not yn mony but yn thyngs yt he asked (alowayed?) for of me and for 178 bushels of asshes, 28 cords of log wood left at ye of my entry ther, 2 lode pot clay for makyng 12 pots, one lode of bryk clay for makyng of bryks, 4 stones for makyng an oven, 3 syles, 2 payles, 2 shovels, 1 (covlet?), a whele barowe, 4 lb. of safron, 100 of last 4 bushels of fretyng glas and 6 pypes as apareth by hys bylle . . . £18.'[38]

All the materials for a glasshouse are there except sand, it would be good to know just what the ashes were, what part the 'safron' played[39] and where the pot clay came from. Log wood suggests that billets and not copse wood were used. Clay for the making of 12 pots suggests that crucibles were made on the spot. The four stones for making an oven might be large slabs for sieges. The 'fretyng glas' suggests, that they used the intermediate fritting process. The six 'pypes' were probably blow pipes.

Mr T. B. Lennard comments on the letters: 'I have no documents to show whether it [the glass] was merely used for the Mansion House of Knole as the process of manufacturing this glass lasted for at least two or three years, and, for all we know some years longer. The former supposition is perhaps the most probable. Other Kentish landowners appear to have had glass-houses at that period as in the Sydney papers (Letters and Memorials of State, by Collins), a letter from R. Chyte to Sir R. Sydney, dated April 27 1597, refers to "the great glass-house hill towards Penshurst."'

In a letter Pulston reports that 'All the glass he brought home not by horse loade but by carte loade and he handsomely placed in the Chamber where your worship appointed as you shall see at your retorne; there are two locks on the dore to make all fast.'

Kingswood, Cheshire.

A glasshouse site at Kingswood, Delamere, Cheshire, was excavated in 1935 by Prof. R. Newstead, the Rev. Maurice H. Ridgway and Mr George B. Leach. In 1947 the site[40] was again examined by the Rev. M. H. Ridgway, and Mr G. B. Leach,[41] their conclusion is: 'The site explored represents an area on which material from a glasshouse has been dumped. Extensive search in the neighbourhood failed to locate the actual site, although the possibility that it may have been on the spot excavated cannot be completely overuled. The glasshouse from which the debris came made only window glass. The presence of both coloured and painted glass indicates that this was brought to the site as cullet, but eleven fragments of coloured glass with

---

[38] I have converted Roman to Arabic numerals, but I cannot identify all the terms.

[39] In *W.G.*, p. 14, Winbolt says that Mr Buckley explained saffre in the context of sand and ashes as soda from barilla. On p. 15 he equates saffora with barilla, on p. 22 he suggests saffre as a possible variation of sapphire. Zaffre was probably a colouring agent.

[40] Both excavations were hampered by a growing larch plantation.

[41] 'Glasshouse in Delamere Forest, Cheshire,' by R. Newstead in *Chester and N. Wales Arch. Soc.,* N.S., vol. 33 (1939), p. 36. 'Further Notes on the Glasshouse site at Kingswood, Delamere, Cheshire, by the Rev. M. H. Ridgway and G. B. Leach, in *Chester Arch. Soc. Journal*, vol. 27, Pt. 1, p. 133.

selvedged edges and the presence of red molten glass in one of the crucibles seem to indicate that coloured glass was actually made on the site as well ... The date of the glasshouse and of its destruction must still remain obscure.'[42]

The earlier report says of the crucibles: 'The fragments did not admit of reconstruction but appear to belong to one type with bulging sides and everted rims, varying from 13–12 in. in diameter. The bases are flat, and the walls vary in thickness from 0·6 to 0·8 in.'

The later report adds: 'Both inside and outside are coated usually with greenish or brown glaze and in one case with a thin layer of red glass ... The crucibles are made of the same hard grey clay.'

The thin layer of red glass on a crucible fragment is interesting, because the only colour for which there is conclusive evidence of manufacture in the Weald is ruby glass at two glasshouse sites, Nos. 4 and 29.

The size of the crucibles may be much the same as in the Weald, but the rims are different from any I know and the thin walls and bulging sides [barrel-shaped], though similar to the commonest type from Blunden's Wood (No. 33), are unlike the usual thick-walled, bucket-shaped Wealden crucibles.

———

Right at the end of our time, in 1618, Sir William Clavell tried to establish a glasshouse at Church Knowle in Dorset and entered into a contract[43] with Abraham Bigo to build a glasshouse for making green drinking glasses. I know nothing about the venture but it does not seem to have lasted long because Bigo turns up in Ireland a few years later.

Winbolt has notes of other possible glassmaking in southeast England, and quotes an entry in the Parish Registers of Reigate: 1593. Dec. 5. John Brasington alias Folly, Glasman, and Mary Toothe, married.[44] He says that in the Museum at Carshalton, Surrey, 'are glasshouse remains found in Carshalton – several lumps of crucibles with glass adhering and a lump of glass broken out of a crucible. Though greenish, the glass is much clearer than that of any site I have examined, and is probably of later date, perhaps late seventeenth century.[45]'

Jamestown, Virginia.[46]

A complete excavation of a glasshouse of this period (1608) was done at Jamestown.[47] The glasshouse covered an area of 50 ft. by 37 ft., considerably larger than

[42] Writing to me in 1965, the Rev. Maurice H. Ridgway, after he had seen this note, said: 'I think late fourteenth to early fifteenth [century] is still a date I fancy for the Kingswood site.'

[43] Private deeds of the Clavell family, mentioned in the Bulletin of the National Register of Archives, No. 9, 1957, p. 12. I am much indebted to Miss A. Reeve for this reference.

[44] S.C.M., vol. 14, p. 161.   [45] S.C.M., vol. 9, p. 792.

[46] See also Chapter IV, p. 71.

[47] Captain George Percy, younger brother of the ninth Earl of Northumberland, owner of the Petworth estate and glasshouse No. 40, was Governor of Jamestown in 1611. The two glasshouses were probably almost contemporary.

anything except the Woodchester glasshouse, so far (1965) found in England. The whole area was minutely examined by Mr J. C. Harrington (Archaeological Officer of the National Park Service) whose most interesting preliminary report, *Glassmaking at Jamestown*, was published in 1952. He shows the complete lay-out of the glasshouse and gives excellent conjectural reconstructions of the various furnaces (*see* p. 72 and Plate VIII). In spite of this meticulous care he says 'the keenest disappointment was that none of the glass fragments were large enough to show what the original objects had been.' He realized the reason – the use of cullet – and it is interesting to see how the pattern in the Weald also appears in Jamestown. Our sites are usually unrewarding, but we did not have to clear them first of copperhead snakes!

INDEX OF PERSONS AND PLACES

See list of contents on pp. vii for guidance as to subjects discussed in this book. Unless otherwise stated, all places in this index are in Sussex. Compound place-names are indexed under the first word, e.g. Lower Roundhurst will be found under L. Wisborough Green has been abbreviated to Wisborough.

TP 854
G7 K4